End of Chapter Material
to accompany

BIOLOGY
Seventh Edition

Peter H. Raven ▪ George B. Johnson
Jonathan B. Losos ▪ Susan R. Singer

 **Custom Publishing**

Boston   Burr Ridge, IL   Dubuque, IA   Madison, WI   New York
San Francisco   St. Louis   Bangkok   Bogotá   Caracas   Kuala Lumpur
Lisbon   London   Madrid   Mexico City   Milan   Montreal   New Delhi
Santiago   Seoul   Singapore   Sydney   Taipei   Toronto

End of Chapter Material to accompany BIOLOGY

1 2 3 4 5 6 7 8 9 0   PAH PAH   0 9 8 7 6 5 4

ISBN 0-07-310923-1

Editor: Elaine Manke
Production Editor: Sue Culbertson
Printer/Binder: P.A. Hutchison

Contents

FIGURE 1.10

Geometric and arithmetic progressions. A geometric progression increases by a constant factor (e.g., x 2 or x 3 or x 4), while an arithmetic progression increases by a constant difference (e.g., units of 1 or 2 or 3). Malthus contended that the human growth curve was geometric, but the human food production curve was only arithmetic.
What is the effect of reducing the constant factor by which the geometric progression increases? Might this effect be achieved with humans? How?

Answer: It will lead to less food per person, plus eventual starvation, if the slope of the arithmetic line is not increased by technology. Reducing the factor by which the geometric progression increases (lowering the value of the exponent) reduces the difference between numbers of people and amount of food production. It can be achieved by lowering family size or delaying childbearing.

FIGURE 1.14

Molecules reflect evolutionary patterns. Vertebrates that are more distantly related to humans have a greater number of amino acid differences in this vertebrate hemoglobin peptide.
Where do you imagine a snake might fall on the graph? Why?

Answer: A snake would fall somewhere near the bird, as birds and snakes are closely related.

FIGURE 1.15

The molecular clock of cytochrome c. When the time since each pair of organisms diverged in the fossil record is plotted against the number of nucleotide differences in the cytochrome *c* gene, the result is a straight line, suggesting this gene is evolving at a constant rate.
Do you think Dog differs from Cow more than might be expected based on other vertebrates? What might explain this?

Answer: Yes—distance to the line is greater. Random scatter is the most likely explanation: some point is bound to be furthest from the line.

Self Test

1). Which of the following characteristics is *not* a property of life?
      a). responding to stimuli
      b). dividing in two
      c). regulating internal conditions
      d). All of these are characteristics that define life

The correct answer is *b*...
A. Answer *a* is incorrect because all living organisms respond or react to stimuli. Nonliving objects are affected by their environments, a flag waves in the wind, but it is not actually responding to a stimulus.

The correct answer is *b*--dividing in two
B. Although some living organisms reproduce by dividing in two, such as bacteria, not all living organisms divide in two. Also some nonliving objects can also divide in two, such as the "globs" floating inside a lava lamp.

The correct answer is *b*...
C. Answer *c* is incorrect because all living organisms regulate their internal conditions. A set thermostat can regulate the internal temperature of a house, but the house itself is not regulating its internal temperature.

The correct answer is *b*...
D. Answer *d* is incorrect because not all of the characteristics above are properties of life. Answer *b* is not a property of life.

Hint: What makes something "alive"? Anyone could deduce that a galloping horse is alive and a car is not, by why? We cannot say, "If it moves, it's alive," because a car can move and gelatin can wiggle in a bowl. They certainly are not alive. What characteristics do define life? All living organisms share seven basic characteristics: cellular organization, order, sensitivity, growth/development/reproduction, energy utilization, evolutionary adaptation, and homeostasis.

2). The process of inductive reasoning
        a). involves the observation of specific occurrences to construct a general principle.
        b). involves taking a general principle and applying it to a specific situation.
        c). is not used very often in the study of biology.
        d). all of the above

The correct answer is *a*--involves the observation of specific occurrences to construct a general principle
A. Inductive reasoning is used by scientists to explain how the world works. They make many observations and then construct a principle that explains the observations.

The correct answer is *a*....
B. Answer *b* is incorrect because it describes deductive reasoning, not inductive reasoning.

The correct answer is *a*...
C. Answer *c* is incorrect because biologists constantly use inductive reasoning to explain how the world works.

The correct answer is *a*...
D. Answer *d* is incorrect because only *a* is a correct answer. Answer b describes deductive reasoning and answer c is incorrect because biologists constantly use inductive reasoning to explain how the world works.

Hint: Inductive reasoning uses specific observations to construct general scientific principles. *Webster's Dictionary* defines science as systematized knowledge derived from observation and experiment carried on to determine the principles underlying what is being studied. In other words, a scientist determines principles from observations, discovering general principles by careful examination of specific cases.

3). A goal of a scientist is to formulate a hypothesis
        a). that will never be proven false.
        b). that is essentially a theory explaining an observation.
        c). that is just a wild guess.
        d). that will be tested by experimentation.

The correct answer is *d*...
A. Answer *a* is incorrect because an experiment can either lend support to a hypothesis or can prove it false.

The correct answer is *d*...
B. Answer *b* is incorrect because a hypothesis is not the same as a theory. A theory is a scientific explanation supported by a body of experimental evidence and interconnected concepts. A theory is accepted scientific fact.

The correct answer is *d*...
C. Answer *c* is incorrect because scientists formulate hypotheses based on past experience and knowledge of the area. It is not a wild guess, rather it is an educated guess.

The correct answer is *d*--that will be tested by experimentation.
D. A hypothesis is an explanation of an observation. In order to determine if the explanation is correct, a scientist will perform an experiment.

Hint: How do scientists establish which general principles are true from among the many that might be true? They do this by systematically testing alternative proposals. If these proposals prove inconsistent with experimental observations, they are rejected as untrue. After making careful observations concerning a particular area of science, scientists construct a hypothesis, which is a suggested explanation the accounts for those observations. A hypothesis is a proposition that might be true. Those hypotheses that have not yet been disproved by experimentation are retained.

4). An experiment testing a hypothesis will
        a). always support the hypothesis.
        b). always disprove the hypothesis.
        c). include a variable and a control.
        d). not be successful if the hypothesis is rejected.

The correct answer is *c*...
A. Answer *a* is incorrect because frequently the experiments disprove the hypothesis.

The correct answer is *c*...
B. Answer *b* is incorrect because sometimes the experiments support the hypothesis.

The correct answer is *c*--include a variable and a control.
C. In order to test a hypothesis successfully, only one variable can be manipulated at a time and a corresponding control experiment, where the variable is not changed, must be performed to determine the affect of the variable.

The correct answer is *c*...
D. Answer *d* is incorrect because the goal of experimentation is to whittle down all possible hypotheses to only those that are supported by experimentation. Therefore, some hypotheses are expected to be rejected.

Hint: Often we are interested in learning about processes that are influenced by many factors or variables. To evaluate alternative hypotheses about one variable, all other variable must be kept constant. This is done by carrying out two experiments in parallel: in the first experiment, one variable is altered in a specific way to test a particular hypothesis; in the second experiment, called the control experiment, the variable is left unaltered. In all other respects, the two experiments are identical.

5). Darwin's proposal, that evolution occurs through natural selection caused controversy because
        a). it challenged the existence of a Divine Creator.
        b). it challenged the views of earlier philosophers.
        c). it challenged a literal interpretation of the Bible.
        d). the explanation wasn't based on any observations.

The correct answer is *c*...
A. Answer *a* is incorrect because Darwin was not challenging the existence of a Divine Creator, instead arguing that the Creator expressed Himself through the laws of nature, producing changes over time.

The correct answer is *c*...

B. Answer *b* is incorrect because earlier philosophers presented a view of evolution, that living organisms must have changed over time, not that life remained constant and unchanged. Darwin took this view one step further, suggesting a mechanism (natural selection) that drove the changes.

The correct answer is *c*-- it challenged a literal interpretation of the bible.

C. Most people living at the time Darwin published his book believed in a literal interpretation of the bible, accepting the idea of a fixed and constant world. Darwin's explanation of evolution suggested that species changed over time due to pressures of competition through natural selection.

The correct answer is *c*...

D. Answer *d* is incorrect because Darwin based his explanation of evolution through natural selection on observations he made during his five year voyage on the H.M.S. *Beagle*.

Hint: In Darwin's time, most people believed that the various kinds of organisms and their individual structures resulted from direct actions of the Creator (and to this day many people still believe this to be true). Species were thought to be specially created and unchangeable, or immutable, over the course of time. Although Darwin's theory did not challenge the existence of a Divine Creator, he argued that this Creator did not simply create things and then leave them forever unchanged. Instead, Darwin's God expressed Himself through the operation of natural laws that produced change over time, or evolution. These view put Darwin at odds with most people of his time who believed in a literal interpretation of the Bible and accepted the idea of a fixed and constant world.

6). Darwin was convinced that evolution had occurred based on observations that
  a). armadillos on the different islands off the coast of South America had slightly different physical characteristics.
  b). tortoises found on the different Galapagos Islands had different and identifiable shells.
  c). bird fossils that showed modifications from modern-day birds found in the same area.
  d). All of these observations were made by Darwin.

The correct answer is *b*...

A. Answer *a* is incorrect because Darwin observed that present day armadillos in southern South America resembled fossils of armadillo-like animals found in the same area. The key piece of evidence involving Darwin's observations of armadillos was the fossil connection to the past, not the physical characteristics of armadillos on different islands.

The correct answer is *b*-- tortoises found on the different Galapagos Islands had different and identifiable shells.

B. Darwin found tortoises on the Galapagos Islands but noticed that the tortoises on the different islands had different shaped shells, suggesting that they were all related but changed after becoming isolated on an island.

The correct answer is *b*...

C. Answer *c* is incorrect because Darwin observed that living birds on islands more closely resembled those of the closest mainland, not the birds of similar but more distant islands. Darwin's observations about birds did not involve finding fossils of birds.

The correct answer is *b*...

D. Answer *d* is incorrect because only answer *b* describes an observation made by Darwin.

Hint: On the Galapagos Islands, off the coast of Ecuador, Darwin encountered a variety of different finches on the various islands. The 14 species, although related, differed slightly in appearance, particularly in their beaks. Darwin felt is most reasonable to assume all these birds had descended from a common ancestor blown by winds from the South American mainland several million years ago. Eating different foods on different islands, the species had changed during their descent: "descent with modification"—evolution.

7). A key piece of information for Darwin's hypothesis that evolution occurs through natural selection was
        a). the fossil evidence.
        b). his work breeding of pigeons through artificial selection.
        c). Malthus' proposal that death, due to limited food supply, restricts population size.
        d). geographic distribution of similar animals with slight variations in physical characteristics.

The correct answer is c...
A. Answer a is incorrect because although the fossil evidence was an important piece of supporting evidence, it wasn't the <u>key</u> piece of information to explain <u>how</u> change occurs.

The correct answer is c...
B. Answer b is incorrect because although Darwin's experience breeding domestic animals showed him that selection can influence a population, it wasn't the <u>key</u> piece of information explaining the driving force behind the changes that occur in nature.

The correct answer is c-- Malthus' proposal that death, due to limited food supply, restricts population size.
C. Darwin read Thomas Malthus' book in which he described the arithmetic progression of the food supply limits the geometric progression of animal/plant growth. This laid the groundwork of competition limiting survival which is key to the theory of natural selection.

The correct answer is c...
D. Answer d is incorrect because although geographical distribution of animals was an important piece of supporting evidence, it wasn't the <u>key</u> piece of information to explain <u>how</u> change occurs.

Hint: Of key importance to the development of Darwin's insight was his study of Thomas Mathus's *Essay on the Principle of Population*. Malthus pointed out that populations of plants and animals tend to increase geometrically, while their food supply increases only arithmetically. Because populations increase geometrically, virtually any kind of animal or plant, if it could reproduce unchecked, would cover the entire surface of the world within a surprisingly short time. Instead, populations of species remain fairly constant year after year, because death limits population numbers. Malthus's conclusion provided the key ingredient that was necessary for Darwin to develop the hypothesis that evolution occurs by natural selection.

8). Which of the following "new" areas of scientific study could Darwin have used to strengthen his hypothesis?
        a). the age of the earth
        b). the mechanism of inheritance
        c). the expanded fossil record
        d). the geographical distribution of animal species

The correct answer is b...
A. Answer a is incorrect because the exact age of the earth was already in question when Darwin proposed his hypothesis.

The correct answer is b-- the mechanism by which hereditary information is passed on
B. Although a lot of the "new" evidence fills in gaps in Darwin's observations, the description of the mechanism of inheritance provides the explanation of how "change" occurs in organisms and how that change can be passed on to offspring. This is something that Darwin could not explain.

The correct answer is b...
C. Answer c is incorrect because Darwin had already pointed out examples in the fossil record and predicted that "links" would be found in the fossil record.

The correct answer is b...
D. Answer d is incorrect because Darwin had already established that there were variations in characteristics of organisms in different geographical locations.

Hint: Darwin received some of his sharpest criticism in the area of heredity. At that time, no one had any concept of genes or how heredity works, so it was not possible for Darwin to explain completely how evolution occurs. When scientists began to understand the laws of inheritance, the heredity problem with Darwin's theory vanished.

9). What are homologous anatomical structures?
      a). structures that look different but have the similar evolutionary origins
      b). structures that have similar functions but different evolutionary origins
      c). a bat's wing and a butterfly's wing
      d). a bat's wing and a human's leg

The correct answer is a-- structures that may look different but have the similar origins
A. Homologous structures in two organisms were similar in their ancestors and had similar functions but they changed in different ways over time due to pressures from natural selection to the point that they may look different and have different functions but they have similar origins.

The correct answer is a...
B. Answer b is incorrect because these are analogous structures, having similar functions but different origins.

The correct answer is a...
C. Answer c is incorrect because these are analogous structures, having similar functions but different origins.

The correct answer is a...
D. Answer d is incorrect because these two structures aren't related in origin or function. A bat's wing is homologous to a human's arm and hand, not to a human's leg.

Hint: Comparative studies of animals have provided strong evidence for Darwin's theory. In many different types of vertebrates, for example, the same bones are present, indicating their evolutionary past. Forelimbs in different animals are all constructed from the same basic array of bones, modified in one way in the wing of a bat, in another way in the fin of a porpoise, and in yet another way in the leg of a horse. The bones are said to be homologous, that is they have the same evolutionary origin, but they now differ in structure and function.

10). The themes of biology include all of the following except:
      a). chemistry.
      b). cell biology.
      c). genetics.
      d). evolution.

The correct answer is a—chemistry.
A. Although chemistry is discussed in biology, a chemical basis of matter is not unique to living organism and therefore it is not a basic theme of biology.

The correct answer is a...
B. Answer b is incorrect because cell biology is a basic theme of biology, cells being the simplest level of organismal life.

The correct answer is a...
C. Answer c is incorrect because genetics is a basic theme of biology, examining how one generation passes characteristics onto the next generation.

The correct answer is a...
D. Answer d is incorrect because evolution is not only a basic theme of biology, it is the thread that runs through all aspects of biology.

Hint: The basic themes of biology can be viewed through four themes that unify biology. The organization of life is the theme based on the fact that all organisms are composed of cells, life's basic units. The continuity of life is the theme based on the fact that the information that specifies what a cell is like is encoded in a molecule called DNA and this information is passed onto offspring. The unity of life is the theme based on the fact that some of the characteristics of an early ancestor have been preserved in all things alive today. The diversity of life is the theme based on the fact that there is incredible diversity among living things which evolved to fill the varied environments on earth.

Test Your Visual Understanding

1). Which line on the graph indicates the growth of a population if resources were unlimited? Name three factors that limit population growth.
Answer: The blue line represents geometric progression and this type of growth occurs when resources are plentiful. Factors that limit population growth are factors that lead to death. Many factors can lead to death in a population such as limited supplies of food or water, disease, or natural disasters such as floods and fire.

2). By following the general path of evolution, would you say that fungi are more closely related to Archaebacteria or Bacteria? Why?
Answer: Fungi are more closely related to Archaebacteria than to Bacteria because the ancestors to Archaebacteria and Eukarya are on the same branch, which separated from the Bacteria before Archaebacteria and Eukarya groups formed.

Apply Your Knowledge

1). When breeding hunting dogs, the parents are selected for their keen sense of smell, which allows them to find the game (i.e., birds) faster. Breeders predict that this trait will be passed on to the dogs' offspring, producing a family of good hunting dogs. This is artificial selection. Explain how this same trait could be selected for through natural selection in a population of wild dogs.
Answer: A keen sense of smell is vitally important to dogs, especially to dogs in the wild. Unlike a domesticated dog that is fed by its owner, a wild dog is a hunter and needs to track its prey. A keen sense of smell would allow a wild dog a competitive advantage to track down prey compared to other dogs that didn't possess as keen a sense of smell. Through natural selection, the dogs with the keener sense of smell would acquire more food that would aid to its survival. Dogs that survived would have a greater opportunity to produce offspring, some of whom would inherit the keen sense of smell. Eventually, this characteristic would become more prevalent in the population, leading to a change in the make up of the population.

2). Assume four people are stranded on a deserted island and they reproduce once a year. How many people will be on the island after ten years using:
      a). a geometric progression with a factor of two.
      b). an arithmetic progression with a factor of two.

Answer: a). With geometric progression, the population would increase by a constant factor, which in this case is 2. Assuming that all four individuals can reproduce the number of people on the island after 10 years would be 4096:
4x2=8
8x2=16
16x2=32
32x2=64
64x2=18
128x2=256
256x2=512
512x2=1024
1024x2=2048
2048x2=4096

b). With arithmetic progression, the population would increase by a constant difference, which in this case is 2. Assuming that all four individuals can reproduce, the number of people on the island after 10 years would be 24:
4+2=6
6+2=8
8+2=10
10+2=12
12+2=14
14+2=16
16+2=18
18+2=20
20+2=22
22+2=24

FIGURE 2.19

Buffers minimize changes in pH. Adding a base to a solution neutralizes some of the acid present, and so raises the pH. Thus, as the curve moves to the right, reflecting more and more base, it also rises to higher pH values. What a buffer does is to make the curve rise or fall very slowly over a portion of the pH scale, called the "buffering range" of that buffer.

For this buffer, adding base raises pH more rapidly below pH 4 than above it; what might account for this behavior?

Answer: The buffer works over a broad range because it ionizes more completely as pH increases; in essence, there is more acid to neutralize the greater amount of base you are adding. At pH4 none of the buffer is ionized. Thus below that pH, base raises the pH without the ameliorating effects of the ionization of the buffer.

Self Test

1). An atom with a neutral charge must contain
      a). the same number of protons and neutrons.
      b). the same number of protons and electrons.
      c). more neutrons because they are neutral.
      d). the same number of neutrons and electrons.

The correct answer is b...
A. Answer a is incorrect because a neutral atom carries no charge and so it doesn't matter how many neutrons there are in relation to protons. Neutrons are neutral meaning that they carry no charge while protons carry positive charges. In order for an atom to be neutral, it must have equal numbers of protons and electrons.

The correct answer is b--the same number of protons and neutrons.
B. Protons carry positive charges (+1) and electrons carry negative charges (-1), while neutrons carry no charge. If an atom is neutral (containing no charge), there must be an equal number of protons and electrons so that their opposite charges cancel each other out.

The correct answer is b...
C. Answer c is incorrect because neutrons are neutral meaning that they carry no charge and so they don't contribute to the electrical charge of the atom. In order for an atom to be neutral, it must have equal numbers of positively charged protons and negatively charged neutrons.

The correct answer is b...
D. Answer d is incorrect because a neutral atom carries no charge and so it doesn't matter how many neutrons there are in relation to electrons. Neutrons are neutral meaning that they carry no charge while electrons carry negative charges. In order for an atom to be neutral, it must have equal numbers of protons and electrons.

Hint: The positive charges in the nucleus of an atom are counterbalanced by negatively charged electrons orbiting at varying distances around the nucleus. Thus, atoms with the same number of protons and electrons are electrically neutral, having no net charge.

2). Electrons determine the chemical behavior of an atom because
      a). they interact with other atoms.
      b). they determine the charge of the atom.
      c). they can be exchanged between atoms, transferring their energy as the move.
      d). All of these are correct.

The correct answer is d...

A. Answer a is incorrect because although electrons are the outermost particle of the atom and interact with other atoms, that is not the only correct answer.

The correct answer is d...
B. Answer b is incorrect because although electrons determine the charge of the atom (positive, negative, or neutral), that is not the only correct answer.

The correct answer is d...
C. Answer c is incorrect because although electrons can be exchanged between atoms, transferring their energy as the move, that is not the only correct answer.

The correct answer is d—All of these are correct
D. Electrons move around the nucleus in orbitals where they are great distances from the nucleus. Because of these distance, the nuclei of adjoining atoms can not interact with each other, only their electrons can. The number of electrons in relation to protons determines if the atom carries a charge. Electrons can transfer from one atom to another and in doing so, transfers energy from one atom to another.

Hint: The key to the chemical behavior of an atom lies in the arrangement of its electrons in their orbits. The nuclei of two atoms never come close enough in nature to interact and it is for this reason that an atom's electrons determines its chemical behavior. During chemical reactions, electrons are transferred from one atom to another and when an electron is transferred in this way, it keeps its energy of position.

3). The elements within the periodic table are organized by:
      a). the number of protons.
      b). the number of neutrons.
      c). the mass of protons and neutrons.
      d). the mass of electrons.

The correct answer is a--the number of protons.
A. The elements are organized according to their atomic number, which is determined by the number of protons, which is also the number of electrons.

The correct answer is a...
B. Answer b is incorrect because the number of neutrons in an atom has no effect on the placement of that element in the periodic table.

The correct answer is a...
C. Answer c is incorrect because the mass of protons and neutrons determines an atom's atomic mass, not its atomic number and the periodic table is organized according to atomic numbers.

The correct answer is a...
D. Answer d is incorrect because the periodic table is organized according atomic numbers and the mass of the electrons does not affect the atomic number.

Hint: There are 92 naturally occurring elements, each with a different number of protons and a different arrangement of electrons. The elements in the periodic table arranged according to atomic number exhibit a pattern of chemical properties repeated in groups of eight elements.

4). Which of the following statements is *not* true.
      a). Molecules held together by ionic bonds are called ionic compounds.
      b). In NaCl, both sodium and chloride have completely filled outer energy levels of 8 electrons.
      c). A sodium atom is able to form an ionic bond with chloride because sodium gives up an electron and chloride gains an electron.
      d). Ionic bonds can form between any two atoms.

The correct answer is d...
A. Answer a is incorrect because the statement is true. A molecule is a stable association of atoms but when atoms from more than one element associate, it is called a compound. If the atoms that form the compound are ions, then the compound is called an ionic compound.

The correct answer is d...
B. Answer b is incorrect because the statement is true. NaCl is an ionic compound that forms when sodium loses the sole electron from its outer energy level, removing that level and giving it a completely filled outer energy level and chloride gains an electron filling its outer energy level that had 7 electron.

The correct answer is d...
C. Answer c is incorrect because the statement is true. Ionic bonds form between oppositely charged ions. Sodium loses an electron to become a positively charged ion and chloride gains an electron to become a negatively charged ion. These oppositely charged ions attract to form and ionic bond.

The correct answer is d--Ionic bonds can form between any two atoms.
D. This statement is *not* true while all of the other statements are true. Ionic bonds form only between atoms that form ions by gaining or losing electrons but not all atoms form ions. Atoms such as helium are inert and don't usually give up or receive electrons from other atoms. Other atoms, such as carbon, have partially filled outer energy levels but tend to share electrons with other atoms rather than giving up electrons.

Hint: Ionic bonds form when atoms with opposite electrical charges (ions) attract.

5). Oxygen has 6 electrons in its outer energy level; therefore,
        a). it has a completely filled outer energy level.
        b). it can form one double covalent bond or two single covalent bonds.
        c). it does not react with any other atom.
        d). it has a positive charge.

The correct answer is b...
A. Answer a is incorrect because with only 6 electrons in its outer energy level, it needs two more electrons to fill its outer level to satisfy the octet rule.

The correct answer is b--it can form one double covalent bond or two single covalent bonds.
B. Oxygen forms single covalent bonds with two other atoms, sharing an electron with each atom. It can also form a double covalent bond with one other atom, sharing two electrons with the other atom.

The correct answer is b...
C. Answer c is incorrect because with only 6 electrons in its outer energy level, oxygen has not satisfied the octet rule and so it reacts with other atoms in order to fill its outer energy level.

The correct answer is b...
D. Answer d is incorrect because it is not an ion, it tends to remain a neutral atom. But, if oxygen were to become an ion, it is more likely that it would receive 2 electrons from another atom to fill its outer energy level (which would make it a negatively charged ion) rather than give up 6 electrons to become a positively charged ion.

Hint: Molecules often consist of more than two atoms. One reason that larger molecules may be formed is that a given atom is able to share electrons with more than one other atom. An atom that requires two, three, or four additional electrons to fill its outer energy level completely may acquire them by sharing its electron with two or more other atoms.

6). The atomic structure of water satisfies the octet rule by
    a). filling the hydrogen atoms' outer energy levels with 8 electrons each.
    b). having electrons shared between the two hydrogen atoms.
    c). having oxygen form covalent bonds with two hydrogen atoms.
    d). having each hydrogen atom give up an electron to the outer energy level of the
    oxygen atom.

The correct answer is c...
A. Answer a is incorrect because hydrogen has only one *s* orbital which can hold a maximum of 2 electrons. Two electrons fills the outer energy level in hydrogen, *not* 8 electrons.

The correct answer is c...
B. Answer b is incorrect because in the water molecule, covalent bonds form between the oxygen atom and each of the hydrogen atoms. Electrons are *not* shared between the two hydrogen atoms.

The correct answer is c--having oxygen form covalent bonds with two hydrogen atoms.
C. Oxygen has 6 electrons in its outer energy level which requires 2 more electrons in order to be completely filled. It forms single covalent bonds with two hydrogen atoms. The sharing of electrons brings the total number of electrons in the outer level of oxygen to 8 and brings the total number of electrons in the outer level of each hydrogen to 2 (which is a completely filled energy level for the hydrogen atom).

The correct answer is c...
D. Answer d is incorrect because the hydrogen atoms' electrons remain associated with the hydrogen nuclei some of the time but also orbit the oxygen nucleus. The hydrogen atoms do not "give up" their electrons to the outer level in the oxygen atom which would result in the formation of ions.

Hint: Water has a simple atomic structure. It consists of an oxygen atom bout to two hydrogen atoms by tow single covalent bonds. The resulting molecule is stable: it satisfies the octet rule, has no unpaired electrons, and carries no net electrical charge.

7). The partial charge separation in H_2O results from
    a). the electrons' greater attraction to the oxygen atom.
    b). oxygen's higher electronegativity.
    c). a denser electron cloud near the oxygen atom.
    d). All of these are correct.

The correct answer is d...
A. Answer a is incorrect because although the partial charge separation of water molecules results from the electrons' greater attraction to the oxygen atom, this is not the only correct answer.

The correct answer is d...
B. Answer b is incorrect because although the partial charge separation of water molecules results from oxygen's higher electronegativity, that is not the only correct answer.

The correct answer is d...
C. Answer c is incorrect because although the partial charge separation of water molecules results because the electron cloud is denser new the oxygen atom, that is not the only correct answer.

The correct answer is d--all of the above.
D. The partial charge separation of the water molecule results from the stronger attraction of the electrons to the oxygen atom, which means that oxygen has a higher electronegativity compared

to hydrogen. This higher electronegativity means that the electron cloud, which is the area in which one can usually find electrons, is denser near the oxygen atom.

Hint: Both the oxygen and the hydrogen atoms attract the electrons they share in the covalent bonds of a water molecule; this attraction is called electronegativity. However, the oxygen atom is more electronegative than the hydrogen atoms, so it attracts the electrons more strongly than do the hydrogen atoms. As a result, the shared electrons in a water molecule are far more likely to be found near the oxygen nucleus than near the hydrogen nuclei. This stronger attraction for electrons give the oxygen atom two partial negative charges, as though the electron cloud were denser near the oxygen atom than around the hydrogen atoms.

8). The attraction of water molecules to other water molecules is
> a). cohesion.
> b). adhesion.
> c). capillary action.
> d). surface tension.

The correct answer is a--cohesion.
A. In the polar water molecule, the partial negative end of one molecule is attracted to the partial positive end of another molecule. This attraction causes water molecules to "stick" to each other in a process called "cohesion."

The correct answer is a...
B. Answer b is incorrect because adhesion is the attraction of water molecules to molecules of substances other than water.

The correct answer is a...
C. Answer c is incorrect because capillary action is the movement of water molecules through a tube caused by the attraction of water molecules to other substances (adhesion), such as the molecules that make up the glass tube.

The correct answer is a...
D. Answer d is incorrect because surface tension is a property of water that results from the attraction of water molecules for each other, a process called cohesion.

Hint: The polarity of water causes it to be attracted to other polar molecules. When the other molecules are also water, the attraction is referred to as cohesion. When the other molecules are of a different substance, the attraction is called adhesion. The cohesion of liquid water is also responsible for its surface tension. The attraction of water to substances like glass is responsible for capillary action which causes water to up in a glass tube.

9). What two properties of water help it to moderate changes in temperature?
> a). formation of hydration shells and high specific heat
> b). high heat of vaporization and hydrophobic exclusion
> c). high specific heat and high heat of vaporization
> d). formation of hydration shells and hydrophobic exclusion

The correct answer is c...
A. Answer a is incorrect because although the high specific heat is a property of water that helps to moderate changes in temperature, the formation of hydration shells has nothing to do with the moderation of water temperature. The formation of hydration shells is a property of water that helps to make it an effective solvent.

The correct answer is c...
B. Answer b is incorrect because although the high heat of vaporization is a property of water that helps to moderate changes in temperature, hydrophobic exclusion has nothing to do with the moderation of water temperature. Hydrophobic exclusion is the tendency of nonpolar molecules to aggregate when in water, causing these molecules to assume particular shapes.

The correct answer is c--high specific heat and high heat of vaporization.
C. The temperature of a substance is a measure of how rapidly its individual molecules are moving. Because of the hydrogen bonding that occurs between water molecules, a large input of thermal energy is needed to break the hydrogen bonds allowing the molecules to move around more freely, raising the temperature. Therefore, a great deal of energy is needed to increase the temperature of water (high specific heat) and an even greater amount of energy is needed to change liquid water into a gas (high heat of vaporization).

The correct answer is c...
D. Answer d is incorrect because the formation of hydration shells and hydrophobic exclusion are properties of water but they have nothing to do with helping to moderate changes in temperature. The formation of hydration shells is a property of water that helps to make it an effective solvent. Hydrophobic exclusion is the tendency of nonpolar molecules to aggregate when in water, causing these molecules to assume particular shapes.

Hint: Water moderates temperature through two properties associated with hydrogen bonding. Because of the many hydrogen bonds that form between water molecules, a large input of thermal energy is required to break these bonds before the individual water molecules can begin moving about more freely and so have a higher temperature. Water is therefore said to have a high specific heat which is the amount of energy (heat) needed to change the temperature of 1 gram of a substance by 1 degree Celsius (^{O}C). Water also has a high heat of vaporization which is the amount of energy (heat) needed to change 1 gram of liquid into a gas.

10). A substance with a high concentration of hydrogen ions is
      a). called a base.
      b). capable of acting as a buffer.
      c). called an acid.
      d). said to have a high pH.

The correct answer is c...
A. Answer a is incorrect because a base is a substance that combines with hydrogen ions in solution, actually lowering the concentration of hydrogen ions.

The correct answer is c...
B. Answer b is incorrect because a buffer is a substance that acts as a reservoir for hydrogen ions, releasing them or taking them up as necessary to maintain a nearly constant concentration of H^+. A buffer is usually a pair of substances that work in concert, an acid and a base.

The correct answer is c--called an acid.
C. Any substance that dissociates in water to increase the concentration of hydrogen ions is called an acid.

The correct answer is c...
D. Answer d is incorrect because a substance with a high pH has a lower concentration of hydrogen ions. pH is the measurement of hydrogen ion concentration in a solution, the higher the hydrogen ion concentration the lower the pH. Acids have low pHs while bases have high pHs.

Hint: Any stubstance that dissociates in water to increase the concentration of H^+ ions is called an acid. Acidic solutions have pH values below 7. The stronger an acid is, the more H^+ ions it produces and the lower it pH.

Test Your Visual Understanding

1). This figure shows two energy levels (*K* which has an *s* orbital labeled 1*s,* and *L,* which has an *s* orbital labeled 2*s* and three *p* orbitals labeled 2*p*). Knowing that the lower level fills with electrons first followed by the 2*s* orbital and then the *p* orbitals, indicate the number and placement of electrons for the following elements: Carbon (C), Hydrogen (H), Fluorine (F), and Neon (Ne).

Answer:

Carbon:
2 electron in the 1s orbital
2 electrons in the 2 s orbital
2 electrons in the 2p orbitals

Hydrogen:
1 electron in the 1s orbital

Fluorine:
2 electrons in the 1s orbital
2 electrons in the 2s orbital
5 electrons in the 2p orbitals

Neon:
2 electrons in the 1s orbital
2 electrons in the 2s orbital
6 electrons in the 2p orbitals

2). This atom has 7 protons and 7 neutrons. What is its atomic number? What is its atomic mass? Can you predict the number of covalent bonds it will form and explain why? What is this element?

Answer: The atomic number is 7, and the atomic mass is 14. This atom will form three covalent bonds. It has 5 electrons in its outer energy level and in accordance with the octet rule, it will form covalent bonds to bring the number of electrons in its outer energy level to eight. It can achieve this by forming one triple covalent bond, one double covalent bond and one single bond, or three single bonds. Any of these will fulfill the octet rule. This element is nitrogen

Apply Your Knowledge

1). The half-life of radium-226 is 1620 years. If a sample of material contains 16 milligrams of radium-226, how much will it contain in 1620 years? How much will it contain in 3240 years? How long will it take for the sample to contain 1 milligram of radium-226?

Answer: After 1620 (its half-life) half of the radium-226 would be left so:
16mg/2=8mg.
After 3240 (two half-lives) half of a half would be left or:
16mg/2=8mg and then 8mg/2=4mg.
A half-life is 1620 years and so it would take 4 half-lives to get the sample down to 1mg or 4x1620=6480:
After 1 half-life (1620 years)—16mg/2=8mg
After 2 half-lives (3240 years)—8mg/2=4mg
After 3 half-lives (4860 years)—4mg/2=2mg
After 4 half-lives (6480 years)—2mg/2=1mg

2). Scientists find a fossil of a marine animal in the middle of a desert. They use carbon-14 dating to determine how old the fossil is, which would indicate when an ocean covered the desert. There was a 10% (0.10) ratio of ^{14}C compared to ^{12}C in the sample (N_f/N_o) with a ^{14}C half-life ($t1/2$) of 5730 years. Using the equation: $t = [\ln(N_f/N_o)/(-0.693)]$ x t1/2 find the age of the fossil.

Answer: Using the equation: $t = [\ln(N_f/N_o)/(-0.693)]$ x t1/2, the fossil is:
t = [ln(0.10)/(-0.693)] x 5730
t = [(-2.303)/-0.693] x 5730
t = [3.323] x 5730
t = 19,041 years old
An ocean covered the desert 19,041 years ago

15

Inquiry Questions
None for this chapter.

Self Test

1). Proteins, nucleic acids, lipids and carbohydrates all have certain characteristics in common. Which of the following is *not* a common characteristic?
      a). They are organic, which means they are all living substances.
      b). They all contain the element carbon.
      c). They contain simpler units that are linked together making larger molecules.
      d). They all contain functional groups.

The correct answer is a--They are organic which means they are all living substances.
A. It is true that true that all four of these substances are organic but that does *not* mean that they are alive. When we say that these are all organic that means that they all contain the element carbon. Living organisms are composed of primarily organic molecules but the molecules themselves are not living.

The correct answer is a...
B. Answer b is incorrect because all four of these substances contain carbon, carbon bonded to other carbon atoms or bonded to other types of atoms such as oxygen, hydrogen, nitrogen, or sulfur.

The correct answer is a...
C. Answer c is incorrect because all four of these substances are composed of simpler subunits that link together to make large macromolecules. The subunits of proteins are amino acids. The subunits of nucleic acids are nucleotides. The subunits of lipids include glycerol and fatty acid chains. The subunits of carbohydrates include glucose.

The correct answer is a...
D. Answer d is incorrect because all four of these substances contain functional groups. Functional groups are groups of atoms that have defined chemical properties no matter where they occur. Phosphate, a functional group found as part of phospholipids or nucleic acids, has the same chemical property regardless of what type of molecule it is attached to.

Hint: Organic molecules are those whose chemical compounds contain carbon. The frameworks of biological molecules consist predominantly of carbon atoms bonded to other carbon atoms or to atoms of oxygen, nitrogen, sulfur, or hydrogen.

2). A peptide bond forms by:
      a). a condensation reaction.
      b). dehydration synthesis.
      c). the formation of a covalent bond.
      d). all of these.

The correct answer is d...
A. Answer a is incorrect because although a peptide bond forms by a condensation reaction, this isn't the only correct answer.

The correct answer is d...
B. Answer b is incorrect because although a peptide bond forms by dehydration synthesis, this isn't the only correct answer.

The correct answer is d...
C. Answer c is incorrect because although a peptide bond forms by the formation of a covalent bond, this isn't the only correct answer.

The correct answer is d--all of these.
D. A covalent bond that forms between two amino acids is called a peptide bond. This bond forms when a hydrogen from the amino group of one amino acid and an -OH from the carboxyl group of a second amino acid are lost as a water molecule, resulting in the formation of a covalent bond. The loss of water in a reaction is referred to as a condensation reaction or dehydration synthesis.

Hint: In addition to its R group, each amino acid, when ionized, has a positive amino group (NH_3^+) at one end and a negative carboxyl group (COO^-) at the other end. The amino and carboxyl groups on a pair of amino acids can undergo a condensation reaction, losing a molecule of water and forming a covalent bond. A covalent bond that links two amino acids is called a peptide bond.

3). Protein motifs are considered a type of
      a). primary structure.
      b). secondary structure.
      c). tertiary structure.
      d). quaternary structure.

The correct answer is b...
A. Answer a is incorrect because motifs involve hydrogen bonding between amino acids within the peptide. Primary structure involves peptide bonds forming the main backbone of the peptide.

The correct answer is b--secondary structure
B. Motifs are sometimes called "supersecondary structure" because motifs are a combination of secondary structural elements held in place by hydrogen bonding. For example, the alpha turn alpha motif is a combination of alpha helix structures that form a specific shape to the protein, which allows the protein to bind to the DNA double helix.

The correct answer is b...
C. Answer c is incorrect because motifs involve hydrogen bonding between amino acids within the peptide. Tertiary structure involves large scale folding of the peptide, which brings the motifs into the appropriate positions and folds the nonpolar side groups of amino acids toward the interior of the protein by hydrophobic exclusion.

The correct answer is b...
D. Answer d is incorrect because motifs involve hydrogen bonding between amino acids within the peptide. Quaternary structure involves the association of two or more polypeptide chains into a functional protein.

Hint: The structure of proteins is traditionally discussed in terms of four levels of structure, primary, secondary, tertiary, and quaternary but two additional levels of structure are increasingly distinguished by molecular biologists: motifs and domains. The elements of secondary structure can combine in proteins in characteristic ways called motifs or sometimes "supersecondary structure."

4). The substitution of one amino acid for another
      a). will change the primary structure of the polypeptide.
      b). can change the secondary structure of the polypeptide.
      c). can change the tertiary structure of the polypeptide.
      d). All of these are correct.

The correct answer is d...
A. Answer a is incorrect because although the amino acid substitution would change the primary structure, that isn't the only correct answer.

The correct answer is d...
B. Answer b is incorrect because although the amino acid substitution could change the secondary structure, that isn't the only correct answer.

The correct answer is d...
C. Answer c is incorrect because although the amino acid substitution could change the tertiary structure, that isn't the only correct answer.

The correct answer is d—All of these are correct.
D. A substitution of one amino acid for another will definitely change the primary structure of the polypeptide because the primary structure is determined by the sequence of amino acids. But, substituting amino acids could also greatly affect the secondary structure. If the amino acid that was lost in the substitution formed hydrogen bonds with other amino acids and the substituted amino acid cannot form those hydrogen bonds, the secondary structure is disrupted. For the same reasons, the tertiary structure could be disrupted.

Hint: Proteins consist of long amino acid chains folded into complex shapes with nonpolar amino acids literally shoved to the interior of the protein with the polar and charged amino acids restricted to the outside surface of the protein. The specific amino acid sequence of a protein is its primary structure. The amino acids form hydrogen bonds with each other within the polypeptide forming its secondary structure. The final folded shape of a globular protein, which positions the various motifs and folds nonpolar side groups into the interior, is called a protein's tertiary structure.

5). Chaperone proteins function by
      a). providing a protective environment in which proteins can fold properly.
      b). degrading proteins that have folded improperly.
      c). rescuing proteins that folded incorrectly and allow them to refold into the proper configuration.
      d). providing a template for how the proteins should fold.

The correct answer is c...
A. Answer a is incorrect because the chaperone proteins appear to correct a misfolded protein, suggesting that they play a more active role in the process, rather than just providing an environment for protein folding.

B. The correct answer is c...
Answer b is incorrect because chaperone proteins are not degradative proteins. A misfolded protein may eventually be degraded but the chaperone proteins do not have that function; proteolytic enzymes in the cell serve that function.

The correct answer is c--rescuing proteins that folded incorrectly and allow them to refold into the proper configuration.
C. A newly synthesized protein folds into its secondary structure but subsequent folding occurs by trial and error. This process is aided by chaperone proteins, which seem to recognize improperly folded proteins and unfolds them, giving them another chance to fold correctly.

The correct answer is c...
D. Answer d is incorrect because if chaperone proteins served as a template for protein folding, then there would need to be a chaperone protein specific to each type of protein. Less than two dozen chaperone proteins have been identified; far less than would be needed if they served as templates.

Hint: Molecular biologists have now identified more than 17 kinds of proteins that act as molecular chaperones. Many are heat shock proteins, produced in greatly elevated amounts is a cell is exposed to elevated temperatures; high temperatures cause proteins to unfold, and heat shock chaperone proteins help the cell's proteins refold.

6). Which of the following lists the purine nucleotides?
   a). adenine and cytosine
   b). guanine and thymine
   c). cytosine and thymine
   d). adenine and guanine

The correct answer is d...
A. Answer a is incorrect because although adenine is a purine base, cytosine is a pyrimidine base.

The correct answer is d...
B. Answer b is incorrect because although guanine is a purine base, thymine is a pyrimidine base.

The correct answer is d..
C. Answer c is incorrect because cytosine and thymine are pyrimidine bases.

The correct answer is d--adenine and guanine
D. Adenine and guanine are purine nucleotide bases. Cytosine, thymine (found in only in DNA), and uracil (found only in RNA) are pyrimidine nucleotide bases.

Hint: Two types of organic bases occur in nucleotides. The first type, purines, are large, double-ring molecules found in both DNA and RNA; they are adenine (A) and guanine (G). The second type, pyrimidines, are smaller, single-ring molecules; they include cytosine (C, in both DNA and RNA), thymine (T, in DNA only), and uracil (U, in RNA only).

7). The two strands of a DNA molecule are held together through base-pairing. Which of the following best describes the base-pairing in DNA?
   a). Adenine forms two hydrogen bonds with thymine.
   b). Adenine forms two hydrogen bonds with uracil.
   c). Cytosine forms two hydrogen bonds with guanine.
   d). Cytosine forms two hydrogen bonds with thymine.

The correct answer is a--Adenine forms two hydrogen bonds with thymine.
A. Because of how the nitrogenous bases line up along a strand of the DNA molecule, the six-sided ring structure of adenine can form two hydrogen bonds with the six-sided ring in thymine. Cytosine and guanine are not able to form hydrogen bonds with adenine. Uracil is also able to form hydrogen bonds with adenine but uracil is not a base found in DNA, only in RNA.

The correct answer is a...
B. Answer b is incorrect because adenine forms two hydrogen bonds with uracil in the formation of an RNA molecule, not DNA. Uracil is not found in DNA.

The correct answer is a...
C. Answer c is incorrect because although cytosine and guanine are complementary base pairs in DNA, they form three hydrogen bonds between themselves, not two.

The correct answer is a...
D. Answer d is incorrect because cytosine base pairs with guanine, not with thymine.

Hint: Each step of DNA's helical staircase is a base-pair, consisting of a base in one chain attracted by hydrogen bonds to a base opposite it on the other chain. These hydrogen bonds hold the two chains together as a duplex. The base-pairing rules are rigid: adenine can only pair with thymine (in DNA) or with uracil (in RNA), and cytosine can only pair with guanine.

8). A characteristic common to all lipids is
   a). that they contain long chains of C-H bonds.
   b). that they are insoluble in water.
   c). that they have a glycerol backbone.
   d). All of these are characteristics of all lipids.

The correct answer is b...
A. Answer a is incorrect because although many lipids contain long chains of C-H bonds, called fatty acid chains/tails, not all lipids have fatty acid tails. Some lipids have multi-ringed structures, such as cholesterol.

The correct answer is b--that they are all soluble in water.
B. Lipids are a varied group of molecules with a common characteristic that they are insoluble in water. Lipids contain a high proportion of C-H bonds that are nonpolar, which makes the molecules nonpolar. Only polar or charged molecules are soluble in water.

The correct answer is b...
C. Answer c is incorrect because although many lipids have a 3-carbon glycerol backbone structure, not all lipids have glycerol. Some lipids have multi-ringed structures, such as cholesterol.

The correct answer is b...
D. Answer d is incorrect because only option b is a characteristic common to all lipids. Options a and c are not characteristics common to all lipids, for example steroids have multi-ringed structures and don't have long chains of C-H bonds or a glycerol backbone.

Hint: Lipids are a loosely defined group of molecules with one main characteristic: they are insoluble in water. The most familiar lipids are fats and oils. Lipids have a very high proportion of nonpolar carbon-hydrogen (C-H) bonds, and so lipid molecules will cluster together, exposing what polar groups they have to the water.

9). Carbohydrates have many functions in the cell. Which of the following is an *incorrect* match of the carbohydrate with its function?
   a). sugar transport in plants--disaccharides
   b). energy storage in plants--starches
   c). energy storage in plants--lactose
   d). sugar transport in humans--glucose

The correct answer is c...
A. Answer a is incorrect because plants *do* use disaccharides to transport sugars throughout the plant body. Sugar in a disaccharide form is less readily metabolized during transport.

The correct answer is c...
B. Answer b is incorrect because plants *do* store energy in long polymers called polysaccharides. Starch is a polysaccharide formed in plants by linking glucose molecules together.

The correct answer is c--energy storage in plants/lactose
C. Plants store energy in different forms, such as starch, cellulose, and amylopectin but *not* as lactose. Lactose is a disaccharide found in the milk produced by mammals that supplies energy to their young.

The correct answer is c...
D. Answer d is incorrect because humans *do* transport sugar throughout their bodies in the form of glucose. Glucose is required by the cells throughout the body and needs to be readily available so it is not converted to a disaccharide or any other form for transport.

Hint: Organisms store the metabolic energy contained in monosaccharides by converting them into disaccharides, which are linked together into insoluble forms. These insoluble polysaccharides are long polymers of monosaccharides. Plant polysaccharides formed from glucose are called starches.

10). Which of the following carbohydrates is associated with plants?
    a). glycogen
    b). amylopectin
    c). chitin
    d). levo-glucose

The correct answer is b...
A. Answer a is incorrect because glycogen is a highly branched glucose storage molecule found in animals. This polysaccharide, like starch in plants, forms an insoluble mesh of glucose, made available to the animal as needed.

The correct answer is b--amylopectin
B. Amylopectin is a branched polysaccharide of glucose. In plants, this starch forms cross-links which results in a mesh of glucose. Energy is stored in these molecules as starch granules in chloroplasts and other plant organelles.

The correct answer is b...
C. Answer c is incorrect because chitin is a structural carbohydrate found in insects, fungi, and certain other organisms. Chitin forms a tough, resistant surface material. Cellulose is a similar structural carbohydrate found in plants.

The correct answer is b...
D. Answer d is incorrect because levo-glucose is "left-handed" form of glucose, which doesn't occur naturally in plants. l-sugars, as they are called, are usually synthesized in the lab but have been found in trace amounts in red algae, snail eggs, and seaweed.

Hint: Plant polysaccharides formed from glucose are called starches. The starch with the simplest structure is amylose, which is composed of many hundreds of glucose molecules linked together in long unbranched chains. Most plant starch is a somewhat more complicated variant of amylose called amylopectin.

Test Your Visual Understanding

1). The amino acids of a polypeptide affect the shape of the protein. Assume this is a section of a longer polypeptide chain. Predict where each of the following amino acid pairs would be found in the protein—facing toward the outside or folded in toward the interior—and explain why:
a). Both amino acids are valine.
b). One amino acid is aspartic acid, and the other is serine.
c). Both amino acids are glycine.
d). One amino acid is alanine, and the other is isoleucine
Answer:
a). Valine is a nonpolar amino acid and is repelled by water, therefore this section of the polypeptide chain would be folded in toward the interior away from the watery environment.
b). Aspartic acid is a charged amino acid and serine is a polar amino acid; both are attracted to water, therefore this section of the polypeptide chain would be facing toward the outside.
c). Glycine is a polar amino acid and is attracted to water, therefore this section of the polypeptide chain would be facing toward the outside.
d). Alanine and isoleucine are both nonpolar amino acids and are repelled by water, therefore this section of the polypeptide chain would be folded in toward the interior away from the watery environment.

2). Describe the DNA template that produced this molecule of RNA by indicating the DNA bases that are complementary to the RNA bases numbered.
Answer:

#1--A
#2--T
#3--G
#4--C
#5--T
#6--A
#7--C

Apply Your Knowledge
1). How many molecules of water are used up in the breakdown of a polypeptide 15 amino acids in length?
Answer: A polypeptide that has fifteen amino acids is held together by fourteen peptide bonds. One molecule of water is consumed in the breaking of a peptide bond, therefore:
1 molecule of water x number of peptide bonds or:
1 x 14 = 14 water molecules

2).Why do you suppose the monosaccharide glucose is circulated in the blood of humans rather than a disaccharide, such as sucrose, which is the transport sugar found in plants?
Answer: Humans use glucose in metabolic pathways for the generation of cellular energy. Glucose flows into metabolic pathways directly. A disaccharide, such as sucrose, would require an additional step before entering into a metabolic pathway. Therefore, it is more efficient for humans to transport sugar in the blood as glucose. Plants, on the other hand, use the carbohydrates they produce as building blocks of cellular tissues, therefore, the transportation of carbohydrates as sucrose is more efficient in plants.

None for this chapter.

Self Test

1). Which of the following is necessary and sufficient for life?
- a). complexity
- b). heredity
- c). growth
- d). all of these

The correct answer is b...
A. Answer a is incorrect because non-living objects can have complexity, for example a computer has complexity. So, although complexity is a necessary property (possessed by all life) it is not sufficient to define life (possessed only by living organisms).

The correct answer is b--heredity
B. Although all of the properties are necessary for life, meaning that they are possess by all living things only heredity is a property that is possessed only by living organisms. All living organisms have complexity and the ability to grow but non-living things may also possess these properties so they are not sufficient to define life.

The correct answer is b...
C. Answer c is incorrect because non-living objects can grow, for example soap bubbles grow when air is blown into them. So, although growth is a necessary property (possessed by all life), it is not sufficient to define life (possessed only by living organisms).

The correct answer is b...
D. Answer d is incorrect because only answer b is a property of life that is both necessary and sufficient. Non-living objects can have complexity, for example a computer has complexity. So, although complexity is a necessary property (possessed by all life), it is not sufficient to define life (possessed only by living organisms). Non-living objects can grow, for example soap bubbles grow when air is blown into them. So, although growth is a necessary property (possessed by all life), it is not sufficient to define life (possessed only by living organisms).

Hint: The criteria of cellular organization, sensitivity, growth, development, reproduction, regulation, and homeostasis, although necessary for life, are not sufficient to define life. One ingredient is missing--a mechanism of the preservation of improvement--heredity.

2). Which of the following most accurately describes the origins of life on earth?
- a). Special creation: Life-forms were put on earth by supernatural or divine forces.
- b). Extraterrestrial origin: The earth may have been infected by life from another planet.
- c). Spontaneous origin: Life evolved from inanimate matter to increasing levels of complexity.
- d). None of these are accurate.

The correct answer is d...
A. Answer a is incorrect because although the hypothesis of special creation could be true, we are not able to test it experimentally and so it is a hypothesis that can't be supported or rejected. Therefore, it can not be considered a "scientific" hypothesis.

The correct answer is d...
B. Answer b is incorrect because although the hypothesis of extraterrestrial origin could be true and there is some scientific evidence that adds support to this hypothesis, we can not yet say that it is the most accurate description of the origin of life on earth.

The correct answer is d...
C. Answer c is incorrect because although the hypothesis of spontaneous origin could be true and there is some scientific evidence that adds support to this hypothesis, we can not yet say that it is the most accurate description of the origin of life on earth.

The correct answer is d--none of the above.
D. We don't yet know how life began on the earth and so none of the three hypotheses can be said to *most accurately* describe the origins of life on earth. However, only extraterrestrial origin and spontaneous origin are scientifically-testable hypotheses and so only these two hypotheses can be tested experimentally.

Hint: Any one of the three possible explanations of the origins of life on earth might be true. However, we are limiting the scope of inquiry to scientific matters, and only extraterrestrial and spontaneous origins permit testable hypotheses to be constructed--that is, explanations that can be tested and potentially disproved.

3). Which of the following proposals assumes that the earth had a reducing atmosphere low in oxygen?
        a). Life evolved deep in the earth's crust.
        b). Life evolved under frozen oceans.
        c). Life evolved at the ocean's edge.
        d). Life evolved at deep-sea vents.

The correct answer is c...
A. Answer a is incorrect because if life formed deep in the ocean's crust, there would be no interaction with the atmosphere and so it wouldn't matter if the atmosphere was or was not a reducing atmosphere.

The correct answer is c...
B. Answer b is incorrect because if life formed under frozen oceans, there would be no interaction with the earth's atmosphere and so it wouldn't matter if the atmosphere was or was not a reducing atmosphere.

The correct answer is c--at the ocean's edge.
C. The atmosphere of early earth was hot and chemicals in the water and atmosphere under went chemical reactions to produce other molecules. If oxygen had been present in the atmosphere, it would have reacted with the newly formed molecules, breaking them down into water and carbon dioxide. Therefore, a reducing atmosphere with little oxygen would be necessary for life to begin at the ocean's edge.

The correct answer is c...
D. Answer d is incorrect because if life formed at deep-sea vents, there would be no interaction with the earth's atmosphere and so it wouldn't matter if the atmosphere was or was not a reducing atmosphere.

Hint: By studying the earth's history, we know that the atmosphere of early earth was very hot, improving the likelihood of chemical reactions. In a hot atmosphere composed of carbon dioxide, nitrogen gas, water vapor, hydrogen gas and elements other than oxygen, molecules could form at the water/air interface through chemical reaction. Such an atmosphere is said to be a reducing atmosphere. If oxygen were present in the atmosphere, it would react with the newly formed molecules, breaking them down to form carbon dioxide and water.

4). Scientists have created synthetic nucleotide-like molecules in the laboratory that are able to replicate. This seems to support which hypothesis of chemical evolution?
   a). an RNA-first hypothesis
   b). a protein-first hypothesis
   c). a peptide-nucleic acid first hypothesis
   d). All of the hypotheses are supported by these results.

The correct answer is a--an RNA-first hypothesis
A. A primary argument of the RNA first hypothesis is that a hereditary molecule would need to have been first so that molecules could form consistently. Critics of this argue that nucleic acids are too complex to form spontaneously and need enzyme to guide their synthesis. The creation of synthetic nucleotide-like molecules in the lab suggests that it is possible for nucleotides to form on their own.

The correct answer is a...
B. Answer b is incorrect because the synthesis of a nucleotide-like molecule in the laboratory that is able to replicate is in direct opposition to the protein first argument that suggests that nucleic acids are too complex to form spontaneously and would require enzymes in order to replicate.

The correct answer is a...
C. Answer c is incorrect because the peptide-nucleic acid first hypothesis suggests that the first molecule was a combination of the two types of organic molecules that would be simple enough to form spontaneously and would replicate itself. However, the synthesis of a nucleotide-like molecule in the laboratory that replicates suggests that a peptide component is not required.

The correct answer is a...
D. Answer d is incorrect because only option a is supported by these results. The results do not support b because synthesis of a nucleotide-like molecule in the laboratory that is able to replicate is in direct opposition to the protein first argument that suggests that nucleic acids are too complex to form spontaneously and would require enzymes in order to replicate. And the results do not support c because the synthesis of a nucleotide-like molecule in the laboratory that replicates suggests that a peptide component is not required.

Hint: Deciding which came first, RNA or proteins, is a chicken-and-egg paradox. In an effort to shed light on this problem, Julius Rebek and a number of other chemists have created synthetic nucleotide-like molecules in the laboratory that are able to replicate. Moving even further, Rebek and his colleagues have created synthetic molecules that could replicate and "make mistakes." This simulates mutations, a necessary ingredient for the process of evolution.

5). A key link needed between bubbles and cells is
   a). that they needed a hereditary molecule.
   b). that they needed to grow and bud off new bubbles.
   c). that they needed to incorporate enzymes.
   d). that they needed to form spontaneously.

The correct answer is a--that they needed a hereditary molecule.
A. While microspheres (or the other names given to these bubble structures) could form readily in water and could incorporate organic molecules, in order to make the jump to cells, they required a means of reproducing which would pass genetic information onto offspring bubbles.

The correct answer is a...
B. Answer b is incorrect because although growing and budding off new bubbles would have been an important step in the jump from bubble to cell, this wouldn't assure that anything that was incorporated into the first bubble would be passed on to the budding bubbles.

The correct answer is a...
C. Answer c is incorrect because although the incorporation of enzymes helped a bubble exist longer, once the bubble popped, it was gone. Hereditary molecules were needed to assure that molecular information was passed on to other bubbles.

The correct answer is a...
D. Answer d is incorrect because although the bubble needed to originally form spontaneously, each new cell could not form spontaneously. Once hereditary molecules were incorporated in to the bubbles this allowed them a method to reproduce, assuring that the "daughter" bubbles were like the "parent" bubble.

Hint: Whether the early bubbles that gave rise to cells were lipid or protein remains an unresolved argument. While it is true that lipids microspheres (coacervates) will form readily in water, there appears to be no mechanism for their heritable replication. On the other hand, one can imagine a heritable mechanism for protein microspheres. The discovery that RNA can act as an enzyme to assemble new RNA molecules on an RNA template has raised the interesting possibility that perhaps the first components of cells were RNA molecules. That stable RNA became surrounded by microspheres.

6). Prokaryotes were the only life-form on the earth
        a). for about 1.5 billion years.
        b). for about 1 billion years.
        c). for about 2.5 billion years.
        d). for more than 2.5 billion years.

The correct answer is b...
A. Answer a is incorrect because the prokaryotes existed alone on the earth less than 1.5 billion years. The eukaryotes appear in the fossil record about 1.5 billion years ago, but prokaryotes had already been around for about 1 billion years.

The correct answer is b--1 billion years.
B. The earliest microfossils of prokaryotes were found in rock about 2.5 billion years old. The fossil record shows eukaryotes appearing about 1.5 billion years ago, which means that prokaryotes existed alone for about 1 billion years.

The correct answer is b...
C. Answer c is incorrect because although prokaryotes appear in the fossil record 2.5 billion years ago, eukaryotes appear about 1.5 billion years ago and so that ended the prokaryote's sole existence.

The correct answer is b...
D. Answer d is incorrect because the prokaryotes don't appear much before 2.5 billion years and so it is not likely that they've been around for more than 2.5 billion years. Also, eukaryotes appear about 1.5 billion years ago and so that ended the prokaryote's sole existence.

Hint: What do we know about the earliest life-forms? The fossils found in ancient rocks show an obvious progression from simple to complex organisms, beginning about 2.5 billion years ago. Life may have been present earlier, but rocks of such great antiquity are rare, and fossils have not yet been found in them. The earliest evidence of life appears in microfossils, fossilized forms of microscopic life. Judging from the fossil record, eukaryotes did not appear until about 1.5 billion years ago.

7). The first organisms may have been a type of archaebacteria similar to present day organisms called
        a). extreme halophiles.
        b). prokaryotes.
        c). extreme thermophiles.
        d). eubacteria.

The correct answer is c...
A. Answer a is incorrect because although extreme halophiles live in harsh salty conditions, this doesn't mimic early earth which was a high temperature environment.

The correct answer is c...
B. Answer b is incorrect because prokaryote is the name given to all single-celled organisms that lack a true nucleus. Although the earliest life-form was a prokaryote, scientists have been able to narrow that down even further to a specific type of archaebacteria.

The correct answer is c--extreme thermophiles.
C. The extreme thermophiles are a group of archaebacteria that live at very high temperatures and so would have thrived in the conditions of early earth.

The correct answer is c...
D. Answer d is incorrect because eubacteria is the second major group of prokaryotes (the other group is archaebacteria). The first organisms were probably more closely related to archaebacteria rather than to eubacteria.

Hint: Thermophiles have been found living comfortably in boiling water. Indeed, many kinds of thermophilic archaebacteria thrive at temperatures of $110^{\circ}C$ ($230^{\circ}F$). Because thermophiles live at high temperatures similar to those that may have existed when life first evolved, microbiologists speculate that thermophilic archaebacteria may be relics of earth's first organisms.

8). The infolding of outer membrane seen in prokaryotes is believed to have given rise to which of the following?
      a). mitochondrion
      b). chloroplast
      c). endoplasmic reticulum
      d). all of these structures

The correct answer is c...
A. Answer a is incorrect because the mitochondrion is believed to have evolved from energy-producing endosymbiotic bacteria that resided in larger bacterial cells, ultimately becoming part of that larger cells.

The correct answer is c...
B. Answer b is incorrect because the chloroplast is believed to have evolved from photosynthetic endosymbiotic bacterial that resided in larger bacterial cells, ultimately becoming part of the larger cells.

The correct answer is c--endoplasmic reticulum
C. Eukaryotic cells have an extensive network of internal membranes called the endoplasmic reticulum (ER) that extends between the nucleus and the surface of the cell. Substances are transported throughout the cell through these passageways. Bacteria have infoldings of their outer membranes that may have expanded and evolved into the more complex eukaryotic ER.

The correct answer is c...
D. Answer d is incorrect because only answer c is believed to have evolved from the infoldings of the outer membrane. Both the mitochondrion and the chloroplast were believed to have evolved from endosymbiotic bacteria that resided in larger bacterial cells, ultimately becoming part of those cells.

Hint: Many bacteria have infoldings of their outer membranes extending into the cytoplasm and serving as passageways to the surface. The network of internal membranes in eukaryotes called endoplasmic reticulum (ER) is thought to have evolved from such infoldings, as is the nuclear envelope, an extension of the ER network that isolates and protects the nucleus.

9). All organisms fall into one of _____ domains that include _____ kingdoms.
  a). six/three
  b). six/six
  c). three/three
  d). three/six

The correct answer is d...
A. Answer a is incorrect because there are three domains and six kingdoms.

The correct answer is d...
B. Answer b is incorrect because there are only three domains, not six, however, there are six kingdoms.

The correct answer is d...
C. Answer c is incorrect because although there are three domains, there are six kingdoms.

The correct answer is d--three/six
D. There are three domains, which is a larger more generalized group of organisms. The three domains have been established based on three general cell types: Archae (which includes the archaebacteria), Bacteria (which includes the eubacteria), and Eukarya (which includes all eukaryotes). Under these three domains are six kingdoms: Archaebacteria (Archae), Eubacteria (Bacteria), Protista (Eukarya), Fungi (Eukarya), Plantae (Eukarya), and Animalia (Eukarya).

Hint: Confronted with the great diversity of life on earth today, biologists have attempted to categorize similar organisms in order to better understand them, giving rise to the science of taxonomy. We can generalize that all living things fall into one of three domains that include six kingdoms.

10). Which of the following statements is false.
  a). Life may have evolved on Mars.
  b). In order for life to evolve anywhere, carbon is required.
  c). A large ocean exists under the icy surface of Europa.
  d). It is possible that life may have evolved on some other planet.

The correct answer is b...
A. Answer a is incorrect because the statement is true. Mars is now a frozen, arid planet but that has not always been the case. Billions of years ago, it is believed that mars was a warmer planet, flowing with water, and had a carbon dioxide atmosphere--conditions not different from early earth. Therefore it is reasonable to assume that life had evolved on mars at some time.

The correct answer is b--In order for life to evolve anywhere, carbon is required.
B. This statement is false. It is easy to assume that because carbon was the basis of the evolution of life on earth that carbon is absolutely necessary for life. However, other elements such as silicon have similar chemical properties of those in carbon (requiring four electrons to fill its outer energy level) and could likely form the backbone of another type of "organic" molecule.

The correct answer is b...
C. Answer c is incorrect because the statement is true. Europa is covered with ice but photos of Europa reveal a sea of liquid water beneath the surface of the ice. In coming decades satellite missions are scheduled to explore this ocean for life.

The correct answer is b...
D. Answer d is incorrect because the statement is true. The universe has 10^{20} stars similar to our sun and it seems likely that at least some of these stars have planets. Life could form on one of these planets that was the right size and distance from the its star to create conditions favorable for the evolution of life.

Hint: We should not overlook the possibility that life processes might have evolved in different ways on other planets. A functional genetic system, capable of accumulating and replicating changes and thus of adaptation and evolution, could theoretically evolve from molecules other than carbon, hydrogen, nitrogen, and oxygen in a different environment. Silicon, like carbon, needs four electrons to fill its outer energy level, and ammonia is even more polar that water. Perhaps under radically different temperature and pressures, these elements might form molecules as diverse and flexible as those carbon has formed on earth.

Test Your Visual Understanding

1). Match the following descriptions with the appropriate numbered step in the figure that explains a bubble hypothesis.

a). Bombarded by the sun's ultraviolet radiation, lightning, and other energy sources, the simple organic molecules released from the bubbles reacted to form more complex organic molecules.
b). Volcanoes erupted under the sea, releasing gases enclosed in bubbles.
c). The more complex organic molecules fell back into the sea in raindrops. There, they could be enclosed in bubbles and begin the process again.
d). When the bubbles persisted long enough to rise to the surface, they popped, releasing their contents to the air.
e). The gases, concentrated inside the bubbles, reacted to produce simple organic molecules.
Answer:
1—b
2—e
3—d
4—a
5—c

Apply Your Knowledge

1). In Fred Hoyle's science fiction novel, *The Black Cloud*, the earth is approached by a large interstellar cloud of gas that orients itself around the sun. Scientists soon discover that the cloud is feeding on the sun, absorbing the sun's energy through the excitation of electrons in the outer energy levels of cloud molecules, in a process similar to the photosynthesis that occurs on earth. Different portions of the cloud are isolated from each other by associations of ions created by this excitation. Electron currents pass between these portions, much as they do on the surface of the human brain, endowing the cloud with self-awareness, memory, and the ability to think. Using electrical discharges, the cloud is able to communicate with humans and describe its history. It tells scientists that it originated as a small extrusion from an ancestral cloud, and that since then it has grown by the absorption of molecules and energy from stars like our sun, on which it has been feeding. Soon the cloud moves off in search of other stars. Is it alive?

Answer:
1). The cloud appears alive possessing several fundamental properties of life including internal organization (such as cellular organization), sensitivity, growth, regulation, and homeostasis. However, a key property of life that the cloud does not seem to possess is that of heredity. Although the cloud grows, it does not seem capable of reproducing offspring that carry characteristics passed on from the parent. Without this key characteristic, the cloud would not be considered alive.

Self Test

1). What type of microscope would you need to view a cellular structure that is 5 nm in size?
    a). a light microscope
    b). an electron microscope
    c). a compound microscope
    d). no microscope can resolve down to 5 nm

The correct answer is b...
A. Answer a is incorrect because a light microscope, depending on the magnification of the lenses, can only view a structure about 200 nm in size. Any smaller than that, the wavelengths of light begin to overlap, reducing resolution.

The correct answer is b--an electron microscope
B. An electron microscope uses electron bombardment to view a structure and an electron's wavelength is much shorter than that of visible light. A structure 5 nm in size can easily be resolved by an electron microscope.

The correct answer is b...
C. Answer c is incorrect because although a compound microscope is able to increase the magnification of an image, it still uses visible light. The shortest wavelength of visible light is about 400 nm so even with increased magnification, the compound microscope would never be able to distinguish a structure 5 nm in size.

The correct answer is b....
D. Answer d is incorrect because an electron microscope is able to resolve an object much less than 5 nm in size.

Hint: Light microscopes, even compound ones, are not powerful enough to resolve many structures within cells. For example, a membrane is only 5 nanometers thick. Why not just add another magnifying stage to the microscope and so increase its resolving power? Because when two objects are closer that a few hundred nanometers, the light beams reflecting from the two images start to overlap. The only way two light beams can get closer together and still be resolved is if their "wavelengths" are shorter. One way to avoid overlap is by using a beam of electrons rather than a beam of light.

2). Which of the following is *not* found in prokaryotic cells?
    a). ribosomes
    b). cell wall
    c). nucleus
    d). photosynthetic membranes

The correct answer is c...
A. Answer a is incorrect because ribosomes are one of the few cellular structures that bacteria have. Ribosomes are the site of protein synthesis and bacteria carry out this process on ribosomes that float in their cytoplasm.

The correct answer is c...
B. Answer b is incorrect because bacteria do have cell walls. The cell walls in bacteria are of a unique chemical composition of carbohydrates and proteins. The cell wall is necessary to maintain the shape of the bacterial cell and keep it from rupturing.

The correct answer is c--nucleus
C. Although bacteria do not contain any cellular organelles to speak of, the nucleus if the one organelle that separates the eukaryotes from the prokaryotes. Eukaryotic cells have their DNA sequestered in the nucleus, sheltered from the rest of the cells while the DNA in prokaryotic cells is exposed to the cytoplasm.

The correct answer is c...
D. Answer d is incorrect because photosynthetic bacteria have extensive infoldings of their plasma membranes that contain the pigments necessary for photosynthesis. This is the extent of compartmentalizing in bacterial cells.

Hint: If you were to look at an electron micrograph of a bacterial cell, you would be struck by the cell's simple organization. There are few, if any, internal compartments, and while they contain simple structures like ribosomes, most have not membrane-bound organelles, the kinds so characteristic of eukaryotic cells. Nor do bacteria have a true nucleus. The entire cytoplasm of a bacterial cell is one unit would not internal support structure. Consequently, the strength of the cell comes primary from its rigid wall.

3). Which of the following statements is incorrect.
   a). DNA in the nucleus is usually coiled into chromosomes.
   b). The nucleolus is the site of ribosomal RNA synthesis.
   c). Some substances can pass into and out of the nucleus.
   d). Red blood cells can not synthesize RNA.

The correct answer is a--DNA in the nucleus is usually coiled into chromosomes.
A. DNA is *not* usually coiled into chromosomes. RNA can not be synthesized from DNA unless the DNA is expanded into long threadlike strings called chromatin. DNA coils up into chromosomes only during cell division. Because a cell spends most of its time growing and making RNA, not in dividing, the DNA is usually not coiled into chromosomes.

The correct answer is a...
B. Answer b is incorrect because the statement is true. The nucleolus is the site of ribosomal RNA synthesis. The cell produces a lot of ribosomal RNA and so there is a special area in the cell where this type of RNA synthesis occurs; it is called the nucleolus.

The correct answer is a...
C. Answer c is incorrect because the statement is true. The nucleus contains protein-lined pores that allow some substances to pass into and out of the nucleus. The substances that pass into the nucleus are primarily proteins and the substances that pass out the of nucleus are primarily RNA molecules.

The correct answer is a...
D. Answer d is incorrect because the statement is true. Red blood cells lose their nuclei when they mature and without an nucleus there is no DNA. Without DNA no RNA can be synthesized.

Hints: The DNA of eukaryotes is divided into several linear chromosomes. Except when the cell is dividing, its chromosomes are fully extended into threadlike strands, called chromatin, of DNA complexed with protein. This open arrangement allows proteins to attach to specific nucleotide sequences along the DNA. Without this access, DNA could not direct the day-to-day activities of the cell.

4). Which of the following matches are not correct.
   a). ribosomes -- rough ER
   b). protein synthesis -- smooth ER
   c). rough ER -- export of proteins out of cell
   d). smooth ER -- cells in intestine

The correct answer is b...
A. Answer a is incorrect because ribosomes match correctly with rough ER. Endoplasmic reticulum that has ribosomes associated with the membrane is called rough ER because it has a rough, pebbled appearance.

The correct answer is b--protein synthesis -- smooth ER
B. This is not a correct match. Protein synthesis occurs on the ribosomes associated with the rough ER, not the smooth ER. The smooth ER is involved in the synthesis of carbohydrates and lipids.

The correct answer is b...
C. Answer c is incorrect because rough ER matches correctly with export of proteins out of the cell. Proteins that are synthesized on ribosomes associated with the rough ER, enter the cisternal space of the rough ER and eventually are transported to the plasma membrane and out of the cell.

The correct answer is b...
D. Answer d is incorrect because smooth ER matches correctly with cells of the intestine and liver. Smooth ER contains proteins involved in the synthesis of carbohydrates and lipids. Cells such as those found in the intestines carry out extensive lipid synthesis and therefore have abundant amounts of smooth ER.

Hint: The ER surface regions that are devoted to protein synthesis are heavily studded with ribosomes, large molecular aggregates of protein and ribonucleic acid (RNA) that translate RNA copies of genes into proteins. Through the electron microscope, these ribosome-rich regions of the ER appear pebbly, like the surface of sandpaper, and they are therefore called rough ER.

5). Which is the following is *not* produced by the Golgi apparatus?
    a). glycolipids
    b). glycoproteins
    c). liposomes
    d). secretory vesicles

The correct answer is c...
A. Answer a is incorrect because glycolipids are produced by the Golgi apparatus. Lipids manufactured on the smooth ER are transported to the Golgi apparatus and are modified as they pass through. Lipids are modified by the addition of a short sugar chain onto the lipid, producing a glycolipid.

The correct answer is c...
B. Answer b is incorrect because glycoproteins are produced by the Golgi apparatus. Proteins manufactured on the rough ER are transported to the Golgi apparatus and are modified as they pass through. Proteins are modified by the addition of a short sugar chain onto the protein, producing a glycoprotein.

The correct answer is c--liposomes
C. Liposomes are not produced by the cell, but rather are synthetic "membrane" vesicles, developed as a delivery system of drugs or other substances into the cell.

The correct answer is c...
D. Answer d is incorrect because secretory vesicles are produced by the Golgi apparatus. The formation of secretory vesicles is the last step in the modification process of proteins and lipids in the Golgi apparatus. After the molecules have passed through the Golgi apparatus they come to the *trans* face of the Golgi where they are packaged into secretory vesicles for distribution throughout the cell or to the plasma membrane to be released from the cell.

Hint: Liposomes are synthetically manufactured vesicles that contain any variety of desirable substances (such as drugs), and can be injected into the body. Because the membrane of liposomes is similar to plasma and organelle membranes, these liposomes serve as an effective and natural delivery system to cells and may prove to be of great therapeutic value.

6). What is the difference between a primary lysosome and a secondary lysosome?
       a). Primary lysosomes are larger than secondary lysosomes.
       b). Primary lysosomes are active, while secondary lysosomes are inactive.
       c). Primary lysosomes have a low pH while, secondary lysosomes have a high pH.
       d). Primary lysosomes have low levels of protons, while secondary lysosomes have high levels of protons.

The correct answer is d...
A. Answer a is incorrect because a secondary lysosome which has fused with a vesicle or organelle will actually be larger than the inactive primary lysosome.

The correct answer is d...
B. Answer b is incorrect because lysosome doesn't become active until it fuses with a substance (old organelle or vesicle) that is to be digested. Prior to fusing with a substance the lysosome is inactive and is called a primary lysosome. Once it binds to the substance, its enzymes become activated and it is called a secondary lysosome.

The correct answer is d...
C. Answer c is incorrect because primary lysosomes are inactive and therefore they have a high pH (basic). Once the lysosome fuses with a substance to be digested, its pH drops (it becomes acidic) and it then is called a secondary lysosome.

The correct answer is d--Primary lysosomes have low levels of protons, while secondary lysosomes have high levels of protons.
D. The hydrolytic enzymes in lysosomes require an acidic environment to become active. When a lysosome is not active, it has a high internal pH and is called a primary lysosome. When a primary lysosome fuses with a substance that is to be digested, it pumps hydrogen ions (protons) to the interior causing the pH to drop. This activates the hydrolytic enzymes and the lysosome becomes a secondary lysosome.

Hint: The digestive enzymes in lysosomes function best in an acidic environment. Lysosomes actively engaged in digestion keep their battery of hydrolytic enzymes fully active by pumping protons into their interiors and thereby maintaining a low internal pH. Lysosomes that are not functioning actively do not maintain an acidic internal pH and are called primary lysosomes. When primary lysosome fuses with a food vesicle or other organelle, its pH falls and its arsenal of hydrolytic enzymes is activated; it is then called a secondary lysosome.

7). Proteins that stay within the cell are produced
       a). on free ribosomes in the cytoplasm.
       b). in the nucleolus.
       c). on ribosomes attached to rough ER.
       d). on ribosomes and pass through the Golgi apparatus.

The correct answer is a--on free ribosomes in the cytoplasm.
A. The cell produces many different proteins, some stay in the cell and some are incorporated into plasma membranes or are transported out the of cell. A protein that is to remain in the cell does not enter the endomembrane system because it can't get back out, so those proteins are produced on free-floating ribosomes in the cytoplasm.

The correct answer is a...
B. Answer b is incorrect because the nucleolus is the site of ribosomal RNA transcription and assembly. No proteins are translated in the nucleus, only in the cytoplasm or in the endomembrane system.

The correct answer is a...
C. Answer c is incorrect because only proteins that are destined to leave the cell are produced on ribosomes attached to the rough ER. Once a protein enters the cisternal space of the rough ER, it remains enclosed in membrane and can not pass back into the cytoplasm.

The correct answer is a...
D. Answer d is incorrect because although all proteins are produce on ribosomes, only those proteins destined to leave the cell pass through the Golgi apparatus. Once a protein enters the endomembrane system, it remains enclosed in membrane and can not pass back into the cytoplasm.

Hint: Proteins that function in the cytoplasm are made by free ribosomes suspended there, while proteins bound within membranes or destined for export from the cell are assembled by ribosomes bound to rough ER.

8). What do chloroplasts and mitochondria have in common?
    a). Both are all present in animal cells.
    b). Both contain their own genetic material.
    c). Both are present in all eukaryotic cells.
    d). Neither is present in plant cells.

The correct answer is b...
A. Answer a is incorrect because animal cells do not contain chloroplasts. Chloroplasts are found only in plant cells and other eukaryotic cells that carry out photosynthesis.

The correct answer is b--They all contain their own genetic material.
B. Mitochondria and chloroplasts contain their own DNA which encode for some of the proteins involved in their unique functions, but some of these proteins are also encoded in the nuclear DNA.

The correct answer is b...
C. Answer c is incorrect because both organelles are not found in all eukaryotic cells. Animal cells contain mitochondria but no chloroplasts. Plant cells contain mitochondria and chloroplasts. All protists contain mitochondria but only some contain chloroplasts. Fungi do not contain chloroplasts.

The correct answer is b...
D. Answer d is incorrect because plant cells have mitochondria and chloroplasts.

Hint: Among the most interesting cell organelles are those in addition to the nucleus that contain DNA. Mitochondria have their own DNA; this DNA contains several genes that produce proteins essential to the mitochondrion's role in oxidative metabolism. Chloroplasts contain DNA, but many of the genes are also located in the nucleus.

9). Which of the following pairs is correctly matched?
    a). actin—MTOC
    b). intermediate fibers—protofilaments
    c). microtubules--"+" / "-" ends
    d). intermediate fibers –cellular movement

The correct answer is c...
A. Answer a is incorrect because actin is not associated with MTOCs. MTOC stands for microtubule-organizing centers, which are nucleation centers where microtubules are assembled. Actin filaments assemble spontaneously not requiring an organizing center.

The correct answer is c...
B. Answer b is incorrect because intermediate fibers are not composed of protofilaments. Microtubules subunits polymerize to form filaments called protofilaments. Intermediate fibers are a heterogeneous group of cytoskeletal fibers composed of different types of protein subunits.

The correct answer is c--microtubules -- "+" / "-" ends
C. Microtubules form from a nucleation center called microtubule-organizing center (MTOC). The polymerizing end of the microtubule, the end farther away from the nucleation center, is called the "+" end and the depolymerizing end of the microtubule, the end nearest to the nucleation center, is called the "-" end.

The correct answer is c...
D. Answer d is incorrect because intermediate fibers are not usually involved in cellular movement. They provide the cell structural stability. Actin and microtubules are involved in cellular movement, both movement of the entire cell and intracellular movement of structures within the cell.

Hint: Microtubules are in a constant state of flux, continually polymerizing and depolymerizing, unless stabilized by the binding of guanosine triphosphate (GTP) to the ends, which inhibits depolymerization. The ends of the microtubule are designated as "+" (away from the nucleation center) or "-" (toward the nucleation center).

10). Which of the following eukaryotic organelles are believed to have evolved through endosymbiosis?
        a). nucleus and mitochondrion
        b). mitochondrion and chloroplast
        c). nucleus and endoplasmic reticulum
        d). chloroplast and endoplasmic reticulum

The correct answer is b...
A. Answer a is incorrect because while the mitochondrion is believed to have evolved through endosymbiosis of a bacterium capable of oxidative metabolism, the nucleus isn't believed to have evolved from endosymbiosis. The nuclear envelope may have evolved from expansion of the infolding of the outer plasma membrane found in some bacteria, but this is not endosymbiosis.

The correct answer is b--mitochondrion and chloroplast.
B. The mitochondrion is believed to have evolved through endosymbiosis of a bacterium capable of oxidative metabolism and the chloroplast possibly from the endosymbiosis of a bacterium capable of photosynthesis. Endosymbiosis is where one organism lives inside another organisms and both organisms benefit from the relationship.

The correct answer is b....
C. Answer c is incorrect because neither the nucleus nor the endoplasmic reticulum is believed to have evolved from endosymbiosis. It is proposed that the nuclear envelope and the endoplasmic reticulum may have evolved from the expansion of the infolding of the plasma membrane in some bacteria, but this is not the same as endosymbiosis.

The correct answer is b...
D. Answer d is incorrect because although it is believed that the chloroplast may have evolved from the endosymbiosis of a bacterium capable of photosynthesis, the endoplasmic reticulum did not evolve this way. It is proposed that the endoplasmic reticulum may have evolved from the expansion of the infolding of the plasma membrane found in some bacteria, this is not the same as endosymbiosis.

Hint: The theory of endosymbiosis proposes that some of today's eukaryotic organelles evolved by a symbiosis in which one species of prokaryote was engulfed by and lived inside another species of prokaryote that was a precursor to eukaryotes. Two key eukaryotic organelles are believed to be the descendants of these endosymbiotic prokaryotes: mitochondria and chloroplasts.

Test Your Visual Understanding

1). From the following list, match the correct label with its numbered leader line in the figure, and describe the function of the organelle in the eukaryotic cell.
cytoskeleton
mitochondrion
nuclear envelope
nucleolus
ribosomes
rough endoplasmic reticulum
smooth endoplasmic reticulum

Answer:

1). 1--Nuclear envelope, function is to control the transport of materials into and out of the nucleus.
2--Nucleolus, function is the localization of DNA that encodes hundreds of copies of rRNA, which allows the rapid generation of large numbers of the molecules needed to produce ribosomes.
3--Smooth ER, function is the synthesis of carbohydrates and lipids.
4--Cytoskeleton, function is the support the shape of the cell, to transport materials throughout the cell, and to move the cell.
5--Mitochondrion, function is the cite of oxidative metabolism in the cell.
6--Rough ER, function is the synthesis of proteins destined to be exported from the cell.
7--Ribosomes, function is the translation of RNA copies of genes into proteins.

Apply Your Knowledge

1). White blood cells (WBCs) circulate throughout the human body. Monocytes make up about 6% of total WBCs, and neutrophils make up about 65% of total WBCs. Monocytes have a diameter of 15 μm, and neutrophils have a diameter of 10 μm. Calculate the surface area and volume of each cell.

Answer:

1). The equation for the surface area of a sphere is $4\pi r^2$

The equation for the volume of a sphere is $4/3\pi r^3$

To calculate either the surface area or volume, we must determine the radius of each cell: $r = 1/2\ d$ (where r is radius and d is diameter) such that:

       radius of monocyte = 1/2 (15) or r = 7.5 μm
       radius of neutrophil = 1/2 (10) or r = 5 μm

Surface area:

       Surface area of monocyte = $4\pi r^2$ or $4\pi 7.5^2$ or $4\pi 56.25$
       Surface area of monocyte = 706.5 $μm^2$

       Surface area of neutrophil = $4\pi r^2$ or $4\pi 5^2$ or $4\pi 25$
       Surface area of neutrophil = 314 $μm^2$

Volume:

       Volume of monocyte = $4/3\pi r^3$ or $4/3\pi 7.5^3$ or $4/3\pi 421.875$
       Volume of monocyte = 1766.25 $μm^3$

       Volume of neutrophil = $4/3\pi r^3$ or $4/3\pi 5^3$ or $4/3\pi 125$
       Volume of neutrophil = 523.33 $μm^3$

Inquiry Questions

None for this chapter.

Self Test

1). Why is the phospholipid molecule so appropriate as the primary structural component of plasma membranes?
    a). Phospholipids are completely insoluble in water.
    b). Phospholipids form strong chemical bonds between the molecules, forming a stable structure.
    c). Phospholipids form a selectively permeable structure.
    d). Phospholipids form chemical bonds with membrane proteins that keep the proteins within the membrane.

The correct answer is c…
A. Answer a is incorrect because if the phospholipid were completely insoluble in water, they wouldn't form hydrogen bonds with water molecules. They would clump together in water like a drop of oil does in water. This type of structure could not form the plasma membrane.

The correct answer is c…
B. Answer b is incorrect because phospholipids do not form chemical bonds between each other. A structure held together by chemical bonds would not offer the flexibility that is necessary for the plasma membrane.

The correct answer is c—Phospholipids form a selectively permeable structure.
A. The lipid bilayer produced by the phospholipid molecules inhibits the passage of water-soluble across the membrane and isolates the interior of the cell from the environment. This is important for cell functions.

The correct answer is c…
B. Answer d is incorrect because phospholipid molecules do not form chemical bonds with membrane proteins. The proteins are kept within the membrane by the same hydrophobic an hydrophilic interactions that formed the lipid bilayer.

Hint: the nonpolar interior of a lipid bilayer impedes the passage of any water-soluble substances through the bilayer, just as a layer of oil impedes the passage of a drop of water. This barrier to the passage of water-soluble substances is the key biological property of the lipid bilayer.

2). Which increases the fluidity of the plasma membrane?
    a). having a large number of membrane proteins
    b). the tight alignment of phospholipids
    c). cholesterol present in the membrane
    d). double bonds between carbon atoms in the fatty acid tails.

The correct answer is d…
A. Answer a is incorrect because number of membrane proteins does not affect the alignment of the phospholipid tails and this alignment is what affects the fluidity of the membrane.

The correct answer is d…
B. Answer b is incorrect because tight alignment of phospholipids *decreases* fluidity, it does not increase it.

The correct answer is d…
C. Answer c is incorrect because cholesterol can increase membrane fluidity but it can also decrease it depending on the temperature.

The correct answer is d—double bonds between carbon atoms in the fatty acid tails.
D. Double bonds between carbon atoms of the fatty acid tails cause kinks in the tails, which keeps the phospholipid molecules from aligning closely together. The farther apart the phospholipid molecules are from each other, the more fluid the membrane becomes.

Hint: Phospholipid bilayers are fluid, with the viscosity of olive oil. Some membranes are more fluid than others, however. The tails of individual phospholipid molecules are attracted to one another when they line up close together. This causes the membrane to become less fluid. The greater the degree of alignment, the less fluid the membrane. Some phospholipid tails do not align well because they contain one or more double bonds between carbon atoms, introducing kinks in the tail. Membranes containing such phospholipids are more fluid than membranes that lack them.

3). Which best describes the structure of a plasma membrane?
     a). proteins embedded within two layers of phospholipids
     b). phospholipids sandwiched between two layers of proteins
     c). proteins sandwiched between two layers of phospholipids
     d). a layer of proteins on top of a layer of phospholipids

The correct answer is a—proteins embedded within two layers of phospholipids.
A. In the aqueous environments of the cell and extracellular fluid, phospholipids orient themselves with their nonpolar tails facing toward each other with their polar phosphorylated heads facing outward. Freeze-fraction microscopy, which splits the membrane apart into two layers of phospholipids showed that protein are embedded within the membrane and not strictly associated with the inside and outside of the membrane.

The correct answer is a...
B. Answer b is incorrect because although some membrane proteins associate with the interior or exterior surfaces of the membrane, many more proteins are embedded in the membrane, projecting through the lipid bilayer.

The correct answer is a...
C. Answer c is incorrect because proteins extend out from the interior region of the lipid bilayer, such that they can not be strictly associated with the interior region of the lipid bilayer.

The correct answer is a...
D. Answer d is incorrect because the membrane consists of two layers of phospholipids, not one, and the proteins are not layered on the membrane but rather extend through the membrane as well as associating with the interior and exterior surfaces.

Hint: A plasma membrane is composed of both lipids and globular proteins. For many years, biologists thought the protein covered the inner and outer surfaces of the phospholipid bilayer like a coat of paint. This however was not consistent with what researchers were learning about the structure of membrane proteins. In 1972, Singer and Nicolson proposed that the globular proteins are inserted into the lipid bilayer.

4). What locks all transmembrane proteins in the bilayer?
     a). chemical bonds that form between the phospholipids and the proteins
     b). hydrophobic interactions between nonpolar amino acids of the proteins and the aqueous environments of the cell
     c). attachment to the cytoskeleton
     d). the addition of sugar molecules to the protein surface facing the external environment

The correct answer is b...
A. Answer a is incorrect because chemical bonds do not form between the phospholipids and the transmembrane proteins. The interior of the lipid bilayer is nonpolar due to the nonpolar tails of the phospholipids and nonpolar regions of membrane proteins associate with the nonpolar interior of the bilayer but this is not due to the formation of chemical bonds.

The correct answer is b-- Hydrophobic interactions between nonpolar amino acids of the proteins and the aqueous environments of the cell.
B. Transmembrane proteins have regions of nonpolar amino acids that are repelled by water. These hydrophobic interactions force the nonpolar amino acids to the interior of the lipid bilayer. The hydrophobic interactions lock the protein into the lipid bilayer.

The correct answer is b...
C. Answer c is incorrect because although some transmembrane proteins are attached to the cytoskeleton, this attachment does not lock the protein within the lipid membrane. Instead, it anchors the proteins in one place so that they can't float around in the membrane.

The correct answer is b...
D. Answer d is incorrect because the addition of sugar molecules to the external surface of the membrane proteins, forming glycoproteins, gives a "sidedness" to the membrane but does not lock the proteins into place.

Hint: Some proteins are anchored to the plasma membrane, like a ship tied up to a dock but other proteins actually transverse the lipid bilayer. The part of the protein that extends through the lipid bilayer, in contact with the nonpolar interior, consists of one or more nonpolar helices or several β-pleated sheets of nonpolar amino acids. Because water avoids nonpolar amino acids much as it does nonpolar lipid chains, the nonpolar portions of the protein are held within the interior of the lipid bilayer.

5). The movement of sodium ions from an area of higher concentration to an area of lower concentration is called _____.
        a). active transport
        b). osmosis
        c). diffusion
        d). phagocytosis

The correct answer is c...
A. Answer a is incorrect because active transport involves the movement of substances, such as ions, from an area of lower concentration to an area of higher concentration.

The correct answer is c...
B. answer b is incorrect because osmosis involved the movement of water molecules from an area of high concentration to an area of lower concentration.

The correct answer is c—diffusion
C. Diffusion is the passive movement of a substance, such as sodium ions, across a membrane from an area of high concentration to an area of low concentration.

The correct answer is c...
D. Answer d is incorrect because phagocytosis is the process by which a cell takes in particulate matter, such as an organism or some other fragment of organic matter by enclosing the particulate matter in a vesicle of membrane.

Hint: Molecules and ions dissolved in water are in constant motion, moving about randomly. This random motion causes a net movement of these substances from regions where their concentration is high to regions where their concentration is lower, a process called diffusion.

6). A cell placed in distilled water will
      a). shrivel up.
      b). swell.
      c). lose water.
      d). result in no net diffusion of water molecules.

The correct answer is b…
A. Answer a is incorrect because distilled water has fewer solutes than a cell, therefore the cell is hyperosmotic compared to the distilled water. Water will flow from a hypoosmotic solution (the distilled water) toward a hyperosmotic solution (the cell).

The correct answer is b—swell
B. The cell is hyperosmotic compared to the distilled water and through osmosis, water molecules will pass from a hypoosmotic solution into a hyperosmotic solution. Water molecules will pass from the distilled water into the cell, causing the cell to swell.

The correct answer is b…
C. Answer c is incorrect because the cell will not lose water in a hypoosmotic solution such as distilled water. Water will instead pass across the cell membrane from the hypoosmotic distilled water into the hyperosmotic cell.

The correct answer is b…
D. Answer d is incorrect because the distilled water is a hypoosmotic solution compared to the cell, which contains a hyperosmotic solution. Water passes from a hypoosmotic solution into a hyperosmotic solution so water will pass into the cell. The only time there is not net diffusion of water molecules between two solutions across a membrane is if the solutions are isosmotic.

Hint: The concentration of all solutes in a solution determines the osmotic concentration of the solution. If two solutions have unequal osmotic concentrations, the solution with the higher concentration is hyperosmotic and the solution with the lower concentration is hypoosmotic. If the osmotic concentrations of two solutions are equal, the solutions are isosmotic.

7). Sucrose cannot pass through the membrane of a red blood cell (RBC) but water and glucose can. Which solution would cause the RBC to shrink the most?
      a). a hyperosmotic sucrose solution
      b). a hyperosmotic glucose solution
      c). a hypoosmotic sucrose solution
      d). a hypoosmotic glucose solution

The correct answer is a—a hyperosmotic sucrose solution
A. A hyperosmotic sucrose solution contains a higher concentration of sucrose than that which is found in the cell, however sucrose cannot pass through the membrane down its concentration gradient. Therefore, in order to establish an osmotic equilibrium, water will diffuse out of the cell from a hypoosmotic solution into the hyperosmotic sucrose solution.

The correct answer is a…
B. Answer b is incorrect because a red blood cell that is placed in a hyperosmotic glucose solution will result in glucose diffusing into the cell from its area of higher concentration, in the solution, to its area of lower concentration, in the cell. This will reduce the osmotic concentration of the glucose solution. While water will still diffuse out of the cell into the hyperosmotic glucose solution, more water will diffuse out of the cell into a hyperosmotic sucrose solution than into a glucose solution.

The correct answer is a…
C. Answer c is incorrect because a cell place in a hypoosmotic sucrose solution will result in the diffusion of water from the solution into the cell, which is hyperosmotic in relation to the solution. The cell will swell, not shrink.

The correct answer is a…
D. Answer d is incorrect because a cell placed in a hypoosmotic glucose solution will result in the diffusion of glucose out of the cell, down its concentration gradient, but also will result in the diffusion of water molecules into the cell until an equilibrium is reached. Overall, the cell will tend to swell rather shrink.

Hint: In cells. A plasma membrane separates two aqueous solutions, one inside the cell (the cytoplasm) and one outside the cell (the extracellular fluid). The direction of the net diffusion of water across this membrane is determined by the osmotic concentrations of the solutions on either side. For example, if the cytoplasm of a cell were hypoosmotic to the extra cellular fluid, water would diffuse out of the cell, toward the solution with the higher concentration of solutes. This loss of water from the cytoplasm would cause the cell to shrink.

8). Which of the following processes requires membrane proteins?
      a). exocytosis
      b). phagocytosis
      c). receptor-mediated endocytosis
      d). pinocytosis

The correct answer is c…
A. Answer a is incorrect because exocytosis is the discharge of material from membrane vesicles at the cell surface. The substance that is expelled from the cell does *not* bind to proteins on the membrane before leaving the cell.

The correct answer is c…
B. Answer b is incorrect because phagocytosis is the process by which large particulate materials are brought into the cell (such as food particles or other organisms). In this process the plasma membrane extends outward and envelops the food particles. Membrane proteins are not required for this process.

The correct answer is c—receptor-mediated endocytosis
C. Receptor-mediated endocytosis is the process whereby specific molecules are brought into the cell through the formation of a membrane bound vesicle. The process is specific in that the molecules to be transported first bind to specific protein receptors on the plasma membrane, which then forms a pit that deepens and seals off into a vesicle.

The correct answer is c…
D. Answer d is incorrect because pinocytosis is the process by which small particulate materials and fluids are brought into the cell. In this process the plasma membrane extends outward and envelops the fluid. Membrane proteins are not required for this process.

Hint: Specific molecules are often transported into eukaryotic cells through receptor-mediated endocytosis. Molecules to be transported first bind to specific receptors on the plasma membrane. The transport process is specific because only that molecule has a shape that fits snugly into the receptor. The plasma membrane of a particular kinds of cell contains a characteristic battery of receptor types, each for a different kind of molecule.

9). Exocytosis involves
- a). the ingestion of large organic molecules or organisms.
- b). the use of ATP.
- c). the uptake of fluids from the environment.
- d). the discharge of materials from cellular vesicles.

The correct answer is d...

A. Answer a is incorrect because exocytosis is the expelling of substances from the cell, not the ingestion of large organic molecules or organisms. The ingestion of large particulate matter is the process of phagocytosis.

The correct answer is d...

B. Answer d is incorrect because exocytosis does not require the direct involvement of ATP. Cellular energy may be required indirectly for the process of exocytosis but there is not a binding site for ATP in the membrane or vesicle containing the substance to be expelled.

The correct answer is d...

C. Answer c is incorrect because exocytosis is the expelling of substances from the cell, not the ingestion of fluids from the environment. The ingestion of fluids is the process of pinocytosis.

The correct answer is d—the discharge of materials from cellular vesicles.

D. Exocytosis is the expelling of materials from the cell through the formation of membrane-bound vesicles that fuse with the plasma membrane.

Hint: The reverse of endocytosis is exocytosis, the discharge of material from vesicles at the cell surface. Proteins and other molecules are secreted from cells in small packets called vesicles, whose membranes fuse with the plasma membrane, releasing their contents to the cell surface.

10). Molecules that are transported into the cell *up* their concentration gradients do so by
- a). facilitated diffusion.
- b). osmosis.
- c). coupled transport
- d). none of the above

The correct answer is c...

A. Answer a is incorrect because facilitated diffusion involves the transport of molecules down their concentration gradients, not up them.

The correct answer is c...

B. Answer b is incorrect because osmosis is the diffusion of water molecules from an area of low solute concentration to an area of high solute concentration. This is actually down the concentration gradient for water.

The correct answer is c—coupled transport

C. In coupled transport, molecules are transported up their concentration gradients by the cotransport of a second substance down its concentration gradient. The concentration gradient for the second substance is so large (established by the input of cellular energy, ATP) that the movement down its concentration gradient can actually "pull" another molecule across the membrane up its concentration gradient. Active transport also transports molecules up their concentration gradients with the direct input of cellular energy, but this was not an option provided.

The correct answer is c...

D. Answer d is incorrect because although answer options a and b are not correct, answer option c is correct.

Hint: Many molecules are transported into cells up a concentration gradient through a process that uses ATP indirectly. The molecules move hand-in-hand with sodium ions or protons that are moving down their concentration gradients. This coupled transport has two components: establishing the down gradient and traversing the up gradient. ATP is used to establish the sodium ion or proton down gradient, which is greater than the up gradient of the other molecule to be transported. Coupled transport proteins carry the molecule and either a sodium ion or proton together across the membrane.

Test Your Visual Understanding

1). In this figure of a transmembrane protein, what colored area of the protein contains nonpolar amino acids? What colored area contains polar amino acids? What colored area contains amino acids carrying a positive or negative charge?
Answer: The nonpolar amino acids are found within the interior nonpolar region of the lipid bilayer, so the pink colored areas contain nonpolar amino acids. The polar amino acids are found associated with the external environment, so the purple colored areas contain polar amino acids. Charged amino acids are polar and so these amino acids would be found in the purple colored areas of the protein.

2). Match the function of the membrane protein with the appropriate numbered figure:
   a). cell surface receptor
   b). transporter
   c). cell surface identity marker
   d). enzyme

Answer:
1--b
2--d
3--a
4--c

Apply Your Knowledge

1). If during the action of the sodium-potassium pump, 150 molecules of ATP are used, how many sodium ions are transported across the membrane?
Answer: 450 sodium ions.
Solution: Every time the sodium-potassium pump undergoes its conformational change, 3 sodium ions are transported across the membrane and 1 ATP molecule is required. If 150 ATP molecules have been used by the sodium-potassium pump, then the pump has undergone its conformational change 150 times, and has transported 150 x 3 Na^+ ions/time, or 450 total sodium ions.

2). If a cell's cytoplasm were hyperosmotic to the extracellular fluid, how would the concentration of solutes in the cytoplasm compare with that in the extracellular fluid? Assuming the membrane was permeably only to water, in which direction would water move?
Answer: The contents of the cell would contain more solutes than the extracellular fluid, which would be hypoosmotic compared to the cell. Assuming that the membrane was permeably only to water, water would move into the cell, toward the area with more solutes.

3). Cholera, a disease caused by a bacterial infection of *Vibrio cholerae,* results in severe diarrhea leading to dehydration. A toxin released by the bacterium causes the release of chloride ions (Cl-) from cells lining the small intestines and inhibits the uptake of sodium ions (Na+) by these cells. Explain how this disruption of cellular ion concentrations would result in extreme dehydration.
Answer: Under normal conditions, the chloride ions remain in the cells lining the lumen of the small intestine. This creates an overall negative charge within the cells that drives positively charged sodium ions into the cells creating a hyperosmotic condition in the cells. Water moves

into the cells by osmosis. The diarrhea that occurs in cholera results from the bacterial infection, which causes the increased concentrations of Cl- and Na+ in the lumen of the small intestine. Elevated concentrations of these two ions results in the lumen of the small intestines becoming hyperosmotic compared to the cells lining the intestines. This in turn causes the diffusion of large amounts of water through osmosis into the lumen of the intestine from the cells and blood stream.   The water passes out of the body as diarrhea, leaving the body dehydrated.

4). Cystic fibrosis is a genetic disease that results in thick mucus secretions that clog up air passages in the lungs. Faulty chloride ion channels keep Cl- and Na+ in the cells that line the airways increasing the intracellular ion concentrations. How does this cause the mucus in the airways to become thick?

Answer: This is a similar situation of that seen in cholera but in the opposite direction. Normally, chloride ions (Cl-) pass out of the cells lining the airways through chloride ion channels. Sodium ions (Na+) follow the Cl- out of the cells due to the electrochemical gradient created by the movement of Cl-. The movement of ions out of the cells makes the cells hypoosmotic compared to the lumen of the airways. Water passes out of the cells and blood stream through osmosis and into the airways, thinning the mucus that flushes out impurities. In cystic fibrosis, the chloride channel doesn't function properly so Cl- remains in the cells, likewise Na+ remains in the cells. The cells are hyperosmotic compared to the lumen of the airways so water remains in the cells and bloodstream. Without water passing into the airways, the mucus becomes thick and clogs the airways.

Inquiry Questions
None for this chapter.

Self Test

1). Which of the following techniques has recently aided the study of receptor proteins?
   a). protein purification
   b). monoclonal antibodies
   c). isolation of cell signal molecules
   d). all of these

The correct answer is b...
A. Answer a is incorrect because protein purification is not a recent technique; it has been used in biology for quite some time. But, if biologists relied just on the purification of proteins as a means of studying receptor proteins, we wouldn't be all that far along in our understanding because there are so many proteins in the cell and searching for a particular receptor protein to purify is like looking for a needle in a haystack.

The correct answer is b--monoclonal antibodies
B. Antibodies are specific proteins produced by cells of the immune system that can bind to other proteins. This type of immune system cell can be exposed to a certain type of receptor protein and produce antibodies against that protein. The immune cell then divides to produce many copies of itself (clones) that produce that one type of antibody (mono). The monoclonal antibody binds to the particular receptor protein to isolate if from the thousands of other proteins in the cell.

The correct answer is b...
C. Answer c is incorrect because the isolation of cell signal molecules would involve just as many challenges as the isolation of receptor proteins. There are thousands of chemical signals and so the isolation of these chemical signals doesn't take us any closer to characterizing the receptors to which they bind.

The correct answer is b..
D. Answer d is incorrect because only answer option b is correct. Answer a is incorrect because protein purification is not a recent technique. It is used in the study of receptor proteins but wasn't a technique that advanced the process of characterizing receptor proteins. Answer c is incorrect because there are just as many signal molecules as there are receptors so studying the signal molecules is just as difficult as studying the receptors.

Hint: The characterization of receptor proteins has presented a very difficult technical problem, because of their relative scarcity in the cell. However, two recent techniques have enabled cell biologists to make rapid progress in this area: monoclonal antibodies and gene analysis.

2). Which of the following describes autocrine signaling?
   a). Signal molecules released by cells diffuse through the extracellular fluid to other cells.
   b). Signal molecules enter the organism's circulatory system and travel throughout the body.
   c). Signal molecules are released from a cell and bind to receptors on its own plasma membrane.
   d). Signal molecules are released into a narrow space between cells called a synapse.

The correct answer is c...
A. Answer a is incorrect because signal molecules that are released from a cell and diffuse through extracellular fluid to other cells describes paracrine signaling.

The correct answer is c...
B. Answer b is incorrect because signal molecules that are released from a cell and enter the organism's circulatory system and travel throughout the body describes endocrine signaling.

The correct answer is c--Signal molecules are released from a cell and bind to receptors on its own plasma membrane.
C. Autocrine signaling is the process whereby a cell communicates with itself (talks to itself). This process is thought to play a role in reinforcing developmental changes.

The correct answer is c...
D. Answer d is incorrect because signal molecules that are released into a narrow space between cells called a synapse describes synaptic signaling, a special type of signaling that occurs in the nervous system.

Hint: Cells communicate through any of four basic mechanisms, depending primarily on the distance between the cells. In addition to using these four basic mechanisms, some cells actually send signals to themselves, secreting signals that bind to specific receptors on their own plasma membranes. This process is called autocrine signaling.

3). Intracellular receptors usually bind
        a). water-soluble signals.
        b). large molecules that act as signals.
        c). signals on the cell surface.
        d). lipid-soluble signals.

The correct answer is d...
A. Answer a is incorrect because intracellular receptors are found inside the cell and a signal must pass through the plasma membrane in order to bind to the receptor. Water-soluble molecules can not pass through the cell membrane so they can not bind to intracellular receptors.

The correct answer is d...
B. Answer b is incorrect because intracellular receptors are found inside the cell and a signal must pass through the plasma membrane in order to bind to the receptor. Large molecules, even if they are lipid-soluble, would not diffuse through the plasma membrane very easily.

The correct answer is d...
C. Answer c is incorrect because intracellular receptors are found inside the cell and so are not able to bind to signals on the cell surface. The signal must pass into the cell through the plasma membrane.

The correct answer is d--lipid-soluble signals.
D. Intracellular receptors are found inside the cell and so the signals to which they bind must also be inside the cell. Therefore, signals that bind to intracellular receptors are either very small molecules or are lipid-soluble.

Hint: Many cell signals are lipid-soluble or very small molecules that can readily pass across the plasma membrane of the target cell and into the cell, where they interact with a receptor.

4). Which of the following is *not* a type of cell surface receptor?
        a). chemically gated ion channels
        b). intracellular receptors
        c). enzymic receptors
        d). G-protein-linked receptors

The correct answer is b...
A. Answer a is incorrect because chemically gated ion channels are a type of cell surface receptor. Chemically gated ion channels extend through the membrane and bind to signals on

the surface of the cell. Binding of the signal opens an ion channel that allows ions to enter the cell.

The correct answer is b--DNA-binding receptors
B. Intracellular receptors are receptors that are found inside the cell or inside the nucleus. They are not present on the cell surface and are not a type of cell surface receptor.

The correct answer is b...
C. Answer c is incorrect because enzymic receptors are a type of cell surface receptor. An enzymic receptors is a cell surface receptor that acts as an enzyme or is linked to an enzyme. When the signal binds to a enzymic receptor on the surface of the cell, it activates the enzyme to elicit a response in the cell.

The correct answer is b...
D. Answer d is incorrect because G-protein-linked receptors are a type of cell surface receptor. G-protein-linked receptors are the largest group of cell surface receptors. These receptors act indirectly on enzymes or ion channels with the aid of an assisting protein called a guanosine triphosphate (GTP)-binding protein, or G protein.

Hint: Cell surface receptors convert an extracellular signal to an intracellular one, responding to the binding of the signal molecule by producing a change within the cell's cytoplasm. Most of a cell's receptors are cell surface receptors, and almost all of them belong to one of three receptor superfamilies: chemically gated ion channels, enzymic receptors, and G-protein-linked receptors.

5). Which of the following is not a second messenger?
        a). adenylyl cyclase
        b). cyclic adenosine monophosphate
        c). calcium ions
        d). cAMP

The correct answer is a--adenylyl cyclase
A. Adenylyl cyclase not a second messenger but it is an enzyme involved in the production of a second messenger, cAMP. Adenylyl cyclase is activated inside the cell by a G protein. The activated G protein stimulates the enzyme adenylyl cyclase, which catalyzes the synthesis of cAMP. cAMP then goes on to initiate the appropriate cellular change.

The correct answer is a...
B. Answer b is incorrect because cyclic adenosine monophosphate is a second messenger, also referred to as cAMP. Cyclic adenosine monophosphate is activated through a G protein and triggers changes in the cell such as the activation of other enzymes.

The correct answer is a...
C. Answer c is incorrect because calcium ions act as second messengers in the cell. Calcium ion (Ca^{++}) levels are usually very low inside the cytoplasm of the cell while outside the cell and in special organelles, Ca^{++} levels are quite high. When calcium ion channels are activated, Ca^{++} rushes into the cell and activates various calcium-sensitive proteins. These proteins initiate a variety of cellular activities.

The correct answer is a...
D. Answer d is incorrect because cAMP is a second messenger. cAMP stands for cyclic adenosine monophosphate. cAMP is activated through a G protein and triggers changes in the cell such as the activation of other enzymes.

Hint: Some enzymic receptors and most G-protein-linked receptors carry the signal molecule's message to the target cell by utilizing other substances to relay the message within the cytoplasm. These other substances, small molecules or ions commonly called second messengers alter the behavior of particular proteins by binding to them and changing their shape.

The two most widely used second messengers are cyclic adenosine monophosphate (cAMP) and calcium.

6). The amplification of a cellular signal requires all but which of the following?
    a). a second messenger
    b). DNA
    c). a signal molecule
    d). a cascade of protein kinases

The correct answer is b...
A. Answer a is incorrect because a second messenger is required for the amplification of a cellular signal. A second messenger such as cAMP is usually activated following the activation of a G protein. The second messenger goes on to activate protein kinases or other proteins in the cell.

The correct answer is b--DNA
B. While DNA can sometimes be involved in the amplification of a cellular signal, it is usually not involved in the actual amplification steps.

The correct answer is b...
C. Answer c is incorrect because a signal molecule is the first step of the amplification process--it gets the whole thing moving. The signal molecule binds to a receptor, which activates a G protein or a second messenger. Most signaling molecules are found in such low concentrations that their activation of cellular processes would take a great deal of time without the amplification of the signal.

The correct answer is b...
D. Answer d is incorrect because a cascade of protein kinases is the heart of the amplification process. Second messengers that were activated by a G protein in turn activate protein kinases. Each protein kinase molecule activates many enzymes (for example, it adds a phosphate group on many different enzymes). These activated enzyme go on to elicit a response in the cell. Because one protein kinase can activate many other enzymes, the amplification of the signal is sometimes referred to as a protein kinase cascade.

Hint: Both enzyme-linked and G-protein-linked receptors receive signals at the surface of the cell, but the target cell's response rarely takes place there. In most cases the signals are relayed to the cytoplasm or the nucleus by second messengers, which influence the activity of one or more enzymes or genes and so alter the behavior of the cell. But most signaling molecules are found in such low concentrations that their diffusion across the cytoplasm would take a great deal of time unless the signal is amplified. Therefore, most enzyme-linked and G-protein-linked receptors use a chain of other protein messengers to amplify the signal as it is being relayed to the nucleus.

7). MHC proteins are
    a). molecules that determine a person's blood type.
    b). large molecules that pass through the membrane many times.
    c). identity markers present on the surface of an individual's cells.
    d). different for each type of tissue in the body.

The correct answer is c...
A. Answer a is incorrect because the molecules that determine a person's blood type are glycolipids on the surface of red blood cells, not MHC proteins.

The correct answer is c...
B. Answer b is incorrect because although MHC can be rather large molecules, they only pass through the membrane once; they are called single-pass proteins.

The correct answer is c--identity markers present on the surface of an individual's cells.
C. MHC proteins (stands for major histocompatibility complex proteins) are proteins present on the membrane of all of the cells of a given individual. Practically every individual makes a different set of MHC proteins so that these can serve as identity tags for each individual.

The correct answer is c...
D. Answer d is incorrect because MHC proteins are cell surface markers that distinguish between "self" and "nonself" cells. All of the cells of a given individual have the same "self" markers. The cells of different tissues in the body have different tissue-specific identity markers but these are usually glycolipids, not MHC proteins.

Hint: The immune system uses other cell surface markers to distinguish between "self" and "nonself" cells. All of the cells of a given individual, for example, have the same "self" markers, called major histocompatibility complex (MHC) proteins. Because practically every individual makes a different set of MHC proteins, they serve as distinctive identity tags for each individual.

8). Sheets of cells are formed from which type of cell junctions?
      a). tight junctions
      b). anchoring junctions
      c). communication junctions
      d). none of these

The correct answer is a--tight junctions
A. Tight junctions encircle each cell, forming connections between the plasma membranes of the cells. The junctions between neighboring cells are so securely attached that there is no space between them for leakage, forming a sheet of cells.

The correct answer is a...
B. Answer b is incorrect because anchoring junctions function in attaching cells to each other or to the extracellular matrix. These junctions do not form sheets of cells.

The correct answer is a...
C. Answer c is incorrect because communication junctions form openings between the plasma membranes of adjacent cells, essentially connecting the cytoplasms of adjacent cells. While these junctions form tight connections between adjacent cells, they don't usually occur in an entire layer of cells forming sheets.

The correct answer is a...
D. Answer d is incorrect because there is a correct answer--answer a.

Hint: Tight junctions connect the plasma membranes of adjacent cells in a sheet, preventing small molecules from leaking between the cells and through the sheet. This allows the sheet of cells to act as a wall, keeping molecules to one side or the other.

9). Cadherin can be found in which of the following?
      a). tight junctions
      b). anchoring junctions
      c). communication junctions
      d). adherens junctions

The correct answer is b...
A. Answer a is incorrect because tight junctions involve the connection of the plasma membranes of adjacent cells, forming sheet of cells. Cadherin is not involved in this process.

The correct answer is b--anchoring junctions.
B. Anchoring junctions mechanically attach the cytoskeleton of a cell to the extracellular matrix or to the cytoskeletons of other cells. Cadherin is a protein that creates a critical link in some but

not all anchoring junctions however, cadherin appears in no other types of cell junctions except for anchoring junctions.

The correct answer is b...
C. Answer c is incorrect because communication junctions involve the formation of passageways between cells allowing molecules to pass directly from one cell into another. Although proteins are involved in connecting up the cytoplasms of adjacent cells, cadherin is not one of these proteins.

The correct answer is b...
D. Answer d is incorrect because although adherens junctions are a type of anchoring junction, it is an anchoring junction that does not use cadherin. Instead the protein integrin is used to anchor the cell to the extracellular matrix.

Hint: Anchoring junctions called desmosomes connect the cytoskeletons of adjacent cells, while hemidesmosomes anchor epithelial cells to a basement membrane. Proteins called cadherins, most of which are single-pass transmembrane glycoproteins, create the critical link.

10). Plasmodesmata are a type of
        a). gap junction.
        b). anchoring junction.
        c). communicating junction.
        d). tight junction.

The correct answer is c...
A. Answer a is incorrect because gap junctions are a type of communicating junction found in animals. In gap junctions, protein channels in adjacent cells line up and attach to one another, creating an open channels between the two cells.

The correct answer is c...
B. Answer b is incorrect because plasmodesmata are a type of communicating junction, not an anchoring junction. An anchoring junction functions in holding cells together or holding cells firmly with their extracellular matrix. Plasmodesmata, on the other hand, form cytoplasmic connections between plant cells.

The correct answer is c--communicating junction.
C. Communicating junctions allow cells to communicate with adjacent cells through direct connections, where chemical signals can pass directly from one cell to another. Plasmodesmata are the type of communicating junction found in plant cells.

The correct answer is c...
D. Answer d is incorrect because plasmodesmata are a type of communicating junction, not a tight junction. A tight junction functions in holding cells together so tightly that substances can not flow between the cells. Tight junctions form a "solid-like" sheet of cells. Plasmodesmata, on the other hand, form cytoplasmic connections between plant cells.

Hint: Many cells communicate with adjacent cells through direct connections, called communicating junctions. Communicating junctions establish direct physical connections that link the cytoplasms of two cells together, permitting small molecules or ions to pass from one to another. In plant, cell-cell junctions occur only a holes or gaps in the walls, where the plasma membranes of adjacent cells can come into contact with each other. Cytoplasmic connections that form across the touching plasma membranes are called plasmodesmata.

1). Match the following labels with the appropriate structures in the figure, and explain where each type of junction is found.
adherens junction
desmosome
gap junction
hemidesmosome
tight junction

Answer:
1). Tight junction with #1, Adherens junction with #2, Desmosomes with #3, Gap junction with #4 and Hemidesmosome with #5
      1--Tight junction
      Tight junctions hold cells together in a sheet, restricting the movement of substances between the cells. Tight junctions are found in cells that line the digestive tract.
      2--Adherens junction
      Adherens junctions are anchoring junctions that use integrin to hold cells together by anchoring to the cells' actin networks. Adherens junctions, as other anchoring junctions are found in tissues that are subject to mechanical stress such as muscle and epithelium.
      3--Desmosomes
      Desmosomes are anchoring junctions that use cadherin to hold cells together by anchoring to the cells' actin networks, or for more stable cell-to-cell connections by anchoring to the cells' intermediate fibers. Desmosomes, as other anchoring junctions are found in tissues that are subject to mechanical stress such as muscle and epithelium.
      4--Gap junction
      Gap junctions are communicating junctions that use protein channels called connexons to create passageways between cells. When the connexons of two adjacent cells are lined up, a direct connection between the cytoplasms of the two cells is made. Small molecules and ions can pass freely between the cells. Gap junctions are found in animal cells.
      5--Hemidesmosome
      Hemidesmosomes are anchoring junctions that use cadherin to hold cells to an extracellular matrix. Hemidesmosomes are found in epithelial cells, holding them to a basement membrane.

Apply Your Knowledge
1). In paracrine signaling, the signal molecule is destroyed by enzymes in 6 milliseconds. The diffusion rate of the signal through the extracellular fluid is 2 nanometer/1 millisecond. How long will the signal last in the extracellular fluid, and what is the farthest distance a target cell can be from the releasing cell to be affected by the signal?
Answer: Enzymes breakdown the signal molecule in 6 milliseconds so the signal can only last for 6 milliseconds in the extracellular fluid. Therefore, the signal has only 6 milliseconds to travel to its target cell. If the signal can travel 2 nanometers/millisecond then:
2 nanometers x 6 milliseconds = 12 nanometers
The farthest distance a target cell can be from the releasing cell is 12 nanometers.

2). At first glance, the signaling systems that involve cell surface receptors may appear rather complex and indirect, with their use of G proteins, second messengers, and often multiple stages of enzymes. What are the advantages of such seemingly complex response systems?
Answer: There are several advantages to response system that is organized in multiple levels. The first is obviously the ability to amplify the signal. With the multiple stages of enzymes, a small amount of a signal is all that is needed to get the response going. This allows for a very high level of sensitivity.

Another advantage is the ability of the cell to use the same "machinery" for different signals--not having to produce new cascade machines to elicit the same response or a related response. If two signals produce the same response, two different G proteins could activate the same adenylyl cyclase and activate the same cascade. Similarly, the same second messenger, for example cAMP could be used in different cascade responses, offering a certain redundancy to the system.

3). *Shigella flexneri* is one of several species of bacteria that cause shigellosis, or bacillary dysentery. Recent evidence has shown that *S. flexneri* cannot spread between the epithelial cells of the intestines without the expression of cadherin by those cells. Why do you suppose it cannot?

Answer: *Shigella flexneri* invades one cell, multiplies and then spreads to contiguous epithelial cells. Cells that are expressing cadherin are closely adhering to their neighboring cells, which makes it easier for *Shigella flexneri* to spread.

Inquiry Questions
None for this chapter.

Self Test

1). An atom gains energy when
      a). an electron is lost from it.
      b). it undergoes oxidation.
      c). it undergoes reduction.
      d). it undergoes an oxidation-reduction reaction.

The correct answer is c...
A. Answer a is incorrect because when an atom loses an electron it also loses the energy of that electron. An atom gains energy when it gains an electron.

The correct answer is c...
B. Answer b is incorrect because when an atom undergoes oxidation, it undergoes the process of losing an electron. When it loses an electron (undergoes oxidation), it loses energy, it does not gains it.

The correct answer is c--when it under goes reduction.
C. During a chemical reaction, when an atom gains an electron it is called reduction. The energy of an electron is transferred when it is transferred and so an atom gains energy when it under goes reduction.

The correct answer is c...
D. Answer d is incorrect because an atom undergoing an oxidation-reduction reaction could be gaining or losing an electron, depending on which side of the equation the atom is on. If the atom gains an electron (undergoes a reduction) it will gain energy; if the atom loses an electron (undergoes an oxidation) it will lose energy.

Hint: When an atom or molecule loses an electron, it is said to be oxidized, and the process by which this occurs is called oxidation. Conversely, when an atom or molecule gains an electron, it is said to be reduced, and the process is called reduction. Therefore, chemical reactions of this sort are called oxidation-reduction (redox) reactions. Energy is transferred from one molecule to another via redox reactions. The reduced form of a molecule thus has a higher level of energy than the oxidized form.

2). Which of the following is concerned with the amount of energy in the universe?
      a). the First Law of Thermodynamics
      b). the Second Law of Thermodynamics.
      c). thermodynamics
      d). entropy

The correct answer is a--The First Law of Thermodynamics.
A. The First Law of Thermodynamics states that energy cannot be created or destroyed; it can only change from one form to another. This means that the amount of energy in the universe is set. The universe will not increase the amount of energy it has or lose energy. Energy will only be converted from one form to another.

The correct answer is a...
B. Answer b is incorrect because The Second Law of Thermodynamics states that the disorder in the universe is continuously increasing. Energy transformations proceed spontaneously to convert matter from a more ordered state to a less ordered state. This law isn't concerned with the amount of energy in the universe, rather that the energy in the universe tends towards a less ordered state.

The correct answer is a...
C. Answer c is incorrect because thermodynamics is the name given to the study of energy and is not concerned with the amount of energy present in the universe, rather it is concerned with following the changes in energy.

The correct answer is a...
D. Answer d is incorrect because entropy is a measurement of the disorder in a system. Entropy is not concerned with the amount of energy in the system, just with the form in which the energy exists (i.e. converting from a more ordered to a less ordered form).

Hint: The first of these universal laws, the First Law of Thermodynamics, concerns the amount of energy in the universe. It states that energy cannot be created or destroyed; it can only change from one form to another (from potential to kinetic, for example).

3). In a chemical reaction, if ΔG is negative, it means that
        a). the products contain more free energy than the reactants.
        b). an input of energy is required to break the bonds.
        c). the reaction will proceed spontaneously.
        d). the reaction is endergonic.

The correct answer is c...
A. Answer a is incorrect because if ΔG is negative, meaning the change in free energy is negative, the product will contain less free energy than the reactants, not more.

The correct answer is c...
B. Answer b is incorrect because if ΔG is negative, it means that the free energy of the product is less than the free energy of the reactant. Because of this, energy is not needed to break the bonds of the product, rather energy is released when the bonds of the product break.

The correct answer is c--the reaction will proceed spontaneously.
C. If the ΔG in a reaction is negative, it means that the products of the reaction contain less free energy than the reactants. This occurs when the product (molecule) is less ordered (has a higher entropy) and/or has less energy in the chemical bonds that hold the molecule together. According to the Second Law of Thermodynamics, disorder is more likely than order, so these types of reactions occur spontaneously--without the input of energy.

The correct answer is c...
D. If the ΔG in a reaction is negative, it means that the product has less free energy than the reactant. The difference in free energy is released in the reaction-energy is given off in the reaction. This type of reaction is called exergonic (meaning "outward energy"), not endergonic (meaning "inward energy").

Hint: In other reactions, the ΔG is negative. The products of the reaction contain less free energy than the reactants; either the bond energy is lower or the disorder is higher, or both. Such reactions tend to proceed spontaneously. A spontaneous reaction may proceed very slowly. These reactions release the excess free energy as heat and are thus said to be exergonic ("outward energy").

4). A catalyst
        a). allows an endergonic reaction to proceed more quickly.
        b). increases the activation energy so a reaction can proceed more quickly.
        c). lowers the amount of energy needed for a reaction to proceed.
        d). is require for an exergonic reaction to occur.

The correct answer is c...
A. Answer a is incorrect because a catalyst, which is a substance that lowers the activation energy, can not allow an endergonic reaction to proceed more quickly. An endergonic reaction

requires the input of energy, which is then stored in the bond of the products. The lower of the input of energy would only keep the endergonic reaction from ever proceeding.

The correct answer is c...
B. Answer b is incorrect because a catalyst is a substance that lowers the activation energy, it *doesn't* increase it. Activation energy is needed even in an exergonic reaction and so although the reaction proceeds spontaneously, it could proceed very slowly if a large activation energy is needed. A catalyst lowers the amount of activation energy needed so the reaction can proceed more quickly.

The correct answer is c--lowers the amount of energy needed for a reaction to proceed.
C. All reactions even, exergonic reactions, require an input of energy in order for the reaction to proceed. This energy is called activation energy. In an endergonic reaction, the activation energy is stored within the bonds of the products, while in an exergonic reaction, the activation energy is released during the reaction. A catalyst is a substance that lowers the amount of energy needed for the reaction (the activation energy) by stressing the bonds so they break more easily.

The correct answer is c...
D. Answer d is incorrect because a catalyst is not required for an exergonic reaction to occur. An exergonic reaction proceeds spontaneously but a large activation energy requirement could mean that the reaction proceeds very slowly. A catalyst increases the speed with which the reaction proceeds, but isn't *required* for it to proceed.

Hint: The rate of an exergonic reaction depends on the activation energy required for the reaction to begin. Reactions with larger activation energies tend to proceed more slowly because fewer molecules succeed in overcoming the initial energy hurdle. However, stressing particular chemical bonds can make them easier to break. The process of influencing chemical bonds in a way that lowers the activation energy needed to initiate a reaction is called catalysis, and substances that accomplish this are known as catalysts.

5). Which of the following statements about enzymes is false?
   a). Enzymes are catalysts within cells.
   b). All the cells of an organism contain the same enzymes.
   c). Enzymes brings substances together so they undergo a reaction.
   d). Enzymes lower the activation energy of spontaneous reactions in the cell.

The correct answer is b...
A. Answer a is incorrect because this statement about enzymes is true. A catalyst is a substance that influences chemical bonds in such a way as to lower the activation energy necessary to start a chemical reaction. A cell uses special proteins, called enzymes to carry out catalysis in the cell.

The correct answer is b--All the cells of an organism contain the same enzymes.
B. This statement about enzymes is false. An organisms contains many different types of cells, each cell type having a different function in the organism. Because different cells perform different functions, they require different chemical reactions. An enzyme is specific to one or only a few different chemical reactions and a particular enzyme is only present in cells that carry out that particular chemical reaction.

The correct answer is b...
C. Answer c is incorrect because this statement about enzymes is true. An enzyme is a protein in the cell that has a unique three-dimensional shape. The reactant(s) of a reaction (called the substrate) associate with areas on the enzyme where the substrate undergoes bond breaking or bond formation.

The correct answer is b...
D. Answer d is incorrect because this statement about enzymes is true. Enzymes are protein catalysts in cells and like any catalyst, they function by lowering the activation energy of a spontaneous reaction so that it proceeds more quickly and easily.

Hint: Thousands of different kinds of enzymes are known, each catalyzing one or a few specific chemical reactions. By facilitating particular chemical reactions, the enzymes in a cell determine the course of metabolism--the collection of all chemical reactions--in that cell. Different types of cells contain different sets of enzymes, and this difference contributes to structural and functional variations among cell types.

6). A multienzyme complex contains
       a). many copies of just one enzyme.
       b). one enzyme and its substrate.
       c). enzymes that catalyze a series of reactions.
       d). side reactions on a substrate.

The correct answer is c...
A. Answer a is incorrect because while an multienzyme complex may contain several copies of a single enzyme, it also contains several different enzymes that work in a series. By clustering enzymes that catalyze a series of reactions, a multienzyme complex offers advantages such as access of substrates to the enzyme, the elimination of side reactions, and the control of the entire enzyme complex rather than control of individual enzymes.

The correct answer is c...
B. Answer b is incorrect because a multienzyme complex contains several different enzymes that work in a series of reactions, not just one enzyme. The association of an enzyme with its substrate is called an enzyme-substrate complex.

The correct answer is c--enzymes that catalyze a series of reactions.
C. As a means of improving efficiency, cells have acquired multienzyme complexes, which are a grouping of enzymes that catalyze different steps of a sequence of reactions. The advantages of multienzyme complexes are: access of substrates to the enzymes, the elimination of side reactions, and the control of the entire enzyme complex rather than control of individual enzymes.

The correct answer is c...
D. Answer d is incorrect because multienzyme complexes do not contain side reactions on a substrate. In fact, multienzyme complexes eliminate side reactions because the reacting substrate never leaves the complex through the series of reactions and so there is never the opportunity for unwanted side reactions.

Hint: Often in cells the several enzymes catalyzing the different steps of a sequence of reactions are loosely associated with one another in non-covalently bonded assemblies called multienzyme complexes.

7). Which of the following has *no* effect on the rate of enzyme-catalyzed reactions?
       a). temperature
       b). pH
       c). concentration of substrate
       d). none of these

The correct answer is d...
A. Answer a is incorrect because temperature does affect the rate of enzyme-catalyzed reactions. An enzyme has an optimal temperature at which it functions. Temperature can alter a protein's shape and so any deviation from an enzyme's optimum temperature can change its three-dimensional shape and distort its active site. The active site may no longer be able to attach its substrate.

The correct answer is d...
B. Answer b is incorrect because pH does affect the rate of enzyme-catalyzed reactions. An enzyme has an optimal pH at which it functions. Proteins contain positively- and negatively-charged amino acid which influence the three-dimensional structure of the protein. Hydrogen ions (which determines pH) in the enzyme's environment affect the distribution of the electrical charges of the enzyme and can alter the enzyme's structure such that it may not function correctly.

The correct answer is d...
C. Answer c is incorrect because the concentration of substrate does affect the rate of enzyme-catalyzed reactions. In order for a reaction to occur, the substrate must be present. A low concentration of the substrate will reduce the rate of enzyme-catalyzed reactions.

The correct answer is d--none of the above
D. All three of these variable affect the rate of enzyme-catalyzed reactions. The three-dimensional shape of the enzyme can be affected by temperature and pH and the concentration of the substrate available and also affect the rate of the reactions.

Hint: The rate of an enzyme-catalyzed reaction is affected by the concentration of substrate, and of the enzyme that works on it. In addition, any chemical or physical factor that alters the enzyme's three-dimensional shape--such as temperature, pH, salt concentration, and the binding of specific regulatory molecules--can affect the enzyme's ability to catalyze the reaction.

8). How is ATP used in the cell to produce cellular energy?
     a). ATP provides energy to drive exergonic reactions.
     b). ATP hydrolysis is coupled to endergonic reactions.
     c). A liberated phosphate group attaches to another molecule, which generates energy.
     d). ATP generates energy by the repulsion of the negatively-charged phosphates.

The correct answer is b...
A. Answer a is incorrect because exergonic reactions in the cell are spontaneous reactions that only require the input of activation energy. While ATP could be used to generate the activation energy required to start an exergonic reaction so much energy would be wasted. Rather, these reactions usually utilize catalysts to lower the activation energy and not ATP.

The correct answer is b--ATP hydrolysis is coupled to endergonic reactions.
B. The hydrolysis of the high-energy bond between the second and third phosphates of the ATP molecules generates considerable energy. When this reaction is coupled to endergonic reactions that require an input of energy, the endergonic reaction can proceed. The coupling of ATP hydrolysis with endergonic reactions drives the metabolic processes of the cell. In fact, so much energy is produced with the hydrolysis of ATP, that the coupled reactions actually become exergonic.

The correct answer is b...
C. Answer c is incorrect because although a phosphate group attaches temporarily to another molecule, this step does not generate the energy needed by the cell.

The correct answer is b...
D. Answer d is incorrect because the repulsion of the negatively-charged phosphates for each other creates very unstable covalent bonds. These bonds are easily broken but it is the breaking of these bonds that generates the energy for the cell, not merely the existence of the high-energy bonds.

Hint: Cells use ATP to drive endergonic reactions. Such reactions do not proceed spontaneously, because their products possess more free energy than their reactants. However, if the cleavage of ATPs terminal high-energy bond releases more energy then the other reaction consumes, the overall energy change of the two coupled reactions will be exergonic (energy releasing) and they will both proceed. Because almost all endergonic reactions require less energy than is released by the cleavage of ATP, ATP can provide most of the energy a cell needs.

9). Anabolic reactions are reactions that
      a). break chemical bonds.
      b). make chemical bonds.
      c). harvest energy.
      d). occur in a sequence.

The correct answer is b…
A). Answer a is incorrect because anabolic reactions are those reactions that build molecules. To build molecules, chemical bonds are made, not broken.

The correct answer is b—make chemical bonds.
B). Anabolic reactions are those reactions that build molecules. To build molecules, chemical bonds are made.

The correct answer is b…
C). Answer c is incorrect because the harvesting of energy involves the breaking of chemical bonds and storing the energy as ATP molecules in the cell.

The correct answer is b…
D). Answer d is incorrect because anabolic reactions are those reactions that build molecules. While several anabolic reactions may occur in sequence, catabolic reactions, reactions that break down molecules, can also occur in sequence.

10). How is a biochemical pathway regulated?
      a). The product of one reaction becomes the substrate for the next.
      b). The end product replaces the initial substrate in the pathway.
      c). The end product inhibits the first enzyme in the pathway by binding to an allosteric site.
      d). All of these are correct.

The correct answer is c...
A. Answer a is incorrect because the biochemical pathway is "built" by the product of one reaction becoming the substrate for the next but it is not regulated in that way.

The correct answer is c...
B. Answer b is incorrect because the end product can not replace the initial substrate. The active site of the first enzyme is specific for the initial substrate and while some competitive inhibitors block enzyme function by blocking the active site, the competitive inhibitor is usually not the end product.

The correct answer is c--the end product inhibits the first enzyme in the pathway by binding to an allosteric site.
C. The goal of a biochemical pathway is to produce an end product. When the cell has enough of the end product it is not necessary, nor efficient, to keep the pathway going. An easy but effective way to regulate a biochemical pathway is to use the end product as a means of determine when the pathway is finished. Many biochemical pathways use a mode of regulation called feedback inhibition, where the end product binds to an allosteric site on the first enzyme, shutting down the enzyme. Once the end product is in short supply again, the inhibitor is released and the pathway turns on again.

The correct answer is c...
D. Answer d is incorrect because only answer c presents a way that biochemical pathways are regulated. Answer a is incorrect because the biochemical pathway is "built" by the product of one

reaction becoming the substrate for the next but it is not regulated in that way. Answer b is incorrect because the end product can not replace the initial substrate. The active site of the first enzyme is specific for the initial substrate and while some competitive inhibitors block enzyme function by blocking the active site, the competitive inhibitor is usually not the end product.

Hint: The regulation of simple biochemical pathways often depends on an elegant feedback mechanism: the end product of the pathway binds to an allosteric site on the enzyme that catalyzes the first reaction in the pathway.

Test Your Visual Understanding

1). In which of these two reactions would the change in free energy, ΔG, be positive? Would the product of this reaction have more or less free energy compared to the reactant? Name this type of reaction.
Answer: The change in panel *a* would result in a positive change in free energy. The product in this reaction would have more free energy than that found in the reactants. This is an endergonic reaction.

2). In which of these two reactions could a catalyst help speed the reaction? How would the catalyst speed the reaction? Name this type of reaction
Answer: The rate of the reaction in panel *b* could be increased with the aid of a catalyst. The catalyst would reduce the amount of energy that is needed to start the reaction, the activation energy of the reaction. The reactant would bind to the catalyst (an enzyme), which would strain the bonds holding the components of the reactant together allowing them to break more easily. This is an exergonic reaction.

Apply Your Knowledge

1). In a biochemical pathway, three ATP molecules are hydrolyzed. The endergonic reactions in the pathway require a total of 17.3 kcal/mole of energy to drive the reactions of the pathway. What is the overall change in free energy of the biochemical pathway? Is the overall pathway endergonic or exergonic?
Answer: The hydrolysis of a molecule of ATP generates 7.3 kcal/mole and so the hydrolysis of three molecules of ATP would generate:
3 x 7.3 kcal/mole = 21.9 kcal/mole.

The endergonic reactions in the pathway require 17.3 kcal/mole and so the overall change in free energy of the pathway would be:

17.3 kcal/mole - 21.9 kcal/mole = -4.6 kcal/mole

The overall pathway is an exergonic reaction and so it would proceed spontaneously as long as the ATP molecules were available.

2). Oxidation-reduction reactions can involve a wide variety of molecules. Why are those involving hydrogen and oxygen of paramount importance in biological systems?
Answer: Oxygen is highly electronegative meaning that it has a strong affinity for electrons and so it is a great reducing agent in redox reactions. Similarly, hydrogen has a low electronegativity and so willingly gives up electrons in redox reactions. Also, oxygen and hydrogen are very abundant in organic molecules and so they are abundant in biological systems.

3). Almost no sunlight penetrates the deep ocean. However, many fish that live there attract prey and potential mates by producing their own light. Where does that light come from? Does its generation require energy?
Answer: The light, called bioluminescence is created through chemical reactions. When chemical bonds are broken during these chemical reactions, the energy released is emitted as light energy and the organism glows. These chemical reactions are endergonic and require the input of energy—ATP.

Self Test

1). In cellular respiration, energy-depleted electrons are donated to an inorganic molecule. In fermentation, what molecule accepts these electrons?
        a). oxygen
        b). an organic molecule
        c). sulfur
        d). an inorganic molecule other than O_2

The correct answer is b…
A. Answer a is incorrect because oxygen is the electron acceptor in aerobic respiration, not in fermentation.

The correct answer is b—an organic molecule
B. In fermentation, oxygen is not present and so this type of cellular respiration is anaerobic. In this case of anaerobic respiration, an organic molecule accepts the energy-depleted electron.

The correct answer is b…
C. Answer c is incorrect because sulfur is an electron acceptor in anaerobic respiration but fermentation is a specific type of anaerobic respiration that uses an organic molecule as the electron acceptor.

The correct answer is b…
D. Answer d is incorrect because an inorganic molecule other than O_2 is used as an electron acceptor in anaerobic respiration but fermentation is a specific type of anaerobic respiration that uses an organic molecule as the electron acceptor.

Hint: The energy in a chemical bond can be visualized as potential energy borne by the electrons that make up the covalent bond. Cells harvest this energy by putting the electrons to work, often to produce ATP. Afterward, the energy-depleted electron (associated with a proton as a hydrogen atom) is donated to some other molecule. When oxygen gas accepts the hydrogen atom, water forms, and the process is called aerobic respiration. When an inorganic molecule other than oxygen accepts the hydrogen, the process is called anaerobic respiration. When an organic molecule accepts the hydrogen atom, the process is called fermentation.

2). Which of the following is *not* a stage of aerobic respiration?
        a). glycolysis
        b). pyruvate oxidation
        c). the Krebs cycle
        d). electron transport chain

The correct answer is a—glycolysis
A. Glycolysis is the first stage in the process of extracting energy from glucose but glycolysis does not use oxygen and so the process is anaerobic, not aerobic. In glycolysis, ATP is made through substrate-level phosphorylation.

The correct answer is a…
B. Answer b is incorrect because pyruvate oxidation is a stage of aerobic respiration. It is the first step in the process of aerobic respiration. A molecule of pyruvate (the end product from glycolysis) is converted into carbon dioxide ad a two-carbon molecule called acetyl-CoA (acetyl-coenzyme A). A molecule of NADH is also produced and enters the electron transport chain.

The correct answer is a...
C. Answer c is incorrect because the Krebs cycle is a stage of aerobic respiration. It is the second step in the process of aerobic respiration, after pyruvate oxidation. The acetyl-CoA, produced in pyruvate oxidation enters a cycle of nine reactions called the Krebs cycle. ATP is made through substrate-level phosphorylation and more molecules of NADH are produced that enter the electron transport chain.

The correct answer is a...
D. Answer d is incorrect because the electron transport chain is a stage of aerobic respiration. It is the third step in the process of aerobic respiration, after pyruvate oxidation and the Krebs cycle. The NADH molecules produced in pyruvate oxidation and the Krebs cycle enter the electron transport chain where they drive the synthesis of a large amount of ATP.

Hint: In most organisms, the processes of substrate-level phosphorylation and aerobic respiration are combined. To harvest energy to make ATP form the sugar glucose in the presence of oxygen, the cell carries out a complex series of enzyme-catalyzed reactions that occur in four stages: the first stage captures energy by substrate-level phosphorylation through glycolysis; the following three stages carry out aerobic respiration by oxidizing the end product of glycolysis.

3). Which steps in glycolysis require the input of energy?
      a). the glucose priming steps
      b). the phosphorylation of glucose
      c). the phosphorylation of fructose 6-phosphate
      d). All of these steps require the input of energy.

The correct answer is d...
A. Answer a is incorrect because although the glucose priming steps which include the first three reactions require the input of energy through two ATP molecules, this is not the only correct answer.

The correct answer is d...
B. Answer b is incorrect because although the phosphorylation of glucose, a step in glucose priming, requires the input of energy through one ATP molecule, this is not the only correct answer.

The correct answer is d...
C. Answer c is incorrect because although the phosphorylation of fructose 6-phosphate, a step in glucose priming, requires the input of energy through one ATP molecule, this in not the only correct answer.

The correct answer is d—all of the above
D. All three steps listed require the input of energy. The glucose priming steps includes the first three reactions of glycolysis in which the glucose molecule is phosphorylated twice. The phosphorylation of glucose in the first reaction and fructose 6-phosphate in the third reaction result from the splitting of ATP molecules which release energy and attach the phosphate groups onto the sugar molecules. Glycolysis could not proceed without this input of energy.

Hint: The first half of glycolysis consists of five sequential reactions that convert one molecule of glucose into two molecules of the three-carbon compound, glyceraldehyde 3-phosphate (G3P). These reactions demand the expenditure of ATP, so they are an energy-requiring process.

Glucose priming. Three reactions "prime" glucose by changing it into a compound that can be cleaved readily into 2 three-carbon phosphorylated molecules. Two of these reactions require the cleavage of ATP, so this step requires the cell to use two ATP molecules.

4). Pyruvate dehydrogenase is a multienzyme complex that catalyzes a series of reactions. Which of the following is *not* carried out by pyruvate dehydrogenase?
      a). a decarboxylation reaction
      b). the production of ATP
      c). producing an acetyl group from pyruvate
      d). combining the acetyl group with a cofactor

The correct answer is b...
A.   Answer a is incorrect because this reaction is carried out by pyruvate dehydrogenase. In the decarboxylation reaction, a carbon is cleaved off of pyruvate and departs the enzyme as CO_2.

The correct answer is b—the production of ATP
B. The multienzyme pyruvate dehydrogenase does not produce ATP during the oxidation of pyruvate. The oxidation of pyruvate produces NADH which goes on to enter the electron transport chain where ATP molecules are formed, but ATP formation is not catalyzed by pyruvate dehydrogenase.

The correct answer is b...
C. Answer c is incorrect because this reaction is carried out by pyruvate dehydrogenase. In liberating a carbon atom from pyruvate through a decarboxylation reaction, an acetyl group is produced.

The correct answer is b...
D. Answer d is incorrect because this reaction is carried out by pyruvate dehydrogenase. After the acetyl group is produced from pyruvate it combines with a cofactor called coenzyme A (CoA) and forms the compound acetyl-CoA.

Hint: The oxidation of pyruvate is a complex reaction involving three intermediate stages and is catalyzed within the mitochondria by a multienzyme complex. Within the complex, component polypeptides pass the substrates from one enzyme to the next, without releasing them. Pyruvate dehydrogenase, the complex of enzymes that removes CO2 from pyruvate, is one of the largest multienzyme complexes. In the course of the reaction, the acetyl group removed from pyruvate combines with a cofactor called coenzyme A (CoA), forming a compound known as acetyl-CoA.

5). How many molecules of CO_2 are produced for each molecule of glucose that passes through glycolysis and the Krebs cycle?
      a). 2
      b). 3
      c). 6
      d). 7

The correct answer is c...
A. Answer a is incorrect because although no CO_2 is produced during glycolysis, 2 molecules of CO_2 are produced during the oxidation of pyruvate (one per each pyruvate molecule that comes from glycolysis). But the 2 acetyl-CoA molecules from the oxidation reaction continue through the Krebs cycle so more than 2 molecules of CO_2 must be produced.

The correct answer is c...
B. Answer b is incorrect because although no CO_2 is produced during glycolysis, 2 molecules of CO_2 are produced during the oxidation of pyruvate (one per each pyruvate molecule that comes from glycolysis). Then the 2 molecules of acetyl-CoA enter the Krebs cycle where 2 more molecules of CO_2 are produced per acetyl-CoA molecules, so more than 3 molecules of CO_2 are produced per molecule of glucose.

The correct answer is c—6

C. Although no CO_2 is produced during glycolysis, each molecule of glucose that enters glycolysis is broken in two, producing two molecules of pyruvate. You must keep this in mind when counting up the number of CO_2 molecules produced through respiration. Each pyruvate molecule produced in glycolysis will yield one molecule of CO_2 during the oxidation of pyruvate and another two molecules of CO_2 during the Krebs cycle, for a total of 3 molecules of CO_2. However, because two pyruvate molecules are produced per molecule of glucose you must double that number to 6 molecules of CO_2.

The correct answer is c...

D. Answer d is incorrect because all of the molecules of CO_2 come from the glucose molecule and glucose only has 6 carbons, therefore a molecule of glucose could not produce 7 molecules of CO_2.

Hint: In the process of aerobic respiration, glucose is entirely consumed. The six-carbon glucose molecule is first cleaved into a pair of three-carbon pyruvate molecules during glycolysis. One of the carbons of each pyruvate is then lost as CO_2 in the conversion of pyruvate to acetyl-CoA; two other carbons are lost as CO_2 during the oxidations or the Krebs cycle. All that is left to mark the passing of the glucose molecule into six CO_2 molecules is its energy.

6). The electrons generated from the Krebs cycle are transferred to _____ and then are shuttled to _____.

a). NAD^+ / oxygen
b). NAD^+ / electron transport chain
c). NADH / oxygen
d). NADH / electron transport chain

The correct answer is b...

A. Answer a is incorrect because although the electrons are transferred to NAD^+, they are not shuttled to oxygen directly. NAD^+ carries the electrons to the electron transport chain where they are eventually transferred to oxygen.

The correct answer is b—NAD^+ / electron transport chain

B. The electrons that are captured from glucose as it passes through glycolysis and the Krebs cycle are transferred to an intermediate electron acceptor, NAD. NAD is reduced to NADH. NADH then shuttles the electrons to the electron transport chain where the energy from the electrons is captured and used to synthesize ATP. Oxygen is the final acceptor of the electrons, forming water as final product of cellular respiration.

The correct answer is b...

C. Answer c is incorrect because NAD^+ is the electron acceptor, not NADH. NAD^+ is reduced to NADH after accepting the electrons and NADH shuttles the electrons to the electron transport chain. From the electron transport chain, the electrons are ultimately passed onto oxygen.

The correct answer is b...

D. Answer d is incorrect because NAD^+ is the electron acceptor, not NADH. NAD^+ is reduced to NADH after accepting the electrons and NADH shuttles the electrons to the electron transport chain.

Hint: Energy captured by NADH is not harvested all at once. Instead of being transferred directly to oxygen, the two electrons carried by NADH are passed along the electron transport chain is oxygen is present. NADH delivers electrons to the top of the electrons transport chain and oxygen captures them at the bottom. The oxygen then joins with the hydrogen ions to form water.

7). The electron transport chain pumps protons
   a). out of the mitochondrial matrix.
   b). out of the intermembrane space and into the matrix.
   c). out of the mitochondrion and into the cytoplasm.
   d). out of the cytoplasm and into the mitochondrion.

The correct answer is a—out of the mitochondrial matrix.
A. Energy from the electrons carried by NADH and another electron carrier, $FADH_2$, drives the actions of proton pumps that are embedded in the inner mitochondrial membrane. These transport proteins pump protons (hydrogen ions) from the inner mitochondrial matrix to the intermembrane space where they accumulate.

The correct answer is a…
B. Answer b is incorrect because the proteins of the electron transport chain pump the protons in the opposite directions, from the matrix into the intermembrane space.

The correct answer is a…
C. Answer c is incorrect because the proteins that pump the protons are located within the inner mitochondrial membrane and so the protons can not be pumped out of the mitochondrion into the cytoplasm.

The correct answer is a…
D. Answer d is incorrect because the proteins that pump the protons are located within the inner mitochondrial membrane and so the protons can not be pumped out of the cytoplasm into the mitochondrion.

Hint: As the electrons harvested by oxidative respiration are passed along the electron transport chain, the energy they release transports protons out of the matrix and into the outer compartment, sometimes called the intermembrane space. Three transmembrane proteins in the inner mitochondrial membrane actually accomplish the transport. The flow of excited electrons induces a change in shape of these pump proteins, which causes them to transport protons across the membrane.

8). What process of cellular respiration generates the most ATP?
   a). glycolysis
   b). oxidation of pyruvate
   c). Krebs cycle
   d). chemiosmosis

The correct answer is d…
A. Answer a is incorrect because glycolysis only generates two molecules of ATP through substrate-level phosphorylation. More ATP is ultimately synthesized from the two NADH molecules produced in glycolysis, but that is through chemiosmosis and not through glycolysis.

The correct answer is d…
B. Answer b is incorrect because the oxidation of pyruvate doesn't generate any molecules of ATP. ATP is ultimately synthesized from the two NADH molecules produced in the oxidation of pyruvate, but that is through chemiosmosis and not through the oxidation of pyruvate.

The correct answer is d…
C. Answer c is incorrect because the Krebs cycle only generates two molecules of ATP through substrate-level phosphorylation. More ATP is ultimately synthesized from the six NADH molecules and two $FADH_2$ molecules produced during the Krebs cycle, but that is through chemiosmosis and not through the Krebs cycle itself.

The correct answer is d—chemiosmosis

C. Chemiosmosis is the process whereby ATP is synthesized by the diffusion protons across the inner mitochondrial membrane into the matrix through ATP synthase channel proteins. The electron transport chain drives chemiosmosis by pumping the protons across this membrane to set up an electrochemical gradient. The electrons from NADH and $FADH_2$ drive the proton pumps. Each molecule of NADH theoretically generates the synthesis of three molecules of ATP and each molecule of $FADH_2$ theoretically generates the synthesis of two molecules of ATP. The contributions of electrons from NADH and $FADH_2$ generate a lot more ATP than any other process in cellular respiration.

Hint: The chemiosmotic model suggests that one ATP molecule is generated for each proton pump activated by the electron transport chain. As the electrons from NADH activate three pumps and those from $FADH_2$ activate two, we would expect each molecules of NADH and $FADH_2$ to generate three and two ATP molecules, respectively for a total of 38 ATPs. However, the net ATP production is decreased by 2 because two molecules of ATP are used to shuttle the NADH molecules produced during glycolysis across the mitochondrial membrane. This reduces the theoretical total of ATP molecules produced during chemiosmosis to 36 ATPs. The actual number of ATPs generated through chemiosmosis is closer to 30.

9). Oxidizing which of the following substances yields the most energy?
   a). proteins
   b). glucose
   c). fatty acids
   d). water

The correct answer is c…

A. Answer a is incorrect because the amino acids of proteins go through a process called deamination where the nitrogen-containing side group is removed and the remaining carbon chain is modified to enter into the Krebs cycle at different points. Because different amino acids ultimately enter the Krebs cycle at different points and do not go through the glycolysis and pyruvate oxidation, they do not generate more energy than carbohydrates.

The correct answer is c…

B. Answer b is incorrect because although glucose is a great source of energy with its numerous C—H bonds, fatty acids are a greater source of energy, producing more molecules of ATP per carbon atom.

The correct answer is c—fatty acids

C. Fatty acids function as the energy storage molecule in the body because the molecule is able to store more energy than carbohydrates or proteins. Fatty acids typically have 16 or more —CH_2 bonds that provide a rich harvest of energy. But even a six-carbon fatty acid, the same number of carbons as glucose, generates more energy than glucose.

The correct answer is c…

D. Answer d is incorrect because water has no carbon bonds and so it has no means of entering respiration, no means of generating energy. Instead, it is a product of respiration.

Hint: How much ATP does the catabolism of fatty acids produce? Compare a hypothetical six-carbon fatty acid with the six-carbon glucose molecule, which generates about 30 molecules of ATP in a eukaryotic cell. The carbons of the fatty acid are removed in twos by enzymes that then bind to coenzyme A, forming acetyl-CoA. This process is called β-oxidation. Each pass through β-oxidation produces one molecule of $FADH_2$ and NADH that enter into the electron transport chain. A six-carbon fatty acid would go through β-oxidation twice producing 2 molecules each of NADH and $FADH_2$ and three molecules of acetyl-CoA. The three molecules of acetyl-CoA produce 3 molecules of ATP, 9 molecules of NADH, and 3 molecules of $FADH_2$. These go into the electron transport chain and produce about 36 molecules of ATP, more energy than glucose.

10). The final electron acceptor in lactic acid fermentation is:
    a). pyruvate
    b). NAD^+
    c). lactic acid
    d). O_2

The correct answer is a—pyruvate
A. Pyruvate, the end product of glycolysis becomes the final electron acceptor in the absence of oxygen in certain cells, such as muscle cells. NAD^+ must be regenerated for glycolysis to continue and so pyruvate accepts the hydrogen atom (and electrons) from NADH and in doing so, the pyruvate converts into lactic acid.

The correct answer is a…
B. Answer b is incorrect because NAD^+ is the electron acceptor during glycolysis, not in fermentation. The goal of fermentation is to recycle NAD^+ so another electron acceptor is used, pyruvate.

The correct answer is a…
C. Answer c is incorrect because lactic acid is the end product of lactic acid fermentation, not the final electron acceptor. Pyruvate accepts the hydrogen atom (and electrons) from NADH, thereby producing lactic acid and recycling NAD^+.

The correct answer is a…
D. Answer d is incorrect because lactic acid fermentation is an anaerobic process and oxygen is not involved. In fact, if oxygen is present, lactic acid fermentation does not occur.

Hint: Most animal cells use an enzyme called lactate dehydrogenase to transfer a hydrogen atom from NADH back to the pyruvate that is produced by glycolysis. This reaction converts pyruvate into lactic acid and regenerates NAD^+ from NADH.

Test Your Visual Understanding

Answer the following questions related to this figure, which shows the process of chemiosmosis.
1). In the figure, proton pumps are transporting hydrogen ions across the membrane. What is the driving force of this pump? What type of membrane transport is the proton pump? Explain.
Answer: The driving force of the proton pump is the reduction of the protein with electrons transferred to the protein from NADH. These electrons carry energy and the energy is transferred to the pump and allows it to transport hydrogen ions (protons) across the inner mitochondrial membrane. The proton pump is a type of active transport. The pump requires energy to transport the protons that it receives, not from ATP, but rather from electrons transferred from NADH. It pumps protons across the membrane against their concentration gradient. The proton pump can also be viewed as couple transport because the actions of the proton pump are coupled to the actions of ATP synthase so even though both processes are not functioning in the same protein pump, they are coupled transport systems.

2). Why is this process called chemiosmosis? What is the force driving the synthesis of ATP? How could the process of ATP synthesis be inhibited or shut down?
Answer: This process is called chemiosmosis because the chemical formation of ATP is driven by a diffusion force similar to osmosis, the protons diffuse from an area of higher concentration to an area of lower concentration. The force driving the synthesis of ATP is the steep electrochemical gradient established by the actions of the proton pump. The proton pump pumps hydrogen ions across the membrane establishing a chemical gradient, the protons are higher in the intermembrane space than in the matrix. On top of the chemical gradient, an electrical gradient is also established. The pumping of the hydrogen ions across the membrane makes the intermembrane space more positively-charged compared to the matrix, such that the positively-charged hydrogen ions are driven toward the more negatively-charged matrix. This strong

electrochemical gradient is a very strong driving force—energizing the ATP synthase protein to form ATP.

The process of ATP synthesis could be inhibited or shut down with the depletion of NADH in the cell. If there is no NADH carrying electrons, the proton pumps can not function. That is why it is important that the cell recycles NAD^+ so there is a constant supply of NADH.

Apply Your Knowledge

1). How much energy would be generated in the cells of a person who consumed a diet of pyruvate instead of glucose? Calculate the energy generated on a per molecule basis.
Answer: The person would not receive the benefits of energy generated from glycolysis because the pyruvate would enter directly into pyruvate oxidation. For each molecule of pyruvate consumed:

The oxidation of pyruvate to acetyl-CoA would produce:
1 molecule of NADH

One round of the Krebs cycle would produce:
3 molecules of NADH
1 molecule of $FADH_2$
1 molecule of ATP

The electron transport chain would generate:
4 NADH x 2.5 ATP = 9 ATPs
1 $FADH_2$ x 1.5 = 1.5 ATPs

For a total of 11.5 ATP molecules per each pyruvate molecule consumed.

2). As explained in chapter 5, mitochondria are thought to have evolved from bacteria that were engulfed by and lived symbiotically within early eukaryotic cells. Why haven't present-day eukaryotic cells dispensed with mitochondria, placing all of the mitochondrial genes in the nucleus and carrying out all of the metabolic functions of the mitochondria within the cytoplasm?
Answer: The evolution of the eukaryotic cell tended toward compartmentalizing functions as a means of increasing efficiency. By compartmentalizing a function or process, all of the enzymes and substrates for the process could be sequestered in one area increasing the efficiency of reactions taking place. The sequestering of aerobic metabolic functions to the mitochondria and the sequestering of mitochondrial genes help to improve efficiency. The redundancy of some mitochondrial genes to the nucleus is probably more of a "backup" function than of a switching over of the location of the function. It is simply more efficient for all aerobic metabolic functions to be sequestered in the mitochondria.

3). Why do plants typically store their excess energy as carbohydrates rather than fat?
Answer: Because plants are able to produce their own food, it is not necessary for them to have long-term storage of energy provided by fatty acids. Carbohydrate storage is sufficient for plants. When they need more carbohydrates, they just make them. Animals, on the other hand, need to consume their food therefore their bodies have evolved the ability to store energy in more energy-rich molecules for times of famine.

4). If you poke a hole in a mitochondrion, can it still perform oxidative respiration? Can fragments of mitochondria perform oxidative respiration?
Answer: Because oxidative respiration requires the establishment of a concentration gradient of hydrogen ions (protons) a hole in the mitochondrion would allow leakage of protons out of the mitochondrion and would disrupt the proton concentration gradient. Without this gradient, oxidative respiration could not occur. Using that same argument, a fragment of mitochondrial membrane could not perform oxidative respiration. A concentration gradient of protons could not be established across a fragment of membrane, it requires a "closed" system.

None for this chapter.

FIGURE 10.3

Discovery of the light-independent reactions. Blackman measured photosynthesis rates under differing light intensities, CO_2 concentrations, and temperatures. As this graph shows, light is the limiting factor at low light intensities, while temperature and CO_2 concentration are the limiting factors at higher light intensities.
Blackman found that increasing light intensity above 2000 foot-candles did not lead to any further increase in the rate of photosynthesis. Can you suggest a hypothesis that would explain why?

Answer: At 2000 foot-candles, all of the available chlorophyll molecules are in use, at full bore. Adding more photons can't enlist any more chlorophyll molecules, and so it has no effect on the rate.

FIGURE 10.9

Emerson and Arnold's experiment. When photosynthetic saturation is achieved, further increases in intensity cause no increase in output.
Under what experimental conditions would you expect the saturation levels for a given number of chlorophyll molecules to be higher?

Answer: Increasing the temperature or CO_2 concentration should increase the output of individual photocenters and so should raise the rate at which saturation is achieved.

FIGURE 10.13

The enhancement effect. The rate of photosynthesis when red and far-red light are provided together is greater than the sum of the rates when each wavelength is provided individually. This result baffled researchers in the 1950's. Today, it provides the key evidence that photosynthesis is carried out by two photochemical systems with slightly different wavelength optima.
What would you conclude if "both lights on" did not change the relative rate of photosynthesis?

Answer: If exposure to both lights did not increase the rate of photosynthesis, you might conclude that the two photosystems do not act in series, or that there is only one photosystem that absorbs light of either wavelength.

Self Test

1). Within chloroplasts, the semiliquid matrix in which the Calvin cycle occurs is called:
    a). stroma.
    b). thylakoids.
    c). grana.
    d). photosystem.

The correct answer is a—stroma
A. Photosynthesis occurs in cellular structures called chloroplast. Chloroplasts have two compartments that "house" different stages of photosynthesis. The thylakoids house the light reactions that generate the energy needed to build organic molecules. The dark reactions or Calvin cycle occurs in the stroma, the semiliquid matrix that surrounds the thylakoids. The Calvin cycle is the series of reactions that assemble carbon molecules.

The correct answer is a…
B. Answer b is incorrect because the thylakoids are the membrane-bound structures in the chloroplast that house the photosynthetic pigments for the light reactions.

The correct answer is a...
C. Answer c is incorrect because the grana are the columns or stacks of thylakoids. The thylakoids are the membrane-bound structures in the chloroplast that house the photosynthetic pigments for the light reactions.

The correct answer is a...
D. Answer d is incorrect because a photosystem is the name given to the cluster of photosynthetic pigments that are embedded in the thylakoid membrane. The light reactions occur in the photosystems, not the Calvin cycle.

Hint: The internal membranes of the chloroplasts are organized into sacs called the thylakoids, and often numerous thylakoids are stacked on one another in columns called grana. The thylakoid membranes house the photosynthetic pigments of capturing light energy and he machinery to make ATP. Surrounding the thylakoid membrane system is a semiliquid substance called stroma. The stroma houses the enzymes needed to assemble carbon molecules. In the membranes of the thylakoids, photosynthetic pigments are clustered together to form a photosystem.

2). Visible light occupies what part of the electromagnetic spectrum?
   a). the entire spectrum
   b). the entire upper half (with longer wavelengths)
   c). a small portion in the middle
   d). the entire lower half (with shorter wavelengths)

The correct answer is c...
A. Answer a is incorrect because the entire spectrum includes many wavelengths that are not visible to the human eye. Visible light includes the portion of the spectrum with wavelengths between about 400 nm and 740 nm.

The correct answer is c...
B. Answer b is incorrect because the upper half of the spectrum includes radio waves and infrared wavelengths that are not visible to the human eye. Visible light includes the portion of the spectrum with wavelengths between about 400 nm and 740 nm.

The correct answer is c--a small portion in the middle
C. The full electromagnetic spectrum includes energy with wavelengths as long as 100 m and as short as 0.001 nm. The human eye can only detect wavelengths in the range of about 400 nm up to about 740 nm. This area of the spectrum is called visible light.

The correct answer is c...
D. Answer d is incorrect because the lower half of the spectrum includes UV light, X rays, and gamma rays, none of which are visible to the human eye. Visible light includes the portion of the spectrum with wavelengths between about 400 nm and 740 nm.

Hint: Light is a form of electromagnetic energy conveniently thought of as a wave. The shorter the wavelength of light, the greater its energy. Visible light represents only a small part of the electromagnetic spectrum between 400 and 740 nanometers.

3). The colors of light that are most effective for photosynthesis are
   a). red, blue, and violet.
   b). green, yellow, and orange
   c). infrared and ultraviolet
   d). All colors of light are equally effective.

The correct answer is a--red, blue, and violet
A. Chlorophyll is the primary pigment used to absorb light for photosynthesis and so the colors of light that are most effective are those colors absorbed by chlorophyll *a* and *b*. Chlorophyll *a*

absorbs wavelengths of light in the 400-450 nm range (violet to blue light) and 625-740 nm range (red light). Likewise, chlorophyll *b* absorbs wavelengths of light in the 450-475 nm range (blue light) and 600-675 nm range (orange to red light).

The correct answer is a...
B. Answer b is incorrect because light that is absorbed by chlorophylls *a* and *b* would be the most effective for photosynthesis. The middle of the visible light spectrum (the green to orange range) is not absorbed by chlorophylls *a* or *b* and so they would not be effective for photosynthesis. In fact, these wavelengths of light are reflected by the plant's leaves, which is why the leaves appear green to the human eye.

The correct answer is a...
C. Answer c is incorrect because light that is absorbed by chlorophylls *a* and *b* would be the most effective for photosynthesis. Chlorophylls *a* and *b* do not absorb ultraviolet or infrared light and so these wavelengths of light would not be effective for photosynthesis. In fact you can't even use the term "colors" when describing ultraviolet and infrared because these wavelengths do not produce a perception of "color" to the human eye.

The correct answer is a...
D. Answer d is incorrect because light that is absorbed by chlorophylls *a* and *b* would be the most effective for photosynthesis. Only the colors of red, blue, and violet are absorbed by chlorophylls *a* and *b* and so only these colors would be effective for photosynthesis.

Hint: Englemann set out to characterize the action spectrum of photosynthesis, that is, the relative effectiveness of different wavelengths of light in promoting photosynthesis. He found that red and violet light, the two colors most strongly absorbed by chlorophyll, were the most effective for photosynthesis.

4). A photosystem consists of
- a). a group of chlorophyll molecules, all of which contribute excited electrons to the synthesis of ATP.
- b). a pair of chlorophyll *a* molecules.
- c). a group of chlorophyll molecules held together by proteins.
- d). a group of chlorophyll molecules that funnels light energy toward a single chlorophyll *b* molecule.

The correct answer is c...
A. Answer a is incorrect because although any of the chlorophyll molecules in the photosystem can absorb the excitation energy from a photon of light, it is only the reaction center (a single or pair of chlorophyll *a* molecules) which contributes an excited electron to the synthesis of ATP.

The correct answer is c...
B. Answer b is incorrect because a pair of chlorophyll *a* molecules is the reaction center of a photosystem, but a photosystem also includes a whole network of chlorophyll molecules supported by a matrix of proteins and some accessory pigments.

The correct answer is c--a group of chlorophyll molecules held together by proteins.
C. A photosystem consists of a network of chlorophyll molecules held together by a matrix of proteins and some accessory pigments. These chlorophyll molecules capture energy from photons of light, which excite an electron in the chlorophyll molecule. The energy (not the electron) is passed from one chlorophyll molecules to another until it reaches the reaction center. From there, an excited electron from the reaction center is passed to an electron transport chain where ATP is made.

The correct answer is c...
D. Answer d is incorrect because the network of chlorophyll molecules funnels light energy to a reaction center, which is a pair of chlorophyll *a* molecules, not a single chlorophyll *b* molecule.

Hint: Each photosystem is a network of chlorophyll a molecules, accessory pigments, and associated proteins held within a protein matrix on the surface of the photosynthetic membrane. A photosystem channels the excitation energy gathered by any one of its pigment molecules to a reaction center. The reaction center of purple photosynthetic bacteria is a pair of chlorophyll a molecules. The reaction center passes the energy out of the photosystem so it can be put to work driving the synthesis of ATP and organic molecules.

5). Which photosystem is believed to have evolved first?
      a). photosystem I
      b). photosystem II
      c). cyclic photophosphorylation
      d). All photosystems evolved at the same time, but in different organisms.

The correct answer is c...
A. Answer a is incorrect because although Photosystem I is believed to be more closely related to the photosystem found in sulfur bacteria which uses cyclic photophosphorylation, it evolved after that system.

The correct answer is c...
B. Answer b is incorrect because Photosystem II, which uses higher energy lightwaves (shorter wavelengths), is believed to have evolved later, improving the energy-harvesting capabilities of the cell.

The correct answer is c--cyclic photophosphorylation
C. Cyclic photophosphorylation is the name given to the electron transfer process that leads to ATP synthesis in sulfur bacteria. This was the primary form of photosynthetic light reaction for about 1 billion years but was limited in that it was cyclic and so could only be used as a means of harnessing light energy as ATP. The evolution of the two photosystems used in series, expanded the capabilities of the cell to produce carbohydrates.

The correct answer is c...
D. Answer d is incorrect because although cyclic photophosphorylation and Photosystems I and II are found in different organisms, they didn't evolve at the same time. Cyclic photophosphorylation evolved in sulfur bacteria and was the only form of photosynthesis light reaction for about 1 billion years. After that, the combined I and II photosystems evolved in plants and other kinds of bacteria.

Hint: Photosynthetic pigment arrays are thought to have evolved more than 3 billion years ago in bacteria similar to the sulfur bacteria of today. The photosystem found in these bacteria transmits an electron into an electron transport chain that cycles an electron back to the photosystem's reaction center. For more than a billion years, cyclic photophosphorylation was the only form of photosynthetic light reaction that organisms used. However, its major limitation is that it is geared only toward energy production, not toward biosynthesis. After the sulfur bacteria appeared, other kinds of bacteria evolved an improved version of the photosystem: a second more powerful photosystem was combined with the first.

6). Oxygen is produced during photosynthesis when
      a). the carbon is removed from carbon dioxide to make carbohydrates.
      b). hydrogen from water is added to carbon dioxide to make carbohydrates.
      c). water molecules are split to provide electrons for photosystem I.
      d). water molecules are split to provide electrons for photosystem II.

The correct answer is d...
A. Answer a is incorrect because oxygen is a product of the light reactions and not the dark reactions. The dark reactions (the Calvin cycle) produce carbohydrates using the carbon and oxygen from CO_2. Oxygen is produced when a water molecule is split during the light reactions to replenish the electrons lost from the reaction center of Photosystem II.

The correct answer is d...
B. Answer b is incorrect because oxygen is a product of the light reactions and not the dark reactions. The dark reactions (the Calvin cycle) produce carbohydrates using the carbon and oxygen from CO_2 and hydrogens from NADPH. Oxygen is produced when a water molecule is split during the light reactions to replenish the electrons lost from the reaction center of Photosystem II.

The correct answer is d...
C. Answer c is incorrect because although oxygen is produced when a water molecules is split, this reaction occurs to replenish the electron lost from photosystem II, not photosystem I.

The correct answer is d--water molecules are split to provide electrons for photosystem II.
D. The photosystem II loses an electron to the electron transport chain and that electron must be replenished so that photosynthesis can continue. The electrons are supplied to the reaction center of photosystem II by the splitting of a water molecule. The hydrogens replenish the chlorophyll with an electron and oxygen is released.

Hint: This is a two-stage process, called noncyclic photophosphorylation, ejects an electron from photosystem II that are used to synthesize ATP and then passed to $NADP^+$ in photosystem I. The photosystem is replenished with electrons by the splitting of a water molecule. An enzyme in Photosystem II removes electrons one at a time to fill the holes left in the reaction center by departure of light-energized electrons. As soon as four electrons have been removed from the two molecules of water, O_2 is released.

7). During photosynthesis, ATP molecules are generated by
        a). the Calvin cycle.
        b). chemiosmosis.
        c). the electron transport chain.
        d). light striking the chlorophyll molecules.

The correct answer is b...
A. Answer a is incorrect because ATP is generated during the light reactions and the Calvin cycle is considered the dark reactions. The Calvin cycle is the portion of photosynthesis in which carbohydrates are synthesized from CO_2, not the synthesis of ATP. ATP is generated in the light reactions to drive the synthesis of carbohydrates during the Calvin cycle.

The correct answer is b--chemiosmosis.
B. The excited electrons from the photosystem II drive protein pumps that pump protons (hydrogen ions) across the thylakoid membrane into the thylakoid space, which builds up a electrochemical gradient across the membrane. The protons then diffuse across the membrane through transport channels called ATP synthase. The passing of the protons down their electrochemical gradient drives the phosphorylation of ADP producing ATP. The process is called chemiosmosis because it is the movement of chemicals in a process similar to osmosis.

The correct answer is b...
C. Answer c is incorrect because the electron transport chain establishes the electrochemical gradient of protons that drives the synthesis of ATP, but the electron transport chain does not synthesize ATP.

The correct answer is b...
D. Answer d is incorrect because light striking the chlorophyll in the photosystem is the source of energy to drive the electron transport chain, which eventually leads to the synthesis of ATP, but the light striking the chlorophyll does not produce ATP.

Hint: Each thylakoid is a closed compartment into which protons are pumped from the stroma by the b_6-f complex. The splitting of water also produces added protons that contribute to the gradient. The thylakoid membrane is impermeable to protons, so protons cross back out almost exclusively via the channels provided by ATP synthases. As protons pass out of the thylakoid through ATP synthase channels, ADP is phosphorylated to ATP and released into the stroma. This process is called chemiosmosis.

8). The overall purpose of the Calvin cycle is to:
    a). generate molecules of ATP.
    b). generate NADPH.
    c). give off oxygen for animal use.
    d). build organic (carbon) molecules.

The correct answer is d...
A. Answer a is incorrect because ATP is generated during the light reactions of photosynthesis, not during the Calvin cycle. ATP that is produced during the light reactions is used to power the Calvin cycle, which synthesizes carbon molecules from CO_2 and NADPH.

The correct answer is d...
B. Answer b is incorrect because NADPH is produced during the light reactions of photosynthesis. The NADPH that is produced through a reduction reaction becomes the source of hydrogens and energetic electrons to bind carbon atoms together during the Calvin cycle.

The correct answer is d...
C. Answer c is incorrect because of two reasons: 1) oxygen is released during the light reactions of photosynthesis, not as a byproduct of the Calvin cycle and 2). although oxygen is required by animals, it is not the overall purpose of photosynthesis in plants to provide oxygen to animals.

The correct answer is d--build organic (carbon) molecules.
D. The purpose of the Calvin cycle is to build organic molecules that the plant uses as its food source. The plant can then break down these organic molecules during cellular respiration to produce ATP and other byproducts necessary for plant cell function.

Hint: Photosynthesis is a way of making organic molecules from carbon dioxide (CO2). These organic molecules contain many C--H bonds and are highly reduced compared with CO2. To build organic molecules, cells use raw materials provided by the light reactions: energy and reducing power. The key step in the Calvin cycle--the event that makes the reduction of CO2 possible--is the attachment of CO2 to a very special organic molecule.

9). The final product of the Calvin cycle is
    a). RuBP.
    b). G3P.
    c). glucose.
    d). PGA.

The correct answer is b...
A. Answer a is incorrect because RuBP is the 5-carbon molecule that recycles in the Calvin cycle. It binds to CO_2 that produces two molecules of 3-phosphoglycerate (PGA) and it eventually is formed again after glyceraldehyde 3-phosphate (G3P) is released from the Calvin cycle.

The correct answer is b--G3P.
B. G3P, glyceraldehyde 3-phosphate, is formed as a product of the Calvin cycle after three turns of the cycle. G3P is then used to synthesize glucose and other sugars.

The correct answer is b...
C. Answer c is incorrect because although glucose is the ultimate product of photosynthesis, it is not a direct product of the Calvin cycle. The Calvin cycle produces the 3-carbon molecule glyceraldehyde 3-phosphate, which is used to synthesize glucose.

The correct answer is b...
D. Answer d is incorrect because 3-phosphoglycerate (PGA) is first intermediate product in the Calvin cycle, after the carboxylation of ribulose 1,5-bisphosphate (RuBP). PGA is then modified to glyceraldehyde 3-phosphate (G3P) which is the final product of the Calvin cycle.

Hint: With three full turns of the cycle, three molecules of carbon dioxide enter, a molecule of glyceraldehyde 3-phosphate (G3P) is produced, and three molecules of RuBP are regenerated.

10). C_4 photosynthesis is an adaptation to hot, dry conditions in which
      a). CO_2 is fixed and stored in the leaf.
      b). water is stored in the stem.
      c). oxygen is stored in the root.
      d). light energy is stored in chloroplasts.

The correct answer is a--CO_2 is fixed and stored in the leaf
A. At higher temperatures the oxygen levels in the leaf can build up and interfere with carbon fixation. Under these conditions, O_2 binds to rubisco, the enzyme that usually carboxylates ribulose 1,5-bisphosphate, instead oxidizing the molecule. This oxygen modification of ribulose 1,5-bisphosphate ultimately results in the release of CO_2, undoing the Calvin cycle. C_4 plants offset this problem by carboxylating a molecule other than ribulose 1,5-bisphosphate. C_4 plants add CO_2 to the molecule phosphoenolpyruvate (PEP). PEP contributes a CO_2 molecule to ribulose 1,5-bisphosphate, bypassing the actions of rubisco. In this way, CO_2 is fixed by another pathway and stored in the leaf.

The correct answer is a...
B. Answer b is incorrect because C_4 plants do not store water differently, rather they use a different type of carbon fixation. Hot, dry conditions can cause a C_3 plant to have interference in carbon fixation. C_4 plants use different enzymes and intermediate molecules to fix carbon, not affected by hot, dry conditions.

The correct answer is a...
C. Answer c is incorrect because C_4 plants do not store oxygen differently, rather they use a different type of carbon fixation. Hot, dry conditions can cause a C_3 plant to have interference in carbon fixation. C_4 plants use different enzymes and intermediate molecules to fix carbon, not affected by hot, dry conditions.

The correct answer is a...
D. Answer d is incorrect because the problem with hot, dry conditions is not the lack of energy, but rather the build up of oxygen in leaves, which interferes with carbon fixation. C_4 plants use different enzymes and intermediate molecules to fix carbon, not affected by hot, dry conditions.

Hint: Rubisco, the enzyme that catalyzes the key carbon-fixing reaction of photosynthesis has a second enzyme activity that interferes with the Calvin cycle, oxidizing ribulose 1,5-bisphosphate. In this process called photorespiration, O_2 is incorporated into ribulose 1,5-bisphosphate which undergoes additional reactions that actually release CO_2. Photorespiration occurs in plants exposed to high temperature. C_4 plants use a different enzyme, PEP carboxylase, to add a CO_2 to the molecule phosphoenolpyruvate (PEP). This molecule then contributes a CO_2 to ribulose 1,5-bisphosphate in a way that is not affected by high temperatures. C4 therefore, fix carbon in a different way and store the carbon.

Test Your Visual Understanding

1). Match the following labels with their appropriate location on the figure.
a). b_6-f complex
b). H_2O
c). NADP reductase
d). NADPH
e). Photosystem I
f). Photosystem II
g). Water-splitting enzyme

Answer:
1). a--2, b--6, c--4, d--5, e--3, f--1, g--7

Apply Your Knowledge
1). To reduce six molecules of carbon dioxide to glucose via photosynthesis, how many molecules of NADPH and ATP are required?
Answer: For every three molecules of CO_2 that enters the Calvin cycle, one molecule of the three carbon glyceraldehyde 3-phosphate (G3P) is produced. Two molecules of G3P are needed to produce one molecule of glucose. Therefore, the Calvin cycle needs to make a total of 6 turns to produce two molecules of G3P. One turn of the Calvin cycle requires 3 molecules of ATP and 2 molecules of NADPH so for 6 turns:

3 ATP x 6 = 18 ATPs
2 NADPH x 6 = 12 NADPHs

2). What is the advantage of having many pigment molecules in each photosystem but only one reaction center chlorophyll? In other words, why not couple every pigment molecule directly to an electron acceptor?
Answer: If every pigment molecule were coupled to an electron acceptor, there would need to be hundreds of electron acceptors present in the photosystem and hundreds of electron transport chains. Maintaining several electron transport chains would consume a lot of energy. It is more energy economical to have the energy from the sun funneling into one electron acceptor and electron transport chain.

3). The two photosystems, P_{680} and P_{700}, of cyanobacteria, algae, and plants yield an oxidant capable of cleaving water. How might the subsequent evolution of cellular respiration have been different if the two photosystems had not evolved, and all photosynthetic organisms were restricted to the cyclic photophosphorylation used by the sulfur bacteria?
Answer: The evolution of the photosystems from cyclic photophosphorylation resulted in the formation of the oxygen gas that accumulated in the atmosphere. If the photosystems hadn't evolved, oxygen would not have accumulated in the atmosphere. Also, without the evolution of the photosystems, the Calvin cycle would not have evolved because without the photosystem I, NADPH would not be produced to feed hydrogens into the formation of carbohydrates.

4). In theory, a plant kept in total darkness could still manufacture glucose, if it were supplied with which molecules?

Answer: The molecules that are required to produce glucose are the molecules required for the Calvin cycle, which are:

CO_2
ATP
NADPH

Self Test

1). Bacterial cells divide by:
      a). mitosis.
      b). replication.
      c). cytokinesis.
      d). binary fission.

The correct answer is d...
A. Answer a is incorrect because mitosis involves the replication and division of the nucleus and bacterial cells lack a nucleus.

The correct answer is d...
B. Answer b is incorrect because replication is the process by which the cell copies the DNA in the cell. Replication occurs prior to the division of bacterial cells but it is not the process by which the cell divides.

The correct answer is d...
C. Answer c is incorrect because cytokinesis is the division of the cytoplasm in eukaryotic cells, not in bacterial cells.

The correct answer is d--binary fission.
D. Bacterial cells divide by simply dividing in two. Bacterial cells are prokaryotes that literally divide in half after the DNA is replicated.

Hint: In bacteria, which are prokaryotes and lack a nucleus, cell division consists of a simple procedure called binary fission (literally, "splitting in half"), in which the cell divides into two equal or nearly equal halves. The genetic information, or genome, replicates early in the life of the cell.

2). Most eukaryotic organisms have _____ chromosomes in their cells.
      a). 1-5
      b). 10-50
      c). 100-500
      d). over 1,000

The correct answer is b...
A. Answer a is incorrect because while some organisms may have 5 or less chromosomes, most organisms have between 10 and 50 chromosomes.

The correct answer is b--10-50
B. Organisms can have anywhere from 1 to over 1000 chromosomes but most eukaryotes have between 10 and 50 chromosomes.

The correct answer is b...
C. Answer c is incorrect because while some organisms may be between 100 and 500 chromosomes, most organisms have between 10 and 50 chromosomes.

The correct answer is b...
D. Answer d is incorrect because while some organisms may have over 1,000 chromosomes (namely found in plants), most organisms have between 10 and 50 chromosomes.

Hint: Since their initial discovery, chromosomes have been found in the cells of all eukaryotes examined. Their number may vary enormously from one species to another. Most eukaryotes have between 10 and 50 chromosomes in their body cells.

3). Replicate copies of each chromosome are called _____ and are joined at the
_____.
        a). homologues/centromere
        b). sister chromatids/kinetochore
        c). sister chromatids/centromere
        d). homologues/kinetochore

The correct answer is c...
A. Answer a is incorrect because homologues are the two chromosomes in a pair; replicate copies are called sister chromatids. The centromere is the area on the sister chromatids where the two are joined.

The correct answer is c...
B. Answer b is incorrect because although the replicate copies of the chromosomes are called sister chromatids, the area where the two are joined is called the centromere, not the kinetochore. The kinetochore is a protein disk attached to the centromere region of the sister chromatid.

The correct answer is c--sister chromatids/centromere
C. The replicate copies of the chromosome are called sister chromatids. After replication, the sister chromatids stay attached to each other at specific areas of the sister chromatids called centromeres.

The correct answer is c...
D. Answer d is incorrect because homologues are the two chromosomes in a pair; replicate copies are called sister chromatids. The area where the two sister chromatids are joined is called the centromere, not the kinetochore. The kinetochore is a protein disk attached to the centromere region of the sister chromatid.

Hint: The two copies of each chromosome in body cells are called homologous chromosomes, or homologues. Before cell division, each homologue replicates, producing two identical sister chromatids, joined at the centromere, a condensed area found on all eukaryotic chromosomes.

4). During which phase of the cell cycle is DNA synthesized?
        a). G_1
        b). G_2
        c). S
        d). M

The correct answer is c...
A. Answer a is incorrect because G_1 is the primary growth phase of the cell and not the phase in which DNA is synthesized.

The correct answer is c...
B. Answer b is incorrect because G_2 is the second growth phase in which the cell prepares for cell division. The mitochondria and other organelles replicate, chromosomes condense, and the spindle is assembled.

The correct answer is c--S
C. The S phase occurs between the two growth phases (G_1 and G_2). During the S phase, the DNA replicates.

The correct answer is c...
D. Answer d is incorrect because M, which stands for mitosis, is the phase where the microtubule apparatus assembles and the sister chromatids are pulled apart to opposite poles of the cell. This occurs after DNA replication in the S phase.

Hint: The division process of the cell is called the cell cycle and consists of five phases, G_1, S, G_2, M, and C. G_1 is the primary growth phase. This encompasses the major portion of the cell's life span. S is the phase in which the cell synthesizes a replica of the genome. G_2 is the second growth phase in which the cell prepares for cell division. G_1, S, and G_2 together constitute interphase, the portion of the cell cycle between cell divisions.

5). Chromosomes are visible under a light microscope
        a). during mitosis.
        b). during interphase.
        c). when they are attached to their sister chromatids.
        d). All of these are correct.

The correct answer is a--during mitosis
A. The sister chromatids are condensed during mitosis and so they are visible under the light microscope.

The correct answer is a...
B. Answer b is incorrect because they are extended during interphase and so they are invisible during interphase.

The correct answer is a...
C. Answer c is incorrect because while chromosomes are sometimes visible while they are attached to their sister chromatids, this isn't always the case. After the DNA has replicated in the S phase of the cell cycle, the sister chromatids are not visible until condensation, which occurs at the end of the G_2 phase.

The correct answer is a..
D. Answer d is incorrect because the only correct answer is a, during mitosis. Answer b is incorrect because they are extended during interphase and so they are invisible during interphase. Answer c is incorrect because after the DNA has replicated in the S phase of the cell cycle, the sister chromatids are not visible until condensation which occurs at the end of the G_2 phase.

Hint: Interphase is that portion of the cell cycle in which the chromosomes are invisible under the light microscope because they are not yet condensed. In G_2 phase, the sister chromatids begin the long process of condensation, coiling ever more tightly.

6). During mitosis, the sister chromatids are separated and pulled to opposite poles during which stage of mitosis?
        a). interphase
        b). metaphase
        c). anaphase
        d). telophase

The correct answer is c...
A. Answer a is incorrect because interphase is a phase of the cell cycle but it is not a stage of mitosis.

The correct answer is c....
B. Answer b is incorrect because metaphase is the stage of mitosis in which the chromosomes line up along the equatorial plane of the cell (called the metaphase plate) with their centromeres are attached to the kinetochores, which are attached to microtubules.

The correct answer is c--anaphase
C. Anaphase Is a short but active phase of mitosis. The microtubules to which the centromeres are attached shorten and in doing so, pull the centromeres apart which separates the sister

chromatids. The microtubules continue to shorten freeing the sister chromatids and pulling them to opposite poles of the cell.

The correct answer is c...
D. Answer d is incorrect because telophase is the final stage of mitosis. After the chromosomes have been pulled to opposite poles of the cell, the spindle apparatus disassembles and nuclear envelopes begin to form.

Hint: Of all of the stages of mitosis, anaphase, is the shortest and most beautiful to watch. It starts when the centromeres divide. Each centromere splits in two, freeing the two sister chromatids from each other. The centromeres of all the chromosomes separate simultaneously. Freed from each other, the sister chromatids are pulled rapidly toward the poles to which their kinetochores are attached.

7). Cytokinesis is
      a). the same process in plant and animal cells.
      b). the separation of cytoplasm and the formation of two cells.
      c). the final stage of mitosis.
      d). the movement of kinetochores.

The correct answer is b...
A. Answer a is incorrect because the process of cytokinesis is different in plant cells than in animal cells. Animal cells do not have cell walls and so cytokinesis occurs the by the constriction of a belt of actin filaments around the middle of the cell. Plant cells have cell walls and so cytokinesis occurs by the formation of a cell plate, membrane and cell wall components that are deposited at the center of the cell, at right angles to the spindle apparatus.

The correct answer is b--the separation of cytoplasm and the formation of two cells.
B. At the end of mitosis, the eukaryotic cell has partitioned its replicated genomes into two nuclei however cell division is not yet complete. The cell division continues with cytokinesis, which is the partitioning of the cytoplasm into two separate cells. In animal cells, this occurs with the formation of a cleavage furrow, which is the cinching in of the plasma membrane until the cell divides in two. In plants, a plasma membrane forms down the middle of the cells, eventually dividing the cell in two.

The correct answer is b...
C. Answer c is incorrect because cytokinesis is a phase of the cell cycle but it is not a stage of mitosis. Mitosis ends with the separation of the nuclear material, a stage called telophase. Cytokinesis follows the telophase of mitosis.

The correct answer is b...
D. Answer d is incorrect because cytokinesis results in the formation of daughter cells and it is not the movement of kinetochores, which occurs during anaphase.

Hint: Cell division is still not complete at the end of mitosis because the division of the cell proper has not yet begun. The phase of the cell cycle when the cell actually divides is called cytokinesis. It generally involves the cleavage of the cell into roughly equal halves.

8). The eukaryotic cell cycle is controlled at several points; which of these statements is *not* true?
      a). Cell growth is assessed at the G_1/S checkpoint.
      b). DNA replication is assessed at the G_2/M checkpoint.
      c). Environmental conditions are assessed at the G_0 checkpoint.
      d). The chromosomes are assessed at the spindle checkpoint

The correct answer is c...
A. Answer a is incorrect because this is a control point of the cell cycle. At the G_1/S checkpoint, the growth of the cell is assessed to see if the cell has grown enough in size so that cell division can proceed.

The correct answer is c...
B. Answer b is incorrect because this is a control point of the cell cycle. At the G_2/M checkpoint, the replication of DNA synthesis is assessed. If there are errors in the replication process, cell division will not occur, at least not until errors in the DNA have been corrected.

The correct answer is c--environmental conditions are assessed at the G_0 checkpoint
C. The cell does not have a G_0 checkpoint. Occasionally, the cell may go into a resting phase called G_0 instead of proceeding to cell division but there is not a checkpoint at this phase of the cell cycle.

The correct answer is c....
D. Answer d is incorrect because this is a control point of the cell cycle. At the spindle checkpoint, the chromosomes are assessed during metaphase, where the chromosomes line up on the metaphase plate. If there are problems with metaphase, cell division does not go forward.

Hint: Three principal checkpoints control the cell cycle in eukaryotes. Cell growth is assessed at the G_1 checkpoint. Just before the cell enters the S phase, the G_1 checkpoint makes the key decision of whether the cell should divide. The success of DNA replication is assessed at the G_2 checkpoint. This second checkpoint occurs at the end of G_2 and triggers the start of mitosis. The chromosomes are assessed at the spindle checkpoint. This checkpoint occurs at metaphase and triggers the exit from mitosis and cytokinesis.

9). What proteins are used to control cell growth specifically in *multicellular* eukaryotic organisms?
        a). Cdk
        b). MPF
        c). cyclins
        d). growth factors

The correct answer is d...
A. Answer a is incorrect because Cdk is a type of protein that is found in all eukaryotic cells. It controls cell division by phosphorylating other molecules in the cell. Cdk functions in all eukaryotic cells.

The correct answer is d...
B. Answer b is incorrect because MPF (M-phase-promoting factor) is a complex of proteins that is found in all eukaryotic cells. It controls cell division by a type of positive feedback, triggering its own activation through phosphorylation. When the level of activated MPF exceeds the threshold necessary to trigger mitosis, G_2 phase ends. MPF functions in all eukaryotic cells.

The correct answer is d...
C. Answer c is incorrect because cyclins are a type of protein that are found in all eukaryotic cells. Cyclins are regulatory proteins required to activate Cdk. Cdk cannot be active without binding to cyclin. Cyclins function in all eukaryotic cells.

The correct answer is d--growth factors
D. The cells of multicellular eukaryotes must work in concert with each other, some divide while others do not. Cells communicate by releasing proteins called growth factors. Each growing cell apparently binds minute amounts of positive regulatory signals, growth factors that stimulate cell division.

Hint: The cells of multicellular eukaryotes are not free to make individual decisions about cell division, as yeast cells are. The body's organization cannot be maintained without severely limiting cell proliferation, so that only certain cells divide, and only at appropriate times. Each growing cell apparently binds minute amounts of positive regulatory signals called growth factors, proteins that stimulate cell division. When neighboring cells have used up what little growth factor is present, not enough is left to trigger cell division in any one cell.

10). What causes cancer in cells?
      a). damage to genes
      b). chemical damage to cell membranes
      c). UV damage to transport proteins
      d). All of these cause cancer in cells.

The correct answer is a--damage to genes
A. Cancer is a disease of cell division, a failure in the control of cell division. Because cell division is controlled by the action of proteins, a disruption of proteins, by damage to their genes, can trigger the development of cancer.

The correct answer is a...
B. Answer b is incorrect because although chemical damage to cell membrane could cause cell death, it wouldn't disrupt the cell cycle and cancer is the loss of control over cell division.

The correct answer is a...
C. Answer c is incorrect because exposure to UV light can cause cancer but it occurs through the damage to genes, not protein directly.

The correct answer is a...
D. Answer d is incorrect because only answer a causes cancer in cells. Answer b is incorrect because although chemical damage to cell membrane could cause cell death, it wouldn't disrupt the cell cycle and cancer is the loss of control over cell division. Answer c is incorrect because exposure to UV light can cause cancer but it occurs through the damage to genes, not protein directly.

Hint: The unrestrained, uncontrolled growth of cells, called cancer, is essentially a disease of cell division--a failure of cell division control. Recent work has identified one of the culprits. Working independently, cancer scientists have repeatedly identified what has proven to the same gene! Officially dubbed *p53*, this gene plays a key role in the G_1 checkpoint of cell division.

Test Your Visual Understanding

1). Match the mitotic and cell cycle phases with the appropriate figure.

Answer:
      a--Metaphase
      b--Prophase
      c--Interphase
      d--Telophase
      e--Anaphase

Apply Your Knowledge

1). An ancient plant called horsetail contains 216 chromosomes. How many homologous pairs of chromosomes does it contain? How many chromosomes are present in its cells during metaphase?
Answer: 108 homologous pairs; 432 sister chromatids

2). Colchicine is a poison that binds to tubulin and prevents its assembly into microtubules; cytochalasins are compounds that bind to the ends of actin filaments and prevent their elongation.

What effects do you think that these two substances would have on cell division in animal cells?

Answer: Because cell division in animal cells relies on microtubules to pull sister chromatids apart to opposite poles of the cell, colchicine would disrupt the lining up and separating of sister chromatids. Cell division of animal cells also relies on actin filaments to cinch the cell in two during cytokinesis, cytochalasins would disrupt cytokinesis in animal cells.

3). If you could construct an artificial chromosome, what elements would you introduce into it, at a minimum, so that it could function normally in mitosis?

Answer: An artificial chromosome would need to have DNA with an area characteristic of the centromere region, histones and related proteins necessary for condensation, and kinetochores (proteins that associate with centromeres and microtubules). With these structures, the chromosomes would be able to respond to cellular structures in mitosis.

Self Test

1). Fertilization results in
    a). a zygote.
    b). a diploid cell.
    c). a cell with a new genetic combination.
    d). All of these are correct.

The correct answer is d...
A. Answer a is incorrect because although fertilization results in the formation of a zygote, a single cell formed by the fusion of an egg and sperm cell, this is not the only correct answer.

The correct answer is d...
B. Answer b is incorrect because although fertilization results in the formation of a diploid cell, a cell that contains two of each chromosome, this is not the only correct answer.

The correct answer is d...
C. Answer c is incorrect because although fertilization results in the formation of a cell with a new genetic combination because the cell receives half its chromosomes from the father and half from the mother, this is not the only correct answer.

The correct answer is d--All of these are correct.
D. Fertilization is the fusion of two cells, an egg and sperm cell, which each have half the total number of chromosomes. When the cells fuse, they form a zygote, a cell that contains two copies of each chromosome. A zygote is a diploid cell, which again is a cell that contains two copies of each chromosome. Because the chromosomes come from both parents (one half from the mother and one half from the father), each zygote contains a new genetic combination.

Hint: An egg and sperm cell contain half the complement of chromosomes found in other cells. They fuse to form a diploid cell called a zygote. The diploid zygote contains two of each chromosome. Reproduction that involves the alternation of meiosis and fertilization is called sexual reproduction and an outstanding characteristic of this type of reproduction is that the zygote receives half of its chromosomes from its mother and the other half from its father, giving the zygote a new genetic combination.

2). The diploid number of chromosomes in humans is 46. The haploid number is
    a). 138.
    b). 92.
    c). 46.
    d). 23.

The correct answer is d...
A. Answer a is incorrect because 138 is three times the number of chromosomes, the haploid number is half the total number of chromosomes.

The correct number is d...
B. Answer b is incorrect because 92 it twice the number of chromosomes, the haploid number is half the total number of chromosomes.

The correct number is d...
C. Answer c is incorrect because 46 is the total number of chromosome in the human, this is called the diploid number. The haploid number is half the total number of chromosomes.

The correct number is d--23.
D. The haploid number is half the total number of chromosomes and so in the human, the haploid number is half of 46 or 23.

Hint: Two sets of chromosomes are present in the somatic cells of adult individuals, making them diploid cells, but only one set is present in the gametes, which are thus haploid.

3). After chromosome replication and during synapsis,
      a). homologous chromosomes pair along their lengths.
      b). sister chromatids pair at the centromeres.
      c). homologous chromosomes pair at their ends.
      d). sister chromatids pair along their lengths.

The correct answer is a--homologous chromosomes pair along their lengths.
A. After the homologous chromosomes replicate and before they separate during meiosis, the homologues align with each other, forming a physical connection down the length of the chromosome. This connection is called synapsis.

The correct answer is a...
B. Answer b is incorrect because although sister chromatids pair at their centromeres after replication, this is not a characteristic of synapsis. Synapsis is the pairing of homologous chromosomes.

The correct answer is a...
C. Answer c is incorrect because homologous chromosomes pair along the length of their chromosomes during synapsis, not just at their ends.

The correct answer is a...
D. Answer d is incorrect because although the sister chromatids attach each other at the centromeres, they do not pair up along the lengths of the sister chromatids. During synapsis, homologues pair along their lengths, not the sister chromatids.

Hint: The first unique feature of meiosis happens early during the first nuclear division. Following chromosome replication, homologous chromosomes, or homologues pair all along their length. The process of forming these complexes of homologous chromosomes is called synapsis.

4). During which stage of meiosis does crossing over occur?
      a). prophase I
      b). anaphase I
      c). prophase II
      d). telophase II

The correct answer is a--prophase I
A. During prophase I, the homologous pairs of chromosomes are brought into close proximity with each other by the process of synapsis. It is through this close contact that homologous chromosomes are able to exchange bits of DNA with each other. This exchange of genetic information is called crossing over.

The correct answer is a...
B. Answer b is incorrect because crossing over occurs during prophase I, not during anaphase I. During anaphase I, homologous chromosomes with both sister chromatids are separated and pulled toward different poles.

The correct answer is a...
C. Answer c is incorrect because crossing over occurs during prophase I, not during prophase II. During prophase II, the clusters of chromosomes that resulted after telophase I prepare for the

second meiotic division by the breakdown of the nuclear envelope and the formation of a new spindle.

The correct answer is a...
D. Answer d is incorrect because telophase II is the final phase in meiosis and crossing over occurs early on in the process during prophase I. Telophase II is the phase where the nuclear envelope re-forms around the four sets of daughter chromosomes that separated during meiosis.

Hint: In prophase I of meiosis, the DNA coils tighter, and individual chromosomes first become visible under the light microscope as a matrix of fine threads. Because the DNA has already replicated before the onset of meiosis, each of these threads actually consists of two sister chromatids joined at their centromeres. In prophase I, homologous chromosomes become closely associated in synapsis, exchange segments by crossing over, and then separate.

5). Synapsis is the process whereby
        a). homologous pairs of chromosomes separate and migrate toward a pole.
        b). homologous chromosomes exchange chromosomal material.
        c). homologous chromosomes become closely associated.
        d). the daughter cells contain half of the genetic material of the parent cell.

The correct answer is c...
A. Answer a is incorrect because the separation of homologous pairs of chromosomes is the process that occurs during anaphase I and is not synapsis.

The correct answer is c...
B. Answer b is incorrect the process whereby homologous chromosomes exchange chromosomal material is called crossing over, not synapsis.

The correct answer is c--homologous chromosomes become closely associated.
C. Synapsis occurs during prophase I and involves the close association of homologous chromosomes. It is during synapsis, when the homologous chromosomes are closely aligned, that crossing over takes place.

The correct answer is c...
D. Answer d is incorrect because the process whereby the daughter cells contain half of the genetic material is called meiosis or reduction/division.

Hint: During prophase, the ends of the chromatids attach to the nuclear envelope at specific sites so that the members of each homologous pair of chromosomes are brought close together. They then line up side by side.

6). Terminal chiasmata are seen during which phase of meiosis?
        a). anaphase I
        b). prophase I
        c). metaphase I
        d). metaphase II

The correct answer is c...
A. Answer a is incorrect because terminal chiasmata are seen as the homologous chromosomes begin pulling away from each other which occurs in metaphase I, not anaphase I. During anaphase I, the homologous chromosomes have separated from each other and are approaching their poles.

The correct answer is c...
B. Answer b is incorrect because terminal chiasmata are seen as the homologous chromosomes begin pulling away from each other, which occurs in metaphase I, not in prophase I. During

prophase I, synapsis occurs and chiasmata appear but they are not at the terminal ends of the chromosomes.

The correct answer is c--metaphase I
C. During metaphase I, the chiasmata hold the homologous chromosomes together as the centromeres of the homologous pairs are pulled apart. This results in the centromeres staying attached so that homologous chromosomes are pulled apart but the sister chromatids stay connected at the centromeres.

The correct answer is c...
D. Answer d is incorrect because terminal chiasmata are seen as the homologous chromosomes begin pulling away from each other, which occurs in metaphase I, not in metaphase II. Before metaphase II, the homologous chromosomes have been separated and what remains are the sister chromatids. These begin to separate during metaphase II, similar to what occurs during mitosis.

Hint: By metaphase I, the second stage of meiosis I, the nuclear envelope has dispersed and the microtubules form a spindle, just as in mitosis. During diakinesis of prophase I, the chiasmata move down the paired chromosomes from their original points of crossing over, eventually reaching the ends of the chromosomes. At this point, they are called terminal chiasmata. Terminal chiasmata hold the homologous chromosomes together in metaphase I, so that only one side of each centromere faces outward.

7). Which of the following occurs during anaphase I?
     a). Chromosomes cluster at the two poles of the cell.
     b). Crossing over occurs.
     c). Chromosomes align down the center of the cell.
     d). One version of each chromosome moves toward a pole.

The correct answer is d...
A. Answer a is incorrect because the clustering of chromosome at the poles occurs during telophase I, not during anaphase I.

The correct answer is d...
B. Answer b is incorrect because crossing over occurs during prophase I, not during anaphase I.

The correct answer is d...
C. Answer c is incorrect because the aligning of chromosomes down the center of the cell occurs during metaphase I (and during metaphase II with sister chromatids), not during anaphase I.

The correct answer is d--One version of each chromosome moves toward a pole.
D. The microtubules of the spindle fibers attach to the kinetochores on one side of the centromeres. As the microtubules shorten, a version of the homologous chromosome pair moves toward a pole (either the maternal or the paternal chromosome).

Hint: In anaphase I, the microtubules of the spindle fibers begin to shorten. As they shorten, they break the chiasmata and pull the centromeres toward the poles, dragging the chromosomes along with them. Because the microtubules are attached to kinetochores on only one side of each centromere, the individual centromeres are not pulled apart to form two daughter centromeres, as they are in mitosis. Instead, the entire centromere moves to one pole, taking both sister chromatids with it.

8). Mitosis results in two _____ cells, while meiosis results in _____ haploid cells.
     a). haploid/four
     b). diploid/two
     c). diploid/four
     d). haploid/two

The correct answer is c...
A. Answer a is incorrect because although it is correct that meiosis results in four haploid cells, mitosis results in two diploid cells.

The correct answer is c...
B. Answer b is incorrect because although mitosis results in two diploid cells, meiosis results in four haploid cells, not two haploid cells.

The correct answer is c--diploid/four
C. Mitosis results in two daughter cells with the full number of chromosomes so the cells are diploid. Meiosis, on the other hand, involves a reduction in the number of chromosomes so the result is four haploid cells.

The correct answer is c...
D. Answer d is incorrect because mitosis results in the formation of two diploid cells and meiosis results in four haploid cells.

Hint: The final result meiosis is four cells containing haploid sets of chromosomes. No two are alike, because of crossing over in prophase I. The cells that contain these haploid nuclei may develop directly into gametes, as they do in animals. Alternatively, they may themselves divide mitotically, as they do in plants, fungi, and many protists.

9). Genetic diversity is greatest in
     a). parthenogenesis.
     b). sexual reproduction.
     c). asexual reproduction.
     d). binary fission.

The correct answer is b...
A. Answer a is incorrect because although parthenogenesis, which is the development of an adult from an unfertilized egg, generate some genetic diversity with the formation of gametes, there is no fertilization. The process of fertilization adds to the genetic diversity that is in the gametes.

The correct answer is b--sexual reproduction.
B. Sexual reproduction, which involved the formation of gametes through meiosis and the fertilization of the gametes where two gametes fuse to make one diploid cell, offers the greatest potential for genetic diversity. Crossing over, independent assortment, and randomized fertilization all contribute to the genetic diversity of sexual reproduction.

The correct answer is b...
C. Answer c is incorrect because asexual reproduction (no matter the method of asexual reproduction) produces offspring that are genetically identical to the parent. Unless there are mutations, there is no genetic diversity with asexual reproduction.

The correct answer is b...
D. Answer d is incorrect because binary fission is a form of asexual reproduction used by bacteria. Asexual reproduction (no matter the method of asexual reproduction) produces offspring that are genetically identical to the parent. Unless there are mutations, there is no genetic diversity with asexual reproduction.

Hint: While our knowledge of how sex evolved is sketchy, it is abundantly clear that sexual reproduction has an enormous impact on how species evolved today, because of its ability to rapidly generate new genetic combinations. Independent assortment, crossing over, and random fertilization each help generate genetic diversity.

10). Which of the following is not a hypothesis about the evolution of sex?
  a). It evolved to repair damaged DNA.
  b). It evolved as a way to eliminate individuals.
  c). It evolved as a way to eliminate mutations.
  d). It evolved as a way to "store" recessive alleles that may prove beneficial in the future.

The correct answer is b...
A. Answer a is incorrect because this is a hypothesis about the evolution of sexual reproduction. The "DNA Repair Hypothesis" proposes that the pairing of DNA in the synaptonemal complex or even in the fusion of gametes may have provided a mechanism for repairing damaged DNA, especially double-strand breaks.

The correct answer is b--It evolved as a way to eliminate individuals.
B. While sexual reproduction can sometimes alter advantageous traits in individuals, this would not be a pressure that would drive evolution. This would instead work against evolution. If all sexually reproducing individuals were eliminated because of sexual reproduction, then the process would also be eliminated.

The correct answer is b...
C. Answer c is incorrect because this is a hypothesis about the evolution of sexual reproduction. The "Miller's Ratchet" hypothesis proposes that sexual populations can employ recombination to generate individuals with fewer mutations.

The correct answer is b...
D. Answer d is incorrect because this is a hypothesis about the evolution of sexual reproduction. The "Red Queen Hypothesis" proposes that sex in a population allows populations to keep recessive alleles that may prove advantageous in the future. Changes in the environment may select for an allele that may not be present in a large percent of the population but remains "hidden" until it offers an advantage.

Hint: Sex is a great evolutionary advantage for populations or species, which benefits from the variability generated in meiosis by random orientation of chromosomes and by crossing over. However, evolution occurs because of changes at the level of individual survival and reproduction, rather than at the population level, and no obvious advantage accrues to the progeny of an individual that engages in sexual reproduction.

Test Your Visual Understanding

1). Match the following labels with the correct numbers on the figure (Some labels may be used more than once.)
  a). diploid stage (2*n*)
  b). meiosis
  c). fertilization
  d). haploid stage (*n*)
  e). mitosis
Answer:
  a—2
  b—5
  c—1
  d—3
  e—4

2). Human cells spend most of their life cycles in a diploid stage, with only a selected number of cells undergoing meiosis to become haploid. Other organisms spend most of their life cycles in the haploid stage. Look ahead in this text to figures 28.14, 29.13, 29.15, and 30.10. Which of these organisms has a life cycle that is primarily haploid?

Answer: Figures 28.14 and 30.10 are organisms that spend a majority of their life cycles in a haploid stage of development. In figure 28.14, only the briefly formed zygospore is diploid. In figure 30.10, only the briefly formed zygosporangium is diploid.

Apply Your Knowledge

1). An organism has 56 chromosomes in its diploid stage. Indicate how many chromosomes are present in the following, and explain your reasoning:
>   a). somatic cells
>   b). metaphase (mitosis)
>   c). metaphase I (meiosis)
>   d). metaphase II (meiosis)
>   e). gametes

Answer:
>   a). 56 chromosomes would be present in somatic cells, 28 homologous pairs—somatic cells are diploid and would have the full complement of chromosomes.
>   b). 112 chromosomes would be present in mitotic cells at metaphase. Prior to metaphase, the chromosomes replicated and so every chromosome is a pair of identical sister chromatids. So, 56 x 2 = 112 chromosomes.
>   c). 112 chromosomes would be present in meiotic cells in metaphase I. Prior to metaphase I, the chromosomes replicated and so every chromosome is a pair of sister chromatids. So, 56 x 2 = 112 chromosomes. These chromosomes have also undergone crossing over during prophase I so the sister chromatids are no longer identical as in metaphase of mitosis.
>   d). 56 chromosomes would be present in meiotic cells in metaphase II. During metaphase I and anaphase I, homologous pairs of chromosomes were separated so that the resulting cells contained one chromosome of a homologous pair still paired as sister chromatids.
>   e). 28 chromosomes would be present in the gametes. Each gamete would contain one chromosome from each homologous pair. During fertilization, the chromosome will be matched up with its homologue.

2). Humans have 23 pairs of chromosomes. Ignoring the effects of crossing over, what proportion of a woman's eggs contains only chromosomes she received from her mother?

Answer: The chances of a woman's egg receiving *only* maternal chromosomes is 1 in 2^{23} or 8,388,608 and so it is quite improbable that this would occur. Because of independent assortment that occurs during metaphase I of meiosis, it is quite improbable that all of the maternal chromosomes would line up on the same side to be distributed to a single egg.

3). Many sexually reproducing lizard species are able to generate local populations that reproduce by parthenogenesis. Would the sex of these local parthenogenetic populations be male, female, or neuter? Explain your reasoning.

Answer: In parthenogenesis, a haploid egg, which contains the "female" chromosome, undergoes a nuclear division, which means it replicates its DNA but it doesn't undergo cytoplasmic division. The egg becomes diploid and because its is carrying only "female" chromosomes it develops into a female. Populations that arise from parthenogenesis contain only females.

FIGURE 13.36
Correlation between maternal age and the incidence of Down syndrome. As women age, the chances they will bear a child with Down syndrome increase. After a woman reaches 35, the frequency of Down syndrome rises rapidly.
Over a five-year period between ages 20 and 25, the incidence of Down syndrome increases 0.1 per thousand; over a five-year period between ages 35 and 40, the incidence increases to 8.0 per thousand, 80 times as great. The period of time is the same in both instances. What has changed?

Answer: The proportion of egg cells with a chromosomal change producing Down syndrome. Imagine a jar containing 10,000 white marbles. Allow one marble to become red every minute. Now draw out one marble after one minute. The chance of drawing a red one is 1/10,000, or 0.1 per thousand. Wait 80 minutes and pull out another marble. The chance of drawing a red marble is now 80/10,000 or 8 per thousand.

Self Test

1). In order to ensure he had pure-breeding plants for his experiments, Mendel
      a). cross-fertilized each variety with each other.
      b). let each variety self-fertilize for several generations.
      c). removed the female parts of the plants.
      d). removed the male parts of the plants.

The correct answer is b...
A. Answer a is incorrect because cross-fertilizing would introduce variation into the traits he was studying. A true-breeding plant is a plant with no variation for a given trait, for example a true-breeding white flowered plant, self-fertilized would always give rise to white flowered plants.

The correct answer is b--let each variety self-fertilize for several generations.
B. A true-breeding plant is a plant with no variation for a given trait. For Mendel to be certain of his results, he had to be sure that there was no "hidden" variation in the traits for a given plant. To eliminate all variation, Mendel allowed the plants to self-fertilize that way no new alleles were being introduced into the first generation of plants.

The correct answer is b...
C. Answer c is incorrect because in setting up the experiment, he allowed the plants to self-fertilize so the plants still needed the female parts. A plant cannot be fertilized without the female parts of the flower in tact.

The correct answer is b...
D. Answer d is incorrect because in setting up the experiment, he allowed the plants to self-fertilize so the plants still needed the male parts. When Mendel performed the cross experiments, he removed the male parts of the plant in order to control the fertilization of the experimental plants.

Hint: Mendel usually conducted his experiments in three stages. First, he allowed pea plants of a given variety to produce progeny by self-fertilization for several generations. Mendel thus was able to assure himself that the traits he was studying were indeed constant, transmitted unchanged from generation to generation.

2). When two parents are crossed, the offspring are referred to as the
      a). recessives.
      b). testcross.
      c). F_1 generation.
      d). F_2 generation.

The correct answer is c...
A. Answer a is incorrect because the offspring are the next generation and are referred to as first filial. The offspring could be recessive for a given trait (if the parents were both true-breeding recessives) but that is not what they are referred to in this case.

The correct answer is c...
B. Answer b is incorrect because testcross is a type of cross that is performed to confirm the genotype of a dominant phenotype; it is not the name given to the offspring of a parental cross.

The correct answer is c--F_1 generation.
C. The offspring of a parental cross between two true-breeding varieties are referred to as the first filial (*filius* is Latin for "son") abbreviated as F_1.

The correct answer is c...
D. Answer d is incorrect because the F_2 generation is the name given to the offspring of a cross between two individuals from the F_1 generation.

Hint: When Mendel crossed two contrasting varieties of peas, the hybrid offspring did not have flowers of the intermediate color. Instead, in every case the flower color of the offspring resembled their parents. It is customary to refer to these offspring as the first filial, or F_1, generation.

3). A cross between two individuals results in a ratio of 9:3:3:1 for four possible phenotypes. This is an example of a
      a). dihybrid cross.
      b). monohybrid cross.
      c). testcross.
      d). none of these.

The correct answer is a--dihybrid cross.
A. A cross with a ratio of 9:3:3:1 of four possible phenotypes is examining the inheritance of two different traits and it is the result of an F_1 cross so these offspring are hybrids, therefore this is referred to as a dihybrid cross.

The correct answer is a...
B. Answer b is incorrect because a monohybrid cross is used to examine the inheritance of one trait with two possible phenotypes. A cross that is examining four possible phenotypes is looking at the inheritance of two different traits.

The correct answer is a...
C. Answer c is incorrect because a testcross is used to verify the genotype of a dominant phenotype. A testcross can be used to examine one trait or several traits but the 9:3:3:1 ratio would never be achieved with a testcross.

The correct answer is a...
D. Answer d is incorrect because there is a correct answer, answer a. This cross is an example of a dihybrid cross.

Hint: In a cross involving different seed shape alleles and different seed color alleles, all the F_1 individuals were identical, each one heterozygous for both traits. The F_1 individuals of such a cross are dihybrids, individuals heterozygous for both genes. Mendel allowed the dihybrids to self-fertilize. The hypothesis that color and shape genes assort independently thus predicts that the F_2 generation will display a 9:3:3:1 phenotypic ratio.

4). Human height shows a continuous variation from the very short to the very tall. Height is most likely controlled by
          a). epistatic genes.
          b). environmental factors.
          c). sex-linked genes.
          d). multiple genes.

The correct answer is d...
A. Answer a is incorrect because epistatic genes are separate genes that interact such that one gene can interfere with the expression of another gene. Epistasis can influence the phenotypic expression but does not result in a continuous variation as seen with human height.

The correct answer is d...
B. Answer b is incorrect because environmental factors such as nutrition could have some effect on a person's height, but an environmental factor isn't controlling the expression of a gene. Environmental factors, such as temperature, can affect the expression of a gene such as the coloration of an arctic fox's coat, but that doesn't result in a continuous variation as seen with human height.

The correct answer is d...
C. Answer c is incorrect because traits that are sex-linked usually have an inheritance pattern that is expressed more in one sex versus another (usually a trait showing up more in males versus females). However, the inheritance of human height does not exhibit a sex-related inheritance pattern.

The correct answer is d--multiple genes.
D. Few genetic traits are controlled by just one gene, most are the results of two or more genes expressed jointly or sequentially. When two or more genes influence a trait, the trait often shows a range of small differences. If Mendel's flower color had been controlled by multiple genes, he would have seen flowers with a range of color intensities from white to lavender to dark purple, instead of just two colors.

Hint: Few phenotypes are the result of the action of only one gene. Instead, most characters reflect the action of polygenes, many genes that act sequentially or jointly. When multiple genes act jointly to influence a character such as height or weight, the character often shows a range of small differences.

5). In the human ABO blood grouping, the four basic blood types are type A, type B, type AB, and type O. The blood proteins A and B are
          a). simple dominant and recessive traits.
          b). incomplete dominant traits.
          c). codominant traits.
          d). sex-linked traits.

The correct answer is c...
A. Answer a is incorrect because simple dominant and recessive traits only express two phenotypes, the dominant trait and the recessive trait. With the blood grouping, there are four phenotypes, so simple dominant and recessive inheritance can't control them.

The correct answer is c...
B. Answer b is incorrect because incomplete dominant traits show a blending of the parental phenotypes in the heterozygous offspring. With the ABO blood grouping, the parental phenotypes aren't blended; rather they are both expressed fully.

The correct answer is c--codominant traits.
C. A gene may have more than two alleles in a population and there isn't a single dominant allele. Each allele exerts its own effect. They are not expressed jointly where one adds to the expression of another, like in polygenes, nor do they blend their expression as in incomplete dominance, rather all of the alleles have equal effects. In the ABO blood groups, if the A allele is present, the A antibody will appear on the cell and if the B allele is present, the B antibody will also appear on the cell. This is codominance.

The correct answer is c...
D. Answer d is incorrect because sex-related traits are determined by the presence of a gene on the X chromosome and show different inheritance patterns for males and females. The ABO blood grouping alleles are not found on the X chromosome and are not inherited differently in males compared to females.

Hint: A gene may have more than two alleles in a population, and most genes possess several different alleles. Often, no single allele is dominant; instead, each allele has its won effect, and the alleles are considered codominant. A human gene with more than one codominant allele is the gene that determines ABO blood type.

6). Which of the following describes symptoms of sickle cell anemia?
     a). poor blood circulation due to abnormal hemoglobin molecules
     b). sterility in females
     c). failure of blood to clot
     d). failure of chloride ion transport mechanism

The correct answer is a--poor blood circulation due to abnormal hemoglobin molecules
A. Sickle cell anemia is a genetic blood disorder that results from an amino acid substitution in red blood cell's hemoglobin molecule. It causes red blood cells to change shape and stick to other cells. This interferes with the flow of blood through the blood vessels.

The correct answer is a...
B. Answer b is incorrect because this is a symptom of nondisjunction involving the X chromosome and not with sickle cell anemia.

The correct answer is a...
C. Answer c is incorrect because this is a symptom of hemophilia, a blood disorder affecting the clotting capabilities of blood. Hemophilia can be caused by mutations in several different genes, including two genes on the X chromosome.

The correct answer is a...
D. Answer d is incorrect because this is a symptom of cystic fibrosis. Cystic fibrosis is caused by a mutation in a gene that gives rise to a transmembrane protein that regulates the transport of chloride ions across the membrane. When this transport protein is faulty, chloride ions are not transported and thick mucus builds up in the lungs and ducts of the body.

Hint: Sickle cell anemia is a heritable disorder caused by an amino acid substitute in the hemoglobin molecule, the molecule in the red blood cells that transports oxygen throughout the body. The defective hemoglobin molecules cause the red blood cells to become misshapen and to stick to one another. As a result these cells have difficulty moving through the smallest blood vessels where they accumulate, forming clots.

7). What finding finally determined that genes were carried on chromosomes?
    a). heat sensitivity of certain enzymes that determined coat color
    b). sex-linked eye color in fruit flies
    c). the finding of complete dominance
    d). establishing pedigrees

The correct answer is b...
A. Answer a is incorrect because the discovery of heat sensitivity of certain genes in determining coat color in some animals revealed the effects that the environment can have on gene expression but did not determine that genes were carried on chromosomes.

The correct answer is b--sex-linked eye color in fruit flies
B. Morgan determined that the segregation of the eye color trait in fruit flies is a one-to-one correspondence with the segregation of the X chromosome, showing that genes are carried on chromosomes.

The correct answer is b...
C. Answer c is incorrect because Mendel established the finding of complete dominance but he still was not able to say that chromosomes carried the genes that determine the traits of an organism.

The correct answer is b...
D. Answer d is incorrect because establishing a pedigree is a way to reveal the patterns of heredity especially with human heredity where scientists are not able to test inheritance with experimental crosses. Although pedigrees help to establish the dominant and recessive nature of alleles and sex linkage of alleles, they did not provide the evidence linking genes and chromosomes.

Hint: The solution to Morgan's puzzle is that the gene causing the white-eye trait in Drosophila resides only on the X chromosome—it is absent from the Y chromosome. A trait determined by a gene on the X chromosome is said to be sex-linked. Knowing the white-eye trait is recessive to the red-eye trait, we can now see that Morgan's result was a natural consequence of the Mendelian assortment of chromosomes.

8). A genetic map can be used to determine
    a). the relative position of alleles on chromosomes.
    b). restriction sites on chromosomes.
    c). the frequency of recombination between two genes.
    d). all of these.

The correct answer is a--the relative position of alleles on chromosomes.
A. Genetic maps are constructed based on the frequency of crossing over that occurs between two genes. Crossing over occurs more frequently between two genes that are farther apart than between two that are closer together. Using these frequencies, scientists can map out the locations of genes on chromosomes relative to each other.

The correct answer is a...
B. Answer b is incorrect because restriction sites on a chromosome are used to construct a genetic map. The genetic map is not used to identify restriction sites. The genetic map determines the relative position of genes on a chromosome, not the restriction sites.

The correct answer is a...
C. Answer c is incorrect because the frequency of recombination between two genes is the method used to construct a genetic map; the map is not used to determine the frequency of recombination. The genetic map determines the relative position of genes on a chromosome.

The correct answer is a...
D. Answer d is incorrect because only answer a describes the use of a genetic map. Restriction sites and frequencies of recombination are methods used to construct the genetic map, which is used to determine the relative position of genes on chromosomes.

Hint: Because crossing over is more frequent between two genes that are relatively far apart than between two that are close together, the frequency of crossing over can be used to map the relative positions of genes on chromosomes. The results of crossing over can be used to construct a genetic map that measures distance between genes in terms of the frequency of recombination.

9). A Barr body is a(n)
     a). result of primary nondisjunction.
     b). inactivated Y chromosome.
     c). gene that plays a key role in male development.
     d). inactivated X chromosome.

The correct answer is d...
A. Answer a is incorrect because a Barr body is an inactivated X chromosome, not a result of primary nondisjunction. Primary nondisjunction is the failure of sister chromatids to separate during meiosis, resulting in a cell with too many or not enough chromosomes.

The correct answer is d...
B. Answer b is incorrect because a Barr body is an inactivated X chromosome, not an inactivated Y chromosome. The Y chromosome usually does not become inactive in a cell. If it does, the genetic male (XY) actually develops into a female because the individual lacks the *SRY* genes on the Y chromosome that produce the male characteristics.

The correct answer is d...
C. Answer c is incorrect because a Barr body is an inactivated X chromosome, not a gene that plays a key role in male development. The gene that plays a key role in male development is called the *SRY* gene, located on the Y chromosome.

The correct answer is d--inactivated X chromosome.
D. Females inherit two copies of the X chromosome while males only inherit one copy. However, females don't produce twice the amount of proteins encoded on the X chromosome because early on in development, one X chromosome per cell becomes inactive. The inactivated X chromosome, called a Barr body, becomes highly condensed and attaches to the nuclear membrane.

Hint: Although males have only one copy of the X chromosome and females have two, female cells do not produce twice as much of the proteins encoded by the genes on the X chromosome. Instead, one of the X chromosomes in females is inactivated early in embryonic development. Which X chromosome is inactivated varies randomly from cell to cell. The inactivated and highly condensed X chromosome is visible as a darkly staining Barr body attached to the nuclear membrane.

10). Down syndrome in humans is due to
     a). three copies of chromosome 21.
     b). monosomy.
     c). two Y chromosomes.
     d). three X chromosomes.

The correct answer is a--three copies of chromosome 21.
A. Down syndrome is a genetic disorder caused by primary disjunction, where sister chromatids fail to separate during meiosis. When an individual inherits three copies of chromosome 21,

usually inheriting two from the mother, they develop Down syndrome that affects their physical and mental development.

The correct answer is a...

B. Answer b is incorrect because although monosomy is the result of primary disjunction that is also the cause of Down syndrome, monosomy is where one autosomal chromosome is missing. With monosomy, a chromosome is not inherited, usually from the mother, and the fetus usually dies before birth. With Down syndrome, an extra copy of chromosome 21 is inherited (usually from the mother) but the individual often lives but his/her mental and physical development is affected.

The correct answer is a...

C. Answer c is incorrect because the inheritance of two Y chromosomes (from the father) does not cause Down syndrome but rather another genetic disorder called Jacob's syndrome. Both genetic disorders are caused by primary disjunction, where sister chromatids fail to separate during meiosis, but Down syndrome is caused by the presence of an extra autosome (chromosome 21) and Jacob's syndrome is caused by the presence of an extra sex chromosome (Y chromosome). The inheritance of an extra Y chromosome *seems* to have no obvious affect on the XYY male.

The correct answer is a...

D. Answer d is incorrect because the inheritance of three X chromosomes does not cause Down syndrome but rather produces a female with three X chromosomes (each cell containing one X chromosomes and two Barr bodies). The female is normal in most respects but is sterile. Both genetic disorders are caused by primary disjunction, where sister chromatids fail to separate during meiosis, but Down syndrome is caused by the presence of an extra autosome (chromosome 21), not an extra sex chromosome.

Hint: The developmental defect produced by trisomy 21 was first described in 1866 by J. Langdon Down; for this reason, it is called Down syndrome. About 1 in every 750 children exhibits Down syndrome. In humans, the defect is associated with a particular small portion of chromosome 21. In 97% of the human cases examined, all of chromosome 21 is present in three copies. In the other 3%, a small portion of chromosome 21 has been added to another chromosome.

Test Your Visual Understanding

1). The figure shows the results of a dihybrid cross in which Mendel was examining the inheritance of two traits: seed shape (*R* and *r*) and seed color (*Y* and *y*). Consider the results if he had examined three traits. Using these two traits and plant height (*T* and *t*), predict:
      a). the genotypes and phenotypes of the parents.
      b). the genotypic and phenotypic ratios of the F_1 generation.
      c). the genotypes of the eggs and sperm.
      d). the phenotypic ratios of the F_2 generation.

Answer:
      a). The genotype of the parents would be *RRYYTT* x *rryytt* and the phenotypes would be tall plant with round, yellow seeds x dwarf plants with wrinkled, green seeds.
      b). All individuals of the F_1 generation would be the same with the genotype *RrYyTt* and phenotype of tall plants with round, yellow seeds.
      c). There would be no difference in genotype or phenotype of the eggs and sperm, which would be
RYT
RYt
RyT
Ryt
rYT

rYt
ryT
ryt
d). The phenotypic ratio of the F$_2$ generation would be
26/64 are round, yellow, tall
10/64 are round, yellow, dwarf
9/64 are round, green, tall
9/64 are wrinkled, yellow, tall
3/64 are round, green, dwarf
3/64 are wrinkled, yellow, dwarf
3/64 are wrinkled, green, tall
1/64 are wrinkled, green, dwarf

Apply Your Knowledge

1). Phenylketonuria (PKU) is a genetic disorder caused by the mutation of an enzyme, phenylalanine hydroxylase, that breaks down phenylalanine in the cell. If identified at birth, dietary restrictions can control the disease. If not identified, buildup of phenylalanine interferes with brain development. The frequency of PKU in the population is 1 in 12,000 births. How many people with PKU would you expect to find in a population of 250,000?
Answer: To figure out the number of PKU individuals in a population of 250,000 use proportions:

1/12,000 :: ?/250,000

250,000 x 1 = 250,000
250,000/12,000 = 20.83

Therefore, we would expect to find 20.83 individuals with PKU in a population of 250,000.

2). How might Mendel's results and the model he formulated have been different if the traits he chose to study were governed by alleles exhibiting incomplete dominance or codominance?
Answer: If Mendel had selected traits that exhibited incomplete dominance or codominance, he probably wouldn't have identified the patterns of inheritance of dominant and recessive traits. The F$_1$ generation would have expressed a blending of the traits only to have the parental phenotypes reappearing in the F$_2$ generation. He may still have been able to establish the laws of segregation and independent assortment, especially because the heterozygotes would be more easily identified.

Self Test

1). Which of the following experiments suggested that the nucleus is the repository for genetic information?

        a). Hammerling's experiment using *Acetabularia*
        b). Griffith's experiment using *S. pneumoniae* and mice
        c). the Hershey and Chase experiment using bacteriophages
        d). Franklin's X-ray diffraction

The correct answer is a--Hammerling's experiment using *Acetabularia*
A. Hammerling used *Acetabularia* that is a single-celled organism with three defined regions, a cap, a stalk, and a foot. The foot carries the nucleus and Hammerling showed that the foot determined the regeneration of an amputated cap region. These results suggested that the foot held the genetic information needed to regenerate an amputated cap.

The correct answer is a....
B. Answer b is incorrect because Griffith's experiment using *S. pneumoniae* to infect mice demonstrated the principle of transformation where genetic information can be passed from one organism to another.

The correct answer is a...
C. Answer c is incorrect because the Hershey and Chase experiment using bacteriophages demonstrated that the hereditary material in the bacteriophage is DNA and not protein.

The correct answer is a...
D. Answer d is incorrect because Franklin's X-ray diffraction experiments provided information about the three-dimensional structure of the DNA molecule.

Hint: Individuals of the genus *Acetabularia* have distinct foot, stalk, and cap regions: all are differentiated parts of a single cell. The nucleus is located in the foot. Hammerling found that when he amputated the cap from an organism, a new cap regenerated from the remaining portions of the cell. When he amputated the foot, however, no new foot regenerated from the cap and stalk. Hammerling, therefore, hypothesized that the hereditary information resided within the foot of *Acetabularia*.

2). When Hershey and Chase differentially tagged the DNA and proteins of bacteriophages and allowed them to infect bacteria, what did the viruses transfer to the bacteria?

        a). radioactive phosphorus and sulfur
        b). radioactive sulfur
        c). DNA
        d). Both b and c are correct.

The correct answer is c...
A. Answer a is incorrect because the radioactive sulfur which was incorporated into the proteins was found in the medium, not in the bacteria. However, the radioactive phosphorus that was incorporated into the DNA was found inside the bacteria.

The correct answer is c...
B. Answer b is incorrect because the radioactive sulfur, which was incorporated into the proteins, was found in the medium, not in the bacteria.

The correct answer is c--DNA
C. The radioactive phosphorus that was incorporated into the DNA was found inside the bacteria, meaning that the DNA was in the bacteria. This experiment showed that the bacteriophage injects DNA, not proteins, into the bacteria and the DNA is what directs the assembling of the new generation of viruses.

The correct answer is c....
D. Answer d is incorrect because only c is the correct answer. Answer b is incorrect because the radioactive sulfur, which was incorporated into the proteins, was found in the medium, not in the bacteria.

Hint: To identify the hereditary material injected into bacterial cells at the start of an infection, Hershey and Chase used the bacteriophage T2, which contains DNA. They labeled the two parts of the viruses, the DNA and the protein coat, with different radioactive isotopes that would serve as tracers. The isotope of phosphorus, ^{32}P, was used to tag the DNA and the isotope of sulfur, ^{35}S, was used to tag the protein coat. The cells were agitated and rinsed which left only the bacterial cells and their contents. The radioactive phosphorus was found inside the bacteria, not the radioactive sulfur, hence the hereditary information injected into the bacteria was DNA.

3). If one strand of a DNA molecule has the base sequence ATTGCAT, its complementary strand will have the sequence
        a). ATTGCAT
        b). TAACGTA
        c). GCCATGC
        d). CGGTACG

The correct answer is b...
A. Answer a is incorrect because this sequence is identical, not complementary.

The correct answer is b--TAACGTA
B. According to Chargaff's rules: A pairs with T and G pairs with C and so the complementary sequence would be TAACGTA.

The correct answer is b...
C. Answer c is incorrect because A pairs with T not with G, T pairs with A not with C, G pairs with C not with A, and C pairs with G not with T.

The correct answer is b...
D. Answer d is incorrect because A pairs with T not with C, T pairs with A not with G, G pairs with C not with T, and C pairs with G not with A.

Hint: Chargaff observed an important underlying regularity in double-stranded DNA: the amount of adenine present in DNA always equals the amount of thymine, and the amount of guanine always equals the amount of cytosine. These findings are commonly referred to as Chargaff's rules: The proportion of A always equals that of T, and the proportion of G always equals that of C: A=T and G=C.

4). DNA is made up of building blocks called
        a). proteins.
        b). bases.
        c). nucleotides.
        d). deoxyribose.

The correct answer is c...
A. Answer a is incorrect because proteins are not the building blocks of DNA. Proteins associate with DNA in the condensation of the DNA into chromosome, but they are not part of the DNA molecule.

The correct answer is c...
B. Answer b is incorrect because bases, specifically nitrogen-containing bases, are a component of DNA but are not the building blocks of DNA.

The correct answer is c--nucleotides.
C. The DNA molecule is built out of units called nucleotides. Each nucleotide consists of three main components: 1). a sugar (ribose in RNA and deoxyribose in DNA), 2). a phosphate group (PO_4), and 3). a nitrogen-containing base, either a purine or a pyrimidine.

The correct answer is c...
D. Answer d is incorrect because deoxyribose is a component of DNA but it is not the building block of DNA.

Hint: Levene concluded correctly that DNA and RNA molecules are made of repeating units of three components (nitrogen-containing bases, a five-carbon sugar, and a phosphate group). Each unit, consisting of a sugar, phosphate group, and base, is called a nucleotide. The identity of the base distinguished one nucleotide from another.

5). X-ray diffraction experiments conducted by _____ led to the determination of the structure of DNA.
        a). Francis Crick
        b). James Watson
        c). Erwin Chargaff
        d). Rosalind Franklin

The correct answer is d...
A. Answer a is incorrect because Francis Crick along with colleague James Watson worked out a likely structure of DNA using the X-ray diffraction results obtained by Franklin.

The correct answer is d...
B. Answer b is incorrect because James Watson along with colleague Francis Crick worked out a likely structure of DNA using the X-ray diffraction results obtained by Franklin.

The correct answer is d...
C. Answer c is incorrect because Erwin Chargaff identified the base-pairing seen in DNA but didn't determine the structure of DNA.

The correct answer is d--Rosalind Franklin
D. Rosalind Franklin used the technique X-ray diffraction to see a regular pattern of the DNA molecule.

Hint: The significance of the regularities pointed out by Chargaff were not immediately obvious, but they became clear when a British chemist, Rosalind Franklin, carried out an X-ray diffraction analysis of DNA. The diffraction patterns she obtained suggested that the DNA molecule had the shape of a helix, or a corkscrew, with a diameter of about 2 nanometers and a complete helical turn every 3.4 nanometers.

6). Meselson and Stahl proved that
     a). DNA is the genetic material.
     b). DNA is made from nucleotides.
     c). DNA replicates in a semiconservative manner.
     d). DNA is a double helix held together with base-pairing.

The correct answer is c...
A. Answer a is incorrect because the Avery and Hershey and Chase experiments proved that DNA is the genetic material, not Meselson and Stahl.

The correct answer is c...
B. Answer b is incorrect because P. A. Levene determined that DNA is made from nucleotides, not Meselson and Stahl.

The correct answer is c--DNA replicates in a semiconservative manner.
C. Meselson and Stahl used bacteria grown in a heavy isotope of nitrogen, ^{15}N, so that they could follow the replication of new strands of DNA. They determined the semiconservative replication of DNA, where the two strands separate and serve as templates for the formation of a new double helix.

The correct answer is c...
D. Answer d is incorrect because the suggestion that DNA was a double helix held together by base-pairing was proposed by Watson and Crick, not Meselson and Stahl. However, Watson and Crick's model led Meselson and Stahl to their experiment studying replication.

Hint: The three hypotheses of DNA replication were evaluated by Meselson and Stahl using bacteria grown in media that contained a heavy isotope of nitrogen, ^{15}N. New strands of DNA would incorporate the heavy isotope. At the beginning they found all of the DNA was light. After one round of DNA replication there was a hybrid DNA of middle weight. After a second round of DNA replication a heavy form of DNA appeared. Meselson and Stahl interpreted their results that DNA replication was semiconservative, one strand being used as a template for the formation of a new strand.

7). DNA polymerase III can only add nucleotides to an existing chain, so _____ is required.
     a). an RNA primer
     b). DNA polymerase I
     c). helicase
     d). a DNA primer

The correct answer is a--an RNA primer
A. In order for DNA polymerase III to build a new strand of DNA, first a small segment of RNA is made by an RNA polymerase called primase. This section of RNA, called an RNA primer, can then be used as a starting point for the actions of DNA polymerase III. After the DNA strand is built, the RNA primer is cut from the DNA strand and replaced with DNA nucleotides.

The correct answer is a...
B. Answer b is incorrect because DNA polymerase I assists in the actions of DNA polymerase III, but not by starting the DNA strand.

The correct answer is a....
C. Answer c is incorrect because helicase is an enzyme that "unwinds" the DNA for replication. It is not involved in the initiation of DNA synthesis.

The correct answer is a...
D. Answer d is incorrect because although a primer is required, the primer is constructed from RNA nucleotides by the enzyme primase. Later, the RNA primer is spliced out and replaced with DNA nucleotides.

Hint: One of the features of DNA polymerase III is that it can add nucleotides only to a chain of nucleotides that is already paired with the parent strands. Hence, DNA polymerase cannot link the first nucleotides in a new synthesized strand. Instead, another enzyme, an RNA polymerase called primase, constructs an RNA primer, a sequence of about 10 RNA nucleotides complementary to the parent DNA template. DNA polymerase III recognizes the primer and adds DNA nucleotides to it to construct the new DNA strands.

8). Okazaki fragments are
      a). synthesized in the 3' to 5' direction.
      b). found on the lagging strand.
      c). found on the leading strand.
      d). assembled as continuous replication.

The correct answer is b...
A. Answer a is incorrect because all DNA is synthesized in the 5' to 3' direction, not in the 3' to 5' direction. In fact, Okazaki fragments are synthesized in pieces for the very reason that DNA synthesis occurs in the 5' to 3' direction.

The correct answer is b--found on the lagging strand.
B. Replication on the lagging strand is discontinuous because replication occurs in the 5' to 3' direction whereas on the lagging strand the new strand would have to build in the 3' to 5' direction. To synthesize the new strand in the correct direction, small sections of DNA are synthesized in the 5' to 3' direction and are then attached together. These small sections of DNA are called Okazaki fragments.

The correct answer is b....
C. Answer c is incorrect because Okazaki fragments are found on the lagging strand, not on the leading strand. DNA synthesis on the leading strand can proceed in the 5' to 3' direction and so synthesis is continuous. DNA synthesis is discontinuous on the lagging strand where the Okazaki fragments are synthesized and then spliced together.

The correct answer is b....
D. Answer d is incorrect because Okazaki fragments are synthesized in a discontinuous, not a continuous process. DNA replication proceeds in the 5' to 3' direction, but on the lagging strand of the new DNA strand, the synthesis would have to be in the 3' to 5' direction. In order to synthesize DNA in the 5' to 3' direction the DNA is synthesized in small segments in a discontinuous fashion.

Hint: The new strands elongate by different mechanisms. The leading strand, which elongates toward the replication fork, is built up simply by adding nucleotides continuously to its growing 3' end. In contrast, the lagging strand, which elongates away from the replication fork, is synthesized discontinuously as a series of short segments that are later connected. These segments are called Okazaki fragments.

9). Beadle and Tatum's experiment showed that each enzyme is specified by a single
      a). chromosome.
      b). gene.
      c). nucleotide.
      d). mutation.

The correct answer is b...
A. Answer a is incorrect because if a chromosome specified each enzyme, there would need to be many, many more chromosomes in a cell.

The correct answer is b--gene.
B. Beadle and Tatum were able to trace the mutation on the chromosomes of *arg* mutant cells and discovered that the mutations were clustered in three locations, suggesting that they were mutations in a biochemical pathway. Each cluster indicated a different gene; each gene encoded a different enzyme.

The correct answer is b...
C. Answer c is incorrect because a single nucleotide cannot store the information to specify the different enzymes present in a cell. There are only four nucleotides in DNA and thousands of enzymes. A group of nucleotides must encode an enzyme; a group of nucleotides called a gene.

The correct answer is b...
D. Answer d is incorrect because a mutation is a disruption to the normal DNA, not a coding segment of DNA. A mutation can disrupt the formation or functioning of an enzyme, but can't encode an enzyme.

Hint: For each enzyme in the arginine biosynthetic pathway, Beadle and Tatum were able to isolate a mutant strain with a defective form of that enzyme, and the mutation was always located on one of a few specific chromosomal sites. Most importantly, they found there was a different site for each enzyme. Beadle and Tatum concluded that genes produce their effect by specifying the structure of enzymes and that each gene encodes the structure of one enzyme. They called this relationship the one-gene/one-enzyme hypothesis.

10). What was significant about Ingram's work on sickle cell anemia?
      a). The gene for hemoglobin was missing.
      b). Proteins consisted of sequences of amino acids.
      c). A change in one amino acid can affect a protein's structure.
      d). One gene encodes one protein.

The correct answer is c...
A. Answer a is incorrect because sickle cell anemia is caused by an amino acid substitution, not by a missing hemoglobin gene.

The correct answer is c...
B. Answer b is incorrect because Sanger's work on insulin revealed that proteins consist of a sequence of amino acids, not Ingram's work on sickle cell anemia. Sanger was the first to sequence a protein, the protein insulin. It was then that researchers began searching for "errors" in normal amino acid sequences and which led to Ingram's work on hemoglobin.

The correct answer is c--A change in one amino acid can affect a protein's structure.
C. After Sanger announced the amino acid sequence of insulin, researchers began examining the amino acid structures of other proteins. Ingram examined the amino acid sequences of "normal" hemoglobin molecules and compared them to the amino acid sequences of sickle celled hemoglobin. He discovered the differences were due to one amino acid substitution, a valine for glutamic acid.

The correct answer is c...
D. Answer d is incorrect because Beadle and Tatum's research on *Neurospora* actually revealed the relationship between genes and enzymes. They developed the one-gene/one-enzyme hypothesis, not Ingram.

Hint: Vernon Ingram in 1956 discovered the molecular basis of sickle cell anemia, a protein defect inherited as a Mendelian disorder. By analyzing the structures of normal and sickle cell hemoglobin, Ingram, working at Cambridge University, showed that sickle cell anemia is caused by a change from glutamic acid to valine at a single position in the protein. The alleles of the gene encoding hemoglobin differed only in their specification of this one amino acid in the hemoglobin amino acid chain.

Test Your Visual Understanding

1). Based on the information in this figure, can you explain why pyrimidines don't base-pair with each other, and why purines don't base-pair with each other?
Answer: In order that the DNA maintain a diameter of about 2 nm across the double helix, it is necessary the smaller pyrimidines base pair with the larger purines. If two purines were to base-pair, the diameter of the double helix would be larger than 2 nm. Likewise, if two pyrimidines were to base-pair, the diameter of the double helix would be smaller than 2nm.

2). Can you also explain why adenine does not base-pair with cytosine. and why thymine does not base-pair with guanine?
Answer: Hydrogen bonding, which holds the two DNA strands together, determines which nucleotides will form complementary base-pairs. Adenine is able to form two hydrogen bonds and so it lines up with thymine, which is also able to form two hydrogen bonds. Cytosine, which is a smaller nucleotide like thymine, does not base-pair with adenine because their hydrogen-bonding atoms would not line up correctly. Likewise, guanine is able to form three hydrogen bonds and so it lines up with cytosine. which is also able to form three hydrogen bonds. Guanine, which is larger like adenine, does not-base pair with thymine because their hydrogen-bonding atoms would not line up correctly.

Apply Your Knowledge

1). The human genome contain approximately 3 billion (3×10^9) nucleotide base-pairs, and each nucleotide in a strand of DNA takes up about 0.34 nanometers (0.34×10^{-9} meters). How long would the human genome be if it were fully extended?
Answer: 3×10^9 base-pairs x 0.34×10^{-9} meters or:
$(3 \times 10^9) \times (0.34 \times 10^{-9}) = 1.02 \times 10^0$ meters for 1.02 meters long

2). From an extract of human cells growing in tissue culture, you obtain a white, fibrous substance. How would you distinguish whether it was DNA, RNA, or protein?
Answer: First you could test the substance for the presence of amino acids; if present, the substance is a protein. If the substance does not contain amino acids, it is one of the two nucleic acids. To determine which nucleic acid, you can either test the substance for the presence of ribose or deoxyribose or you can test the substance for the presence of thymine or uracil. The presence of thymine or deoxyribose indicates the substance is DNA. The presence of uracil or ribose indicates the substance is RNA.

3). Cells were obtained from a patient with a viral infection. The DNA extracted from these cells consisted of two forms: double-stranded human DNA and single-stranded viral DNA. The base compositions of these two forms of DNA were as follows:

	A	C	G	T
Form 1	22.1%	27.9%	27.9%	22.1%
Form 2	31.3%	31.3%	18.7%	18.7%

Which form was the viral DNA, and which form was the human DNA? Explain your reasoning.
Answer: The single-stranded viral DNA does not have complementary base-pairing and so one would not expect the viral DNA to follow the Chargaff's rule of base-pairing. That being the case, Form 2 would be the viral DNA because the adenine and thymine are not present in equal

proportions and the cytosine and guanine are not in equal proportions. In Form 1, the adenine and thymine are in equal proportions indicating that they are base-paired and the cytosine and guanine are in equal proportions indicating that they are base-paired. Therefore Form 1 is human DNA.

None for this chapter.

Self Test

1). The bases of RNA are the same as those of DNA with the exception that RNA contains
    a). cysteine instead of cytosine.
    b). uracil instead of thymine.
    c). cytosine instead of guanine.
    d). uracil instead of adenine.

The correct answer is b...
A. Answer a is incorrect because both RNA and DNA contain cytosine and neither contains cysteine (which is an amino acid, not a nitrogenous base).

The correct answer is b--uracil instead of thymine.
B. Wherever thymine appears in DNA, the complementary base in RNA that pairs with it is uracil. No thymine is present in RNA and no uracil is present in DNA.

The correct answer is b...
C. Answer c is incorrect because both RNA and DNA contain cytosine and guanine. These two bases are complementary in the DNA double helix and in the DNA–RNA duplex.

The correct answer is b...
D. Answer d is incorrect because RNA contains both uracil and adenine; in fact they are complementary bases in RNA. DNA does not contain uracil, instead adenine base-pairs with thymine, which is not present in RNA.

Hint: As RNA polymerase encounters each DNA nucleotide, it adds the corresponding complementary RNA nucleotide to a growing mRNA strand. Thus, guanine (G), cytosine (C), thymine (T), and adenine (A) in the DNA would signal the addition of C, G, A, and uracil (U), respectively, to the mRNA.

2). Which one of the following is not a type of RNA?
    a). nRNA (nuclear RNA)
    b). mRNA (messenger RNA)
    c). rRNA (ribosomal RNA)
    d). tRNA (transfer RNA)

The correct answer is a--nRNA (nuclear RNA)
A. Although a primary transcript is produced in the nucleus and later modified to form the mRNA molecule, it is not called "nuclear RNA." nRNA is not a type of RNA.

The correct answer is a...
B. Answer b is incorrect because messenger RNA is a type of RNA. mRNA is the molecule that carries the nucleotide sequence from DNA to the cytoplasm where it is transcribed into a protein or enzyme.

The correct answer is a...
C. Answer c is incorrect because ribosomal RNA is a type of RNA. rRNA is the molecule that complexes with proteins in the cytoplasm to form ribosomes, the platform on which proteins are synthesized.

The correct answer is a...
D. Answer d is incorrect because transfer RNA is a type of RNA. tRNA is the molecule that binds to and transfers amino acids to the mRNA–rRNA complex to synthesize proteins.

Hint: The class of RNA found in ribosomes is called ribosomal RNA (rRNA). During polypeptide synthesis, rRNA provides the site where polypeptides are assembled. In addition to rRNA, there are two other major classes of RNA in calls: transfer RNA (tRNA) and messenger RNA (mRNA).

3). Each amino acid in a protein is specified by
        a). several genes.
        b). a promoter.
        c). an mRNA molecule.
        d). a codon.

The correct answer is d...
A. Answer a is incorrect because several genes don't specify an amino acid; not even one gene specifies an amino acid. A gene specifies an entire protein not just one amino acid.

The correct answer is d...
B. Answer b is incorrect because a promoter is a sequence of nucleotides on a DNA template strand that signals the beginning of a gene and is the site of RNA polymerase binding.

The correct answer is d...
C. Answer c is incorrect because a mRNA molecule is the copy of the sequence of nucleotides on the DNA that specifies a gene. The mRNA specifies many amino acids, not just one.

The correct answer is d--a codon.
D. A codon is a three-nucleotide sequence that specifies a specific amino acid. The mRNA contains the codon and the tRNA contains the anticodon.

Hint: Crick and his colleagues reasoned that the genetic code most likely consisted of a series of blocks of information called codons, each corresponding to an amino acid in the encoded protein. They further hypothesized that the information within one codon was probably a sequence of three nucleotides specifying a particular amino acid.

4). The three-nucleotide codon system can be arranged into _____ combinations.
        a). 16
        b). 20
        c). 64
        d). 128

The correct answer is c...
A. Answer a is incorrect because 16 is the number of combinations using a two-nucleotide codon system, not a three-nucleotide codon system.

The correct answer is c...
B. Answer b is incorrect because 20 is the number of amino acids, not the number of combination of nucleotides using a three-nucleotide codon system.

The correct answer is c--64
C. There are 64 different ways to arrange four nucleotides in codons of three nucleotides (4^3 equals 64).

The correct answer is c...
D. Answer d is incorrect because four nucleotides arranged in combinations of three nucleotides would not equal 128 combinations.

Hint: Crick and his colleagues arrived at the number three, because a two-nucleotide codon would not yield enough combinations to code for the 20 different amino acids that commonly occur in proteins. With four DNA nucleotides (G, C, T, and A), only 4^2, or 16, different pairs of nucleotides could be formed. However, the same nucleotides can be arranged in 4^3, or 64, different combinations of three, more than enough to code for the 20 amino acids.

5). The TATA box in eukaryotes is a
      a). core promoter.
      b). – 35 sequence.
      c). – 10 sequence.
      d). 5' cap.

The correct answer is a--a core promoter.
A. This sequence, referred to as the TATA box, is a short sequence that indicates the beginning of a gene to be transcribed. The RNA polymerase binds to this sequence but does not transcribe it; transcription doesn't begin until the RNA polymerase as passed the promoter.

The correct answer is a...
B. Answer b is incorrect because the – 35 sequence is a promoter in bacterial cells. This sequence, TTGACA, is located 35 nucleotides upstream of the position where transcription begins.

The correct answer is a...
C. Answer c is incorrect because the – 10 sequence is a promoter in bacterial cells. This sequence, TATAAT, is located 10 nucleotides upstream of the position where transcription begins.

The correct answer is a...
D. Answer d is incorrect because the 5' cap is a modification made to the mRNA in eukaryotes where the phosphate on the 5' end forms an unusual linkage with GTP. This modification protects the 5' end of the mRNA during its passage from the nucleus to the cytoplasm.

Hint: In eukaryotic DNA, the sequence TATAAA, called the TATA box, is located at – 25 and is very similar to the prokaryotic – 10 sequence but is farther from the start site.

6). The site where RNA polymerase attaches to the DNA molecule to start the formation of RNA is called a(n)
      a). promoter.
      b). exon.
      c). intron.
      d). GC hairpin.

The correct answer is a--promoter.
A. The promoter is a sequence of nucleotides that signals the beginning of a gene to be transcribed but the promoter itself is not transcribed.   There are different promoters but there are similarities in the different promoter sequences.

The correct answer is a...
B. Answer b is incorrect because an exon is a coding region of the DNA, a section of a gene. Exons are found interspersed among introns that are noncoding regions of the DNA. After the RNA is synthesized, the introns are spliced out of the transcript.

The correct answer is a...
C. Answer c is incorrect because an intron is a noncoding region of the DNA. Coding sequences, called exons, are interspersed among the introns. After the RNA is synthesized, introns are spliced out of the transcript.

The correct answer is a...

D. Answer d is incorrect because a GC hairpin is found at the end of the gene, not at the beginning. A GC hairpin is a series of GC nucleotides at the end of a gene which, when transcribed, undergo intramolecular binding to cause a hairpin loop. This loop in the RNA causes the RNA polymerase to pause and results in the dissociation of the RNA and the DNA strands.

Hint: Transcription starts at RNA polymerase binding sites, called promoters, on the DNA template strand. A promoter is a short sequence that is not itself transcribed by the polymerase that binds to it. Striking similarities are evident in the sequences of different promoters.

7). When mRNA leaves the cell's nucleus, it next becomes associated with
    a). proteins.
    b). a ribosome.
    c). tRNA.
    d). RNA polymerase.

The correct answer is b...
A. Answer a is incorrect because the mRNA is used as a template to make proteins; it does not associate with proteins, however, proteins are components of ribosomes which is what the mRNA associates with.

The correct answer is b--a ribosome.
B. The mRNA is the template used by the cell to produce proteins but the ribosome creates a platform on which the mRNA associates with, where proteins are made.

The correct answer is b...
C. Answer c is incorrect because the tRNA doesn't associate with the mRNA until after the mRNA has associated with the ribosome.

The correct answer is b...
D. Answer d is incorrect because the RNA polymerase is the enzyme used to produce the mRNA in the nucleus and doesn't associate with the mRNA after it is produced in and leaves the nucleus.

Hint: In prokaryotes, translation begins when the initial portion of a mRNA molecule binds to a rRNA molecule in a ribosome. The mRNA lies on the ribosome in such a way that only one of its codons is exposed at the polypeptide-making site at any time.

8). If an mRNA codon reads UAC, its complementary anticodon will be
    a). TUC.
    b). ATG.
    c). AUG.
    d). CAG.

The correct answer is c...
A. Answer a is incorrect because the complementary base-pairs for RNA are: A and U, C and G; T (thymine) is not present in RNA.

The correct answer is c...
B. Answer b is incorrect because the complementary base-pairs for RNA are: A and U, C and G; T (thymine) is not present in RNA.

The correct answer is c--AUG.
C. A (adenine) base-pairs with U (uracil) in RNA and so the UA in the codon pairs with AU in the anticodon. C (cytosine) base-pairs with G (guanine) in RNA and in DNA and so the C in the codon pairs with G in the anticodon.

The correct answer is c...
D. Answer d is incorrect because the complementary base-pairs for RNA are: A and U, C and G; therefore U would pair with A, A would pair with U, and C would pair with G.

Hint: In prokaryotes, translation begins when the initial portion of a mRNA molecule binds to a rRNA molecule in a ribosome. The mRNA lies on the ribosome in such a way that only one of its codons is exposed at the polypeptide-making site at any time. A tRNA molecule possessing the complementary three-nucleotide sequence, or anticodon, binds to the exposed codon on the mRNA.

9). The nucleotide sequences on DNA that actually have information encoding a sequence of amino acids are
        a). introns.
        b). exons.
        c). UAA.
        d). UGA.

The correct answer is b...
A. Answer a is incorrect because introns contain noncoding regions of DNA. They are transcribed into mRNA but are spliced out prior to translation so they are not translated into proteins, therefore, they are noncoding regions.

The correct answer is b--exons.
B. Exons are regions of the DNA that contain sequences that encode for proteins. They are scattered among noncoding regions called introns.

The correct answer is b...
C. Answer c is incorrect because UAA is one of the "stop" codons that doesn't encode for an amino acid.

The correct answer is b...
D. Answer d is incorrect because UGA is one of the "stop" codons that doesn't encode for an amino acid.

Hint: A typical eukaryotic gene is not simply a straight sequence of DNA; the order of its units corresponding to the sequence of amino acids in a protein. Instead of DNA units that specifies a protein is broken into many bits called exons that are scattered about within a gene among much longer segments of noncoding DNA called introns.

10). Which of the following statements is correct about prokaryotic gene expression?
        a). Prokaryotic mRNAs must have introns spliced out.
        b). Prokaryotic mRNAs are often translated before transcription is complete.
        c). Prokaryotic mRNAs contain the transcript of only one gene.
        d). All of these statements are correct.

The correct answer is b...
A. Answer a is incorrect because this statement does not accurately describe prokaryotic gene expression. Prokaryotic mRNAs do not contain introns therefore, there are no introns to splice out.

The correct answer is b--Prokaryotic mRNAs are often translated before transcription is complete.
B. Because transcription and translation occur in the same location in prokaryotes (not separated by a nuclear membrane), translation of the mRNA begins before transcription is complete.

The correct answer is b...

C. Answer c is incorrect because this statement does not accurately describe prokaryotic gene expression. Prokaryotic mRNA molecules often contain the transcripts of several genes with related functions (i.e., several enzymes in a pathway).

The correct answer is b...

D. Answer d is incorrect because only answer b accurately describes prokaryotic gene expression. Answer a is incorrect because prokaryotic mRNAs do not contain introns therefore, there are no introns to splice out. Answer c is incorrect because prokaryotic mRNA molecules often contain the transcripts of several genes with related functions (i.e., several enzymes in a pathway).

Hint: Because eukaryotes possess a nucleus, their mRNA molecules must be completely formed and must pass across the nuclear membrane before they are translated. Bacteria, which lack nuclei, often begin translation of a mRNA molecule before its transcription is completed.

Test Your Visual Understanding

1). Match the correct labels from the following list with the lettered boxes in the figure (not all labels will be used).
    replication
    RNA processing
    transcription
    translation
    a). What is this figure illustrating?
    b). Where does process A occur in the eukaryotic cell?
    c). Where does process B occur in the eukaryotic cell?

Answer:
    A—Transcription
    B—Translation
    1a). This figure is illustrating the Central Dogma of gene expression.
    1b). Transcription occurs in the nucleus of eukaryotic cells.
    1c). Translation occurs in the cytoplasm of eukaryotic cells.

Apply Your Knowledge

1). Assume you had four copies per cell of mature mRNA for insulin, a protein made of two polypeptide chains with a total of 51 amino acids. Assume one ribosome can attach onto an mRNA every 20 nucleotides. One amino acid can be translated in 60 milliseconds. How many copies of insulin could be made in three minutes?
Answer: First, figure out how long it takes one ribosome to translate one molecule of insulin:
    51 amino acids x 0.06 seconds (60 milliseconds) = 3.06 seconds
Next, how many insulin molecules can be translated by one ribosome in three minutes (or 180 seconds):
    180/3.06 seconds = 58.8 insulin molecule
Then, figure out how many ribosomes can attach and be working at any given time:
51 amino acids = 51 codons and 51 x 3 = 153 nucleotides such that:
    4 copies x 153 nucleotides/20 binding sites for ribosomes = 30.6 working ribosomes at any given time.
Therefore, one ribosome can build 58.8 molecules of insulin in 3 minutes, so 30.6 ribosomes can build 1,799 molecule of insulin in 3 minutes (58.8 x 30.6 = 1799).

2). The nucleotide sequence of a hypothetical eukaryotic gene is:
TACATACTAGTTAC<u>G</u>TCGCCCGGAAATATC

If a mutation in this gene were to change the fifteenth nucleotide (underlined) from guanine to thymine, what effect do you think it might have on the expression of this gene?

Answer: The mRNA sequence of this gene is:

AUG UAU GAU CAA UG<u>C</u> AGC GGG CCU UUA UAG

The amino acid sequence for this sequence of codons is:

Met-Tyr-Asp-Glu-<u>Cys</u>-Ser-Gly-Pro-Leu-Stop

If the underlined guanine was changed to thymine the mRNA sequence for this codon would be UGU and the amino acid encoded by UGU is Cysteine, the same amino acid encoded by UGC, therefore there would be no effect of this mutation on the production of the protein.

Inquiry Questions
None for this chapter.

Self Test

1). Cutting certain genes out of molecules of DNA requires the use of special
      a). degrading nucleases.
      b). restriction endonucleases.
      c). eukaryotic enzymes.
      d). viral enzymes.

The correct answer is b...
A. Answer a is incorrect because degrading nucleases would degrade all of the DNA molecule. The cutting out of a certain gene requires the actions of an enzyme that is more specific in its target.

The correct answer is b--restriction endonucleases.
B. Restriction endonucleases are produced by bacterial cells as a defense mechanism, to attack and degrade viral DNA that enter the cell. Restriction endonucleases break up the DNA at specific locations and keep the viral DNA from replicating in the bacterial cell.

The correct answer is b...
C. Answer c is incorrect because the enzymes that cut genes out of DNA are bacterial enzymes, not eukaryotic enzymes. However, because DNA is universal, the bacterial enzymes can cut eukaryotic DNA as well as viral DNA. These enzymes can also cut bacterial DNA as long as the DNA is not methylated.

The correct answer is b...
D. Answer d is incorrect because the enzymes that cut genes out of DNA are bacterial enzymes, not viral enzymes. In fact, these bacterial enzymes are a defense mechanism for the bacterial cell, to protect it from viral infections. However, because DNA is universal, the bacterial enzymes can cut eukaryotic DNA in addition to viral DNA.

Hint: Among the natural enemies of bacteria are bacteriophages, viruses that infect bacteria and multiply within them. At some point, they cause the bacterial cells to burst, releasing thousands more viruses. Through natural selection, some types of bacteria have acquired powerful weapons against these viruses: they contain enzymes called restriction endonucleases that fragment the viral DNA as soon as it enters the bacterial cell.

2). Which of the following cannot be used as a vector?
      a). phage
      b). plasmid
      c). bacterium
      d). All can be used as vectors.

The correct answer is c...
A. Answer a is incorrect because a phage is used as a vector. Phages are viruses that attack bacterial cells and can be used to carry recombinant DNA into a bacterial host where the recombinant DNA is then transcribed and translated as host DNA.

The correct answer is c...
B. Answer b is incorrect because a plasmid is used as a vector. A plasmid is a small, circular fragment of DNA found in bacterial cells. A recombinant plasmid can carry foreign DNA into a host bacterial cell where the recombinant DNA is transcribed and translated as host DNA.

The correct answer is c--bacterium
C. A bacterium is often used as a host for recombinant DNA but not a vector.

The correct answer is c...
D. Answer d is incorrect because phages and plasmids are used as vectors, transferring recombinant DNA into a host cell where the recombinant DNA is transcribed and translated as the host DNA.

Hint: The most flexible and common host used for routine cloning is the bacterium *E. coli*. This is not the only host, of course. We now routinely clone eukaryotic DNA, using mammalian tissue culture cells, yeast cells, and insect cells as host systems. Each kind of host/vector system allows particular uses of the cloned DNA.

3). In Cohen and Boyer's recombinant DNA experiments, restriction endonucleases were used to
      a). isolate fragments of cloned bacterial plasmids.
      b). isolate fragments of frog DNA that contained an rRNA gene.
      c). cleave the bacterial plasmid.
      d). All of these are correct.

The correct answer is d...
A. Answer a is incorrect because although they did use restriction endonucleases to isolate a fragment of bacterial plasmids, this isn't the only correct answer.

The correct answer is d...
B. Answer b is incorrect because although they did use restriction endonucleases to isolate a fragment of frog DNA that contained the rRNA gene, this isn't the only correct answer.

The correct answer is d...
C. Answer c is incorrect because although they did use restriction endonucleases to cleave the bacterial plasmid so that they could insert the frog DNA, this isn't the only correct answer.

The correct answer is d--All of these are correct.
D. The recombinant DNA experiments by Cohen and Boyer were multistep experiments in which they first isolated a section of bacterial plasmid using *Eco*RI, then they isolated a fragment of frog DNA that contained the rRNA gene using *Eco*RI, and finally they cleaved the bacterial plasmid with *Eco*RI and incorporated the frog DNA into the plasmid.

Hint: Cohen and Boyer used a restriction endonuclease called *Eco*RI to cut the bacterial plasmid into fragments. They used a fragment 9,000 nucleotides in length as a vector dubbed pSC101. They also used *Eco*RI to cleave DNA that coded for rRNA that they had isolated from the African clawed frog, *Xenopus laevis*. They then mixed the fragments of *Xenopus* DNA with pSC101 plasmids that had be "reopened" by *Eco*RI and allowed bacterial cells to take up DNA from the mixture.

4). A DNA library is
      a). a general collection of all genes sequenced thus far.
      b). a collection of DNA fragments that make up the entire genome of a particular organism.
      c). a DNA fragment inserted into a vector.
      d). all DNA fragments identified with a probe.

The correct answer is b...
A. Answer a is incorrect because a general collection of all genes sequenced thus far is a database but this database would be compiled from many DNA libraries.

The correct answer is b--a collection of DNA fragments that make up the entire genome of a particular organism.

B. An entire genome is usually too large to fit in any one vector and so the DNA is often cut into segments and inserted into many vectors. A DNA library is the collection of all fragments that comprise the entire DNA of the organism.

The correct answer is b…

C. Answer c is incorrect because a DNA fragment inserted into a vector will contain only a very small portion of the entire genome of an organism and a DNA library contains all of the fragments that constitutes the entire genome.

The correct answer is b…

D. Answer d is incorrect because all DNA fragments identified with a probe is a small percentage of the entire genome. A probe is used to identify certain DNA sequences and will identify only a very small portion of the genome while a DNA library reflects the entire genome.

Hint: In order to place a particular gene or DNA sequence into a vector, you must first have a DNA source that contains that sequence. Typically, the source is a collection of DNA fragments representing all of the DNA from an organism. We call this a DNA library.

5). A probe is used in which stage of genetic engineering?
        a). cleaving DNA
        b). recombining DNA
        c). cloning
        d). screening

The correct answer is d…

A. Answer a is incorrect because the cleaving of DNA involves the use of restriction endonucleases to cut the DNA of the vector and the source DNA. This process does not involve the use of RNA probes.

The correct answer is d…

B. Answer b is incorrect because the process of recombining DNA involves the mixing of source DNA fragments with the cleaved vector DNA, resulting in the recombining of the DNAs. A probe is not used in this process.

The correct answer is d…

C. Answer c is incorrect because the cloning process involves the formation of a library of cells that contain recombinant DNA. A probe is not used in this process.

The correct answer is d--screening

D. The screening process involves the examination of the library of clones to find the cells that contain a particular gene from the source DNA. This screening process involves the use of defined growth media and probes to find what the cells had taken DNA up. A radioactive nucleic acid probe that is complementary to the gene of interest is added to the growth media and binds to the colony of cells that contain the gene of interest. The colony that emits radioactivity indicates the presence of the gene.

Hint: The most general procedure for screening clone libraries to find a particular gene is hybridization. In this method, the cloned genes from base-pairs with complementary sequences on another nucleic acid. The complementary nucleic acid is called a probe because it is used to probe for the presence of the gene of interest. As least part of the nucleotide sequence of the gene of interest must be known to be able to construct the probe.

6). The enzyme used in the polymerase chain reaction is
  a). restriction endonuclease.
  b). reverse transcriptase.
  c). DNA polymerase.
  d). RNA polymerase.

The correct answer is c...
A. Answer a is incorrect because restriction endonuclease is an enzyme that cuts DNA at specific sequence sites and is not involved in the polymerase chain reaction.

The correct answer is c...
B. Answer b is incorrect because reverse transcriptase is an enzyme used to synthesize a strand of DNA from a strand of RNA (the reverse process of transcription) and is not involved in the polymerase chain reaction.

The correct answer is c--DNA polymerase.
C. DNA polymerase is the enzyme that synthesizes new complementary strands of DNA and is involved in DNA replication. DNA polymerase cannot build a new strand from scratch; it needs to add on to an existing strand of nucleotides. A primer of RNA is first laid down during replication and the same is done for polymerase chain reaction. The DNA polymerase begins building on a primer that is added to the polymerase chain reaction system.

The correct answer is c...
D. Answer d is incorrect because RNA polymerase is used in the synthesis of RNA molecules and for building primers in DNA replication but it is not used in the polymerase chain reaction because the primers are added to the system not synthesized.

Hint: Once a particular gene is identified within the library of DNA fragments, the final requirement is to make multiple copies of it. A direct approach is to use DNA polymerase to copy the gene sequence of interest through the polymerase chain reaction (PCR).

7). A method used to distinguish DNA of one individual from another is
  a). polymerase chain reaction.
  b). cDNA.
  c). reverse transcriptase.
  d). restriction fragment length polymorphism.

The correct answer is d...
A. Answer a is incorrect because the polymerase chain reaction is used to amplify the quantity of DNA from a small sample. The process copies a segment of DNA, creating a large quantity that can be used for DNA analysis.

The correct answer is d...
B. Answer b is incorrect because cDNA is a DNA copy of a segment of RNA. cDNAs are used when identifying the portion of DNA containing the sequence for a particular protein.

The correct answer is d...
C. Answer c is incorrect because reverse transcriptase is an enzyme used to make a DNA copy of a strand of RNA.

The correct answer is d--restriction fragment length polymorphism.
D. Restriction fragment length polymorphism is a process whereby markers are used to tag specific DNA sequences in DNA from an individual. DNA from the individual is cut into fragments and probed with DNA markers. It is quite rare that two individuals will have the same pattern of DNA markers.

Hint: Often a researcher wishes not to find a specific gene, but rather to identify a particular individual using a specific gene as a marker. One powerful way to do this is by analyzing restriction fragment length polymorphisms, or RFLPs.

8). Inserting a gene encoding a pathogenic microbe's surface protein into a harmless virus produces a

        a). piggyback vaccine.
        b). virulent virus.
        c). active disease-causing pathogen.
        d). pharmaceutical human protein.

The correct answer is a--piggyback vaccine.
A. A vaccine is a substance that triggers the human immune system to mount an attack against a foreign invader. By inserting a pathogenic surface protein gene into a harmless virus, the virus produces the pathogenic surface protein without causing disease. The body produces antibodies against the pathogenic surface protein such that when the pathogen enters the body it is attacked before it can cause disease. A vaccine produced in this way is called a piggyback vaccine.

The correct answer is a...
B. Answer b is incorrect because the insertion of a surface protein gene from a pathogenic microbe does not make a harmless virus virulent.

The correct answer is a...
C. Answer c is incorrect because the insertion of a surface protein gene from a pathogenic microbe does not change a harmless virus into a disease-causing pathogen.

The correct answer is a...
D. Answer d is incorrect because a pharmaceutical human protein is produced by the insertion of a human protein gene into a bacterium where the bacterium begins to produce the human protein, like little protein-producing machines.

Hint: Piggyback vaccines: Another area of potential significance involves the use of genetic engineering to produce subunit vaccines against viruses such as those that cause herpes and hepatitis. Genes encoding part of the protein-polysaccharide coat of the virus is spliced into a fragment of a harmless virus. These viruses begin expressing the disease-causing virus's surface proteins. When inserted into a human, the human begins producing antibodies directed against the coats of the virulent viruses.

9). Although the Ti plasmid has revolutionized plant genetic engineering, one limitation of its use is that it

        a). cannot infect broadleaf plants.
        b). cannot be used on fruit-bearing plants.
        c). cannot transmit prokaryotic genes.
        d). does not infect cereal plants such as corn and rice.

The correct answer is d...
A. Answer a is incorrect because the Ti plasmid, found in the plant bacterium *Agrobacterium tumefaciens*, can infect *only* broadleaf plants which are dicot plants. *Agrobacterium* does not infect monocots plants such as corn, wheat, and rice.

The correct answer is d...
B. Answer b is incorrect because the Ti plasmid, carried into a plant by *Agrobacterium tumefaciens,* can be used on all broadleaf plants that include fruit-bearing plants such as tomato plants, soybean plants, etc.

The correct answer is d...
C. Answer c is incorrect because the Ti plasmid can transmit prokaryotic or eukaryotic genes. Because DNA is universal meaning it is found in all organisms, any fragment of DNA can be placed into any organism.

The correct answer is d...does not infect cereal plants such as corn and rice.
D. The limitation of not being able to infect a cereal plant is not really the limitation of the Ti plasmid itself, but rather the limitation of the bacterium that carries the Ti plasmid. *Agrobacterium tumefaciens* cannot infect cereal plants such as corn, rice, or wheat and so there is no way of getting the Ti plasmid into these plants. However, other methods are being used for genetic engineering in these plants.

Hint: The most successful plant vector has been the Ti plasmid of the plant bacterium *Agrobacterium tumefaciens*, which infects broadleaf plants such as tomato, tobacco, and soybean. Part of the Ti plasmid integrates into the plant DNA and researchers have succeeded in attaching other genes to this portion of the plasmid. Unfortunately, *Agrobacterium* generally does not infect cereals, such as corn, rice, and wheat, but alternative methods can be used to introduce new genes into them.

10). Which of the following is *not* an application of genetic engineering in plants?
   a). nitrogen fixation
   b). DNA vaccines
   c). resistance to glyphosate
   d). production of insecticidal proteins in plants

The correct answer b...
A. Answer a is incorrect because nitrogen fixation is an application of genetic engineering in plants. Plants rely on symbiotic bacteria to fix nitrogen so that it can be used by plants, or in farming, the application of nitrogen to the soil. Using genetic engineering, researchers are attempting to insert nitrogen-fixing genes from bacteria, called *nif* genes, into plants so that they can carry out this necessary process themselves.

The correct answer is b--DNA vaccines
B. The development of DNA vaccines is an application of genetic engineering in animals but not in plants. Animals mount immunological attacks against pathogens that can be stimulated with vaccines, but plants don't carry out this same type of immunological response and so the development of DNA vaccines isn't possible in plants.

The correct answer is b...
C. Answer c is incorrect because resistance to glyphosate is an application of genetic engineering in plants. Glyphosate is a chemical herbicide that is applied to crops in order to kill weeds; unfortunately, it can also kill crops. Through genetic engineering, broadleaf crops have been produced that resist the effects of the herbicide and so aren't affected by the application of the herbicide.

The correct answer is b...
D. Answer d is incorrect because the production of insecticidal proteins in plants is an application of genetic engineering. The goal is to insert genes encoding proteins that are harmful to insects so that insects that eat the plants will die, protecting the plants from insect pests.

Hint: In the future, recombinant viruses may be injected into humans to confer resistance to a wide variety of viral diseases.

Test Your Visual Understanding

1). What process is illustrated in this figure? Where in the cell would you look to find the primary RNA transcript, and where would you look to find the mature mRNA transcript?
Answer: The process illustrated is the production of complementary DNA or cDNA. The primary RNA transcript is present in the nucleus of the cell. The mature mRNA transcript is present in the cytoplasm of the cell. The primary RNA transcript contains introns that are spliced out by enzymes present in the nucleus and from there, the mature mRNA transcript moves out of the nucleus into the cytoplasm.

2). When might researchers use this process—that is, what would they be trying to accomplish?
Answer: Researchers use the production of cDNAs when they require the DNA that codes for the final protein product, which is encoded by the mature mRNA transcript. This is needed when using bacteria to mass produce a eukaryotic protein. If a copy of the DNA for a particular protein was placed in a bacterium, all of the introns in addition to the exons would be transcribed and translated and the protein would not be functional. It is necessary to use the mature mRNA to make the cDNA that can then be inserted into the bacterium so that the functional protein product is made.

Apply Your Knowledge

1). The human genome has about 3 billion base-pairs. Assume you wanted to clone the entire human genome using various vectors, but there is a limit to the size of a DNA fragment that can be inserted in a vector. Following is a list of vectors along with their size limit of DNA fragment. Calculate how many vectors of each type would be needed to generate a library of the human genome.
    a). bacterial plasmid—18 kilo base-pairs
    b). phages—25 kilo base-pairs
    c). YACs—250 kilo base-pairs
Answer:

    1a). The human genome is 3 billion base-pairs or 3×10^9 bp and so the number of bacterial plasmids needed would be:
    3×10^9 bp / 18,000 bp = 166,667 plasmids

    1b). The number of phages needed would be:
    3×10^9 bp / 25,000 = 120,000 phages

    1c). The number of YACs needed would be:
    3×10^9 bp / 250,000 = 12,000 YACs

2). A major focus of genetic engineering has been on attempting to produce large quantities of scarce human proteins by placing the appropriate genes into bacteria and thus turning the bacteria into protein production machines. Human insulin and many other proteins are produced this way. However, this approach does not work for producing human hemoglobin. Even if the proper clone is identified, the fragments containing the hemoglobin genes are successfully incorporated into bacterial plasmids, and the bacteria are infected with the plasmids, no hemoglobin is produced by the bacteria. Why doesn't this experiment work?
Answer: Hemoglobin is a complex protein actually made of four polypeptide chains that are held together in a quaternary structure. There are also four heme groups (iron-containing groups) that are associated with each polypeptide chain. The complexity of this molecule may preclude its synthesis by a bacterial cell. Other genes are most likely involved in the formation of the tertiary and quaternary structures and involved in the incorporation of the heme groups into the polypeptides. A bacterial cell may be able to translate the gene into a polypeptide but the further complexity of the molecule probably restricts its synthesis by bacteria.

Inquiry Questions

FIGURE 17.5
Sequencing DNA. DNA is replicated, and fluorescent nucleotides that halt replication are randomly inserted into different sequences. An automated sequencer determines the base-pair sequence.
Why is it important to know whether or not your primer hybridizes to the template strand in the replication step?

Answer: If your primer copies the template strand, your result will be the sequence of the gene in the 5' to 3' direction. Remember, the newly synthesized sequence will be the complement of the template strand. The complement of the template strand is the coding (gene) sequence. You may want to look at Figure 15.8 and review transcription.

FIGURE 17.14
Corn crop productivity well below its genetic potential due to drought stress. Corn production can be limited by water deficiencies due to the drought that occurs during the growing season in dry climates. Global climate change may increase drought stress in areas where corn is the major crop.
The corn genome has not been sequenced. How could you use information from the rice genome sequence to try to improve drought tolerance in corn?

Answer: You may be able to take advantage of synteny between the rice and corn genome (see Figure 17.9). Let's assume that a drought tolerant gene has already been identified and mapped in rice. Using what is known about synteny between the rice and corn genomes, you could find the region of the corn genome that corresponds to the rice drought tolerance gene. This would narrow down the region of the corn genome that you might want to sequence to find your gene. A subsequent step might be to modify the corn gene that corresponds to the rice gene to see if you can increase drought tolerance.

Self Test

1). Researchers from many labs collaborated to determine the sequence of the human genome. How did labs avoid sequencing the same fragments multiple times?
      a). Each lab could isolate DNA from one particular chromosome to divide the sequencing projects.
      b). Using restriction fragment length polymorphisms, labs could ensure that they were not sequencing the same fragments.
      c). Using short sequences from their respective clones, sequence-tagged sites (STSs), researchers could check to make sure their fragments where not already being sequenced by another group.
      d). By comparing sequences from collaborating labs, researchers could ensure that they were not sequencing the same fragments.

The correct answer is c…
A. Answer a is incorrect because when you isolate genomic DNA from cells it is very difficult to separate one chromosome from the others; this results in isolating total DNA representing each chromosome in a cell.

The correct answer is c…
B. Answer b is incorrect because RFLPs are useful in identifying differences between different individuals, but will not help to identify different DNA fragments. Furthermore, RFLPs represent differences on the SAME DNA molecule from different individuals, but not between different molecules of DNA.

The correct answer is c--Using short sequences from their respective clones, sequence-tagged sites (STSs), researchers could check to make sure their fragments where not already being sequenced by another group.

C. Answer c is correct because STSs can be used to quickly screen a large fragment of DNA for a particular sequence. Because this is a PCR-based screen, it can be carried out very quickly for a large number of STS sites at one time.

The correct answer is c…

D. Answer d is incorrect because if multiple labs were sequencing different regions of the same large DNA fragment, this comparison would not detect the redundancy until the sequences overlapped.

2). Some of your friends are trying to make sense of their genome. To help them out, you draw an analogy between our chromosomes and the interstate highway system. In this analogy, every interstate represents a single chromosome. How could you describe the relationship between chromosomes and genes to your friends using this analogy?

      a). Every mile marker would represent a gene.
      b). Every town would represent a gene.
      c). Every state would represent a gene.
      d). Genes would be defined by the twists and turns on the highway.

The correct answer is b…

A. Answer a is incorrect because genes are not regularly spaced along the chromosome.

The correct answer is b--Every town would represent a gene.

B. Answer b is correct because genes can be spaced along the chromosome much like towns along the highway. Furthermore, single-copy genes are unique in the genome, much like the uniqueness of each town. Finally, genes can be large or small, as can towns.

The correct answer is b…

C. Answer c is incorrect because every state borders immediately with the next state with no intervening regions of highway. There are large regions of chromatin between genes along a chromosome.

The correct answer is b…

D. Answer d is incorrect because the physical shape of a chromosome does not reflect the presence or absence of a gene.

3). Imagine that you broke your mother's favorite vase and had to reconstruct it from the shattered pieces. To do this, you would have to look for pieces with similar ends to join and then progressively glue every piece together. What sequencing strategy does this most closely represent?

      a). shotgun sequencing
      b). contig sequencing
      c). clone-by-clone sequencing
      d). manual sequencing

The correct answer is a--shotgun sequencing

A. Answer a is correct because in the shotgun sequencing strategy, random DNA fragments are sequenced and then overlapping fragments are placed into a contiguous sequence.

The correct answer is a…

B. Answer b is incorrect because a contig is constructed by assembling overlapping sequences; the contig itself is only derived following sequence analysis.

The correct answer is a…
C. Answer c is incorrect because in this sequencing strategy clones that are known to overlap based on physical mapping are selected for sequencing in order.

The correct answer is a…
D. Answer d is incorrect because manual sequencing involves performing individual sequencing reactions without the aid of an automated sequencer to separate the DNA fragments into the correct order.

4). Knowing the sequence of an entire genome
  a). completes our understanding of every gene's function in the organism.
  b). allows us to predict the genetic cause of every disease in the organism.
  c). provides a template for constructing an artificial life-form.
  d). provides the raw data that can then be used to identify specific genes.

The correct answer is d…
A. Answer a is incorrect because simply knowing the sequence of a gene does not lead to a conclusive understanding of the function of the gene. At the very most, sequence analysis can indicate possible biochemical functions of a gene.

The correct answer is d…
B. Answer b is incorrect because identifying the genetic cause of a disease involves very specific genetic analysis in individuals who are affected by the disease; this analysis can sometimes identify the gene affected in these individuals, but is still not guaranteed!

The correct answer is d…
C. Answer c is incorrect because it is impossible to know what portions of a genome function in an organism at any given time, let alone how different genes interact during the development of an organism.

The correct answer is d--provides the raw data that can then be used to identify specific genes.
D. Answer d is correct because analyzing the sequence of a genome for long open reading frames can help to identify protein-coding genes. It is terribly ambitious, however, to identify every gene because there are some genes with very small open reading frames, or no open reading frames at all.

5). If you were to look at the sequence of an entire chromosome, how could you identify which segments might contain a gene?
  a). You could identify large protein-coding regions (open reading frames).
  b). You could look for a match with an expressed sequence tag (EST).
  c). You could look for consensus regulatory sequences that could initiate transcription.
  d). All of these strategies could be used to identify possible genes.
  e). It is impossible to predict genes from sequence data alone.

The correct answer is d…
A. Answer a is incorrect because while many genes encode proteins, this is not the only answer. This requires a large open reading frame. One difficulty with this analysis in genomic DNA, however, is that open reading frames can be interrupted by intron sequences and therefore might be overlooked.

The correct answer is d…
B. Answer b is incorrect because while ESTs are identified by sequencing small regions of complementary DNA (cDNA), this is not the only answer. cDNA is made from mRNA and therefore represents expressed sequences from a given tissue.

The correct answer is d...
C. Answer c is incorrect because while identifying regulatory sequences can identify possible transcription start sites that would lead to expression of a gene, this is not the only answer. This too, is risky because some regulatory-like sequences are not associated with genes at all.

The correct answer is d--All of these strategies could be used to identify possible genes.
D. Answer d is correct because often multiple prediction methods are used to predict the presence of a gene because using only a single prediction method would be very prone to errors.

The correct answer is d...
E. Answer e is incorrect because there are many gene prediction strategies used to analyze genomic DNA for the presence of putative genes.

6). You have been hired to characterize the genome of a novel organism, *Undergraduatus genomicus*. After fully sequencing the 10^6 base-pairs in the genome, you predict that this organism has approximately 10,000 genes. You have a collaborator on this project, however, who has identified 20,000 different expressed sequence tags from this organism. How can you resolve this conflict?
  a). You suggest that your collaborator is an idiot who counted every gene twice!
  b). You suggest that your collaborator may have identified multiple isoforms of the same gene that could arise by alternative splicing.
  c). You fear that you may have underestimated the number of genes, because you forgot that the organism is diploid and you did not count both copies of every gene in your total.
  d). You only identified genes with open reading frames, but most genes do not encode proteins, so your number will be low.

The correct answer is b...
A. Answer a is incorrect because you only collaborate with very talented scientists!!!

The correct answer is b--You suggest that your collaborator may have identified multiple isoforms of the same gene that could arise by alternative splicing.
B. Answer b is correct because ESTs are identified by sequencing small regions of complementary DNA (cDNA). cDNA is made from mRNA and therefore represents expressed sequences from a given tissue.

The correct answer is b...
C. Answer c is incorrect because homologous chromosomes have the same number of genes so would not add to the total number of genes.

The correct answer is b...
D. Answer d is incorrect because while there are non–protein coding genes, most do encode a protein product.

7). In addition to coding sequences, our genome contains
  a). noncoding DNA within genes (i.e., introns).
  b). structural DNA involved in telomeres and centromeres.
  c). simple repetitive DNA.
  d). DNA from transposable elements that have jumped around in the genome.
  e). All of these are present in genomic DNA.

The correct answer is e...
A. Answer a is incorrect because while class II eukaryotic genes often have intron sequences that are removed from the mature mRNA, this is not the only answer.

The correct answer is e…
B. Answer b is incorrect because while there are characteristic DNA sequences that are present at the centromeres and the telomeres of eukaryotic chromosomes, this is not the only answer.

The correct answer is e…
C. Answer c is incorrect because while there are several classes of repetitive DNA in the genome, this is not the only answer.

The correct answer is e…
D. Answer d is incorrect because while there are transposable elements that have moved throughout the genomes of many organisms, this is not the only answer.

The correct answer is e--All of these are present in genomic DNA.
E. Answer e is correct. Our genome contains noncoding DNA with genes (i.e., introns), structural DNA involved in telomeres and centromeres, simple repetitive DNA, and DNA from transposable elements that have jumped around in the genome.

8). Natural variation in the length of tandem repeat sequences (VNTRs) found in the genome can be used to identify individual people by their DNA fingerprint. Why is this possible?
   a). The statement is not true; such variability prevents this from being a useful identification tool.
   b). The changes in repeat length change the DNA synthesis pattern, so the cell cycles have different lengths, making the cells of different people different sizes.
   c). The changes in repeat length occur very infrequently, so there is only one pattern that everybody shares.
   d). The changes in repeat length occur very frequently, so everybody has a unique pattern of different lengths when several repeats are examined.

The correct answer is d…
A. Answer a is incorrect because subtle changes in chromatin structure between individuals is very important in distinguishing each person's DNA fingerprint.

The correct answer is d…
B. Answer b is incorrect because once DNA synthesis begins, it is not affected by the number of tandem repeats; the overall amount of DNA is not significantly different in individuals from one species, so DNA replication will not take longer in one individual than another

The correct answer is d…
C. Answer c is incorrect because VNTRs occur quite frequently and therefore are very useful in identifying an individual's unique DNA restriction fragment length pattern.

The correct answer is d--The changes in repeat length occur very frequently, so everybody has a unique pattern of different lengths when several repeats are examined.
D. Answer d is correct because VNTRs occur quite frequently and therefore are very useful in identifying an individual's unique DNA restriction fragment length pattern.

Test Your Visual Understanding

1). From the information given in the above diagram, construct a contig map of the region presented.
Answer: Review figure 17.3. Your completed contig map should match that shown in Step 3 of figure 17.3.

Apply Your Knowledge

1). Every cell in your body contains the same genomic DNA, yet the proteome of different tissues is unique. How can you explain this?
Answer: The proteome is comprised of the proteins present in any given cell at a specific time.

2). Chromosomes are much like interstate highways. Develop this analogy by assigning a chromosomal counterpart to the following:
        a). the beginning and end of a particular highway
        b). towns along the highway
        c). stretches of highway that pass through wilderness
Answer:
        2a). These are analogous to the telomeres.
        2b). These are analogous to genes.
        2c). These are analogous to the intervening regions of DNA between genes.

3). If you are given a sample of DNA from an unknown organism, how could you determine the origin of the DNA sample?
Answer: Comparing the sequence from the unknown organism with sequences deposited in public sequence databases will allow you to identify likely relatives based on the degree of sequence identity.

Inquiry Questions
None for this chapter.

Self Test

1). Prokaryotes and eukaryotes use several methods to regulate gene expression, but the most common method is
        a). translational control.
        b). transcriptional control.
        c). posttranscriptional control.
        d). control of mRNA passage from the nucleus.

The correct answer is b...
A. Answer a is incorrect because although some genes are regulated by blocking the translation of the mRNA, this is not the most common method of control.

The correct answer is b--transcriptional control.
B. Gene expression is regulated at several levels but the first level, that of transcription, is the most common level in which control is administered. From an energy use standpoint this makes sense, why put the energy into making the transcript only to later block its translation.

The correct answer is b...
C. Answer c is incorrect because posttranscriptional control is any control of gene expression after the primary transcript has been made. This could be blocking the splicing of eukaryotic mRNA, the transport of the mRNA out of the nucleus, or blocking translation of the mRNA. While all of these methods occur, none of them are the most common.

The correct answer is b...
D. Answer d is incorrect because blocking or permitting the passage of the mRNA out of the nucleus is a site of gene regulation, but the most common method occurs before the mRNA is transcribed.

Hint: Gene expression can be regulated at many levels. By far the most common form of regulation in both bacteria and eukaryotes is transcriptional control, that is, control of the transcription of particular genes by RNA polymerase. Other less common forms of control occur after transcription, influencing the mRNA that is produced from the genes or the activity of the proteins encoded by the mRNA.

2). The two protein subunits of the leucine zipper are held together
        a). in the shape of a Y.
        b). by the interaction of leucine amino acids.
        c). by hydrophobic interactions.
        d). All of these are correct.

The correct answer is d...
A. Answer a is incorrect because although the subunits are held together in such a way that they form a Y shape, this isn't the only correct answer.

The correct answer is d...
B. Answer b is incorrect because although the subunits are held together by the interactions of leucine amino acids located on both subunits, this isn't the only correct answer.

The correct answer is d...
C. Answer c is incorrect because although the subunits are held together by hydrophobic interactions between hydrophobic amino acids, this isn't the only correct answer.

The correct answer is d--All of these are correct.
D. Regulatory proteins that contain the leucine zipper motif contain at least two protein subunits. Each subunit contains a cluster of hydrophobic amino acids, usually leucine that hold the subunits together by hydrophobic interactions. The interaction of the subunits arranges the subunits in the shape of a Y.

Hint: Another DNA-binding motif uses two different protein subunits to create a single DNA-binding site. This motif is created where a region on one of the subunits containing several hydrophobic amino acids (usually leucine) interacts with a similar region on the other subunit. This interaction holds the two subunits together at these regions, while the rest of the subunits are separated. Called a leucine zipper, this structure has the shape of a Y.

3). The helix-turn-helix motif contains two helical segments, and in order for the motif to bind DNA, the _____ fits into the major groove of the DNA.
      a). homeodomain
      b). recognition helix
      c). zinc finger
      d). leucine zipper

The correct answer is b...
A. Answer a is incorrect because the homeodomain is a segment of a regulatory protein that is associated with genes that control development and while the homeodomain contains a helix-turn-helix motif as its DNA-binding site, it is not part of that motif.

The correct answer is b--recognition helix
B. In the helix-turn-helix motif the two helical segments are arranged at right angles to each other such that one helical segment butts up against one of the strands of DNA while the other fits snuggly in the major groove. The helical segment that fits in the major groove is called the recognition helix.

The correct answer is b...
C. Answer c is incorrect because a zinc finger is a DNA-binding motif and therefore is not part of the helix-turn-helix motif.

The correct answer is b...
D. Answer d is incorrect because a leucine zipper is a DNA-binding motif and therefore is not part of the helix-turn-helix motif.

Hint: A close look at the structure of a helix-turn-helix motif reveals how proteins containing such motifs are able to interact with the major groove of DNA. Interactions between the helical segments of the motif hold them at roughly right angles to each other. When this motif is pressed against DNA, one of the helical segments (called the recognition helix) fits snugly in the major groove of the DNA molecule, while the other butts up against the outside of the DNA molecule, helping to ensure the proper positioning of the recognition helix.

4). A(n) _____ is a piece of DNA with a group of genes that are transcribed together as a unit.
      a). promoter
      b). repressor
      c). operator
      d). operon

The correct answer is d...
A. Answer a is incorrect because a promoter is the area on the DNA where the RNA polymerase binds and where transcription begins. It is not a group of genes.

The correct answer is d...
B. Answer b is incorrect because a repressor is a protein that binds to a site on the DNA called an operator and blocks the binding of RNA polymerase. It is not a group of genes.

The correct answer is d...
C. Answer c is incorrect because an operator is an area on the DNA, adjacent to the promoter, that binds a repressor. If the repressor is bound to the operator site, RNA polymerase cannot bind to the promoter and transcription is blocked.

The correct answer is d--operon
D. An operon is a group of structural genes that are located adjacent to each other on the prokaryotic genome and are transcribed together as a unit. The same gene regulators control all of the genes.

Hint: The bacterium *Escherichia coli* uses proteins encoded by a cluster of five genes to manufacture the amino acid tryptophan. All five genes are transcribed together as a unit called an operon, producing a single, long piece of mRNA. RNA polymerase binds to a promoter located at the beginning of the first gene, and then proceeds down the DNA, transcribing the genes one after another.

5). What effect would the addition of lactose have on a repressed *lac* operon?
　　　　a). The operator site on the operon would move.
　　　　b). It would reinforce the repression of that gene.
　　　　c). The *lac* operon would be transcribed.
　　　　d). It would have no effect whatsoever.

The correct answer is c...
A. Answer a is incorrect because the operator site is a segment of the DNA and so the operator site is not capable of moving. The operator site would remain in place with the addition of lactose.

The correct answer is c...
B. Answer b is incorrect because the lactose molecule would bind to the repressor and would cause the repressor to disassociate from the operator site. Without a bound repressor protein, the promoter site would be available for the binding of RNA polymerase and the operon would no long be repressed.

The correct answer is c--The *lac* operon would be transcribed.
C. The *lac* operon encodes genes that are needed for the transport and breakdown of the sugar lactose. If lactose is present, the *lac* operon becomes active (by removing a repressor) so that the genes necessary for the metabolism of lactose can be transcribed.

The correct answer is c...
D. Answer d is incorrect because the presence of lactose activates the genes that are necessary to transport and breakdown lactose, therefore the addition of lactose would affect the cell by activating the transcription of the *lac* operon.

Hint: By combining ON and OFF switches, bacteria can create sophisticated transcriptional control systems. A particularly well-studied example is the *lac* operon of *E. coli*. This operon is responsible for producing three proteins that import the disaccharide lactose into the cell and break it down into two monosaccharides: glucose and galactose.

6). A type of DNA sequence that is located far from a gene but can promote its expression is a(n)
    a). promoter.
    b). activator.
    c). enhancer.
    d). TATA box.

The correct answer is c...
A. Answer a is incorrect because a promoter is the DNA sequence to which RNA polymerase binds and begins transcription, it does not make the gene more accessible.

The correct answer is c...
B. Answer b is incorrect because an activator is a protein, not a DNA sequence, that binds to an enhancer region on the DNA and brings the enhancer segment closer to the promoter that increases gene expression.

The correct answer is c--enhancer.
C. An enhancer is a segment of DNA that regulates the expression of a gene that may be hundreds or thousands of nucleotides away. An activator protein binds to the enhancer and brings the enhancer into proximity of the promoter by looping the DNA. When the enhancer is brought closer to the transcription complex, gene expression is increased.

The correct answer is c...
D. Answer d is incorrect because the TATA box is a DNA sequence that appears upstream from the transcription site and is the site where the transcription factor first binds.

Hint: The great advantage of this modular design is that it uncouples regulation from DNA binding, allowing a regulatory protein to bind to a specific DNA sequence at one site on a chromosome and exert its regulation over a promoter at another site, which may be thousands of nucleotides away. The distant sites where these regulatory proteins bind are called enhancers.

7). Which of the following is *not* found in a eukaryotic transcription complex?
    a). activator
    b). RNA
    c). enhancer
    d). TATA-binding protein

The correct answer is b...
A. Answer a is incorrect because activators are found in a human transcription complex. The activator is a protein that binds to an enhancer sequence on the DNA and helps position the RNA polymerase.

The correct answer is b--RNA
B. RNA is not part of any transcription complex. A transcription complex is formed by the association of four different kinds of proteins that position the RNA polymerase for transcription. RNA is the result of transcription, not part of the "machinery" that makes it.

The correct answer is b...
C. Answer c is incorrect because enhancers are found in a human transcription complex. The enhancer is a DNA sequence that binds a regulatory protein that exerts an effect on the promoter.

The correct answer is b...
D. Answer d is incorrect because the TATA-binding protein is found in a human transcription complex. The TATA-binding protein binds to the TATA sequence about 25 nucleotides upstream of the promoter and helps to position the RNA polymerase on the promoter.

Hint: The transcription complex that positions the RNA polymerase at the beginning of a gene is composed of four kinds of proteins. The activator binds to an enhancer sequence, the repressor binds to a silencer sequence, the TATA-binding protein binds to the TATA sequence, and the coactivators hold the different transcription proteins together to form the complex.

8). DNA methylation of genes
        a). inhibits transcription by blocking the base-pairing between methylated cytosine and guanine.
        b). inhibits transcription by blocking the base-pairing between uracil and adenine.
        c). prevents transcription by blocking the TATA sequence.
        d). makes sure that genes that are turned off remain turned off.

The correct answer is d...
A. Answer a is incorrect because the methylation of cytosine to forms 5-methylcytosine has no effect the ability of it to base pair with guanine.

The correct answer is d...
B. Answer b is incorrect because DNA methylation results from the addition of a methyl group to cytosine and therefore is not involved in the base pairing of uracil and adenine.

The correct answer is d...
C. Answer c is incorrect because DNA methylation results from the addition of a methyl group to cytosine and therefore would not affect the TATA sequence that is composed of thymine and adenine.

The correct answer is d--makes sure that genes that are turned off remain turned off.
D. Many inactive mammalian genes are methylated (a methyl group has been added to cytosine producing 5-methylcytosine) and it was once thought that methylation inactivated the genes. It is now believed that inactivated genes are methylated as a means of assuring that inactivated genes remain turned off.

Hint: Methylation is now viewed as blocking accidental transcription of "turned-off" genes. Vertebrate cells apparently possess a protein that binds to clusters of 5-methylcytosine, preventing transcriptional activators from gaining access to the DNA. DNA methylation in vertebrates thus ensures that once a gene is turned off, it stays off.

9). Which of the following are *not* matched correctly?
        a). RNA splicing—occurs in the nucleus
        b). snRNP—splicing out exons from the transcript
        c). poly-A tail—increased transcript stability
        d). All are matched correctly.

The correct answer is b...
A. Answer a is incorrect because this is matched correctly; RNA splicing does occur in the nucleus. The proteins involved in RNA splicing are present in the nucleus and a transcript cannot leave the nucleus until all splicing enzymes have dissociated from the transcript.

The correct answer is b--snRNP—splicing out exons from the transcript
B. snRNP are proteins in the nucleus that splice out introns from the transcript, not exons. Introns are noncoding regions of the DNA and are spliced out before translation.

The correct answer is b...
C. Answer c is incorrect because this is matched correctly; the poly-A tail does increase the stability of the transcript. mRNA molecules that have a longer half-life also have a stable poly-A tail and mRNA molecules, which have less stable poly-A tail sequences, tend to be degraded more quickly.

The correct answer is b...
D. Answer d is incorrect because not all of the answer options are correctly matched. Answer b is incorrectly matched.

Hint: Before the primary transcript is translated, the introns, which comprise on average 90% of the transcript, are removed in a process called RNA processing or RNA splicing. Particles called small nuclear ribonucleoproteins, or snRNPs are though to play a role in RNA splicing.

10). Which of the following is *not* a method of posttranscriptional control in eukaryotic cells?
    a). processing the transcript
    b). selecting the mRNA molecules that are translated
    c). digesting the DNA immediately after translation
    d). selectively degrading the mRNA transcripts

The correct answer is c...
A. Answer a is incorrect because processing the transcript is a method of posttranscriptional control. The transcript is processed by the splicing out of introns and the addition of CAP and poly-A tail segments. These processing steps occur in the nucleus.

The correct answer is c...
B. Answer b is incorrect because selecting the mRNA molecules for translation is a method of posttranscriptional control. Either the selection of a transcript by the association of translation factors or the rejection of a transcript by the association of translation repressor proteins are methods of selecting the mRNA transcripts that will be translated.

The correct answer is c--digesting the DNA immediately after translation.
C. The DNA is never digested. The mRNA may be digested after translation but never the DNA.

The correct answer is c...
D. Answer d is incorrect because the selective degradation of mRNA transcripts is a method of posttranscriptional control. The stability of the mRNA transcript determines how long it will remain active in the cell, able to be translated. The faster the mRNA is degraded, the less likely it will be translated more than once.

Hint: There are several different levels where gene expression can be controlled in eukaryotes: initiation of transcription, RNA splicing, mRNA passage through the nuclear membrane, destruction of the transcript, translation, posttranslational modification.

Test Your Visual Understanding

1). Match the following descriptions with the appropriate lettered panels in the figure, and explain what would be needed to activate the operon if it is not activated.
    i). Operon is OFF because *lac* repressor is bound.
    ii). Operon is OFF because CAP is not bound.
    iii). Operon is ON because CAP is bound and *lac* repressor is not.
    iv). Operon is OFF both because *lac* repressor is bound and CAP is not.
Answer:
    (a)--ii). Operon is OFF because CAP is not bound.
    The repressor is not blocking the operator, so to activate the operon the CAP must be bound to the CAP-binding site
    (b)--iv). Operon is OFF both because *lac* repressor is bound and CAP is not.
    In order for the operon to be active the repressor cannot be bound to the operator because it blocks the RNA-polymerase binding site. Also, the CAP must be bound to help in exposing the RNA-polymerase binding site. Therefore, to activate this operon, the repressor must be removed with lactose and the CAP must be bound due to low glucose levels.

(c)--i). Operon is OFF because *lac* repressor is bound.
The CAP is bound to its binding site but the repressor is also bound at the operator site. Therefore, to activate this operon, the repressor must be removed with lactose.
(d)--iii). Operon is ON because CAP is bound and *lac* repressor is not.
This operon is activated because low glucose levels allows the CAP to bind to its site, helping expose the RNA-polymerase binding site and also the presence of lactose keeps the repressor from binding to the operator site.

Apply Your Knowledge

1). A method of posttranscriptional control is the selective degradation of mRNA transcripts. A transcript encoding a growth factor contains the terminal sequence of AAGCUUGAAU and has a half-life of 40 minutes. Another transcript that encodes an immunoglobin has a terminal sequence of GGAUCGCCAGG and has a half-life of about 2 hours. The half-life is related to the rate of degradation by the equation: $t_{1/2} = 0.693/K$, where $t_{1/2}$ is the half-life, and K is the rate of degradation. Compare the degradation rates of the two transcripts.
Answer:
The degradation rate of the growth factor transcript is:
40 min. = $0.693/K$ or $K = 0.693/40$
$K = 0.0173$ per minute

The degradation rate of the immunoglobin transcript is:
120 min. = $0.693.K$ or $K = 0.693/120$
$K = 0.00578$ per minute

2). All human beings have a rich growth of *E. coli* bacteria in their large intestine. Will the *lac* operon in the bacteria present in a lactose-intolerant individual who is careful never to consume anything with lactose (milk sugar) be activated or repressed? Explain.
Answer: The *lac* operon will not be needed if there is no lactose and so it will be repressed. The *E. coli* bacteria don't need lactose to survive. They use lactose as a source of glucose. If there is no lactose present in the intestine but an alternate source of glucose, the bacteria will survive on the alternate glucose source.

FIGURE 19.22
Gompertz curves. While human populations may differ 25-fold in their mortality rates before puberty, the slopes of their Gompertz curves are about the same in later years.
How do you explain this difference?

Answer: The differences in mortality rates between the different populations are due primarily to the effects of improved nutrition, living conditions, and advances in health care on mortality before puberty. Once a person, any person, passes puberty, his or her likelihood of death is not so markedly influenced by these improvements.

FIGURE 19.23
Hayflick's experiment. Fibroblast cells stop growing after about 50 doublings. Growth is rapid in phases I and II, but slows in phase III, as the culture become senescent, until the final doubling. Cancer cells, by contrast, do not "age."
How do cancer cells overcome this 50-division "Hayflick limit"?

Answer: Cancer cells are able to overcome the Hayflick limit because of mutations disabling the genes that normally act to repress the production of telomerase, an enzyme that adds to telomeres so that their length is not reduced as the cell line proliferates. If their telomeres do not shorten, the cells will keep dividing long after 50 divisions.

Self Test

1). Which of the following series of events represents the path of vertebrate development?
   a). formation of blastula, cleavage, neurulation, cell migration, gastrulation, organogenesis, growth
   b). formation of blastula, cleavage, gastrulation, neurulation, cell migration, organogenesis, growth
   c). cleavage, formation of blastula, gastrulation, neurulation, cell migration, organogenesis, growth
   d). cleavage, gastrulation, formation of blastula, neurulation, cell migration, organogenesis, growth

The correct answer is c...
A. Answer a is incorrect because cleavage occurs before the formation of blastula and gastrulation occurs before neurulation.

The correct answer is c...
B. Answer b is incorrect because cleavage occurs before the formation of blastula.

The correct answer is c--cleavage, formation of blastula, gastrulation, neurulation, cell migration, organogenesis, growth
C. Vertebrates develop in a highly organized and predictable fashion.

The correct answer is c...
D. Answer d is incorrect because gastrulation after formation of blastula.

2). Which of the following statements about *Drosophila* development is FALSE?
   a). *Drosophila* go through four larval instar stages before undergoing metamorphosis.
   b). During the syncytial blastoderm stage, nuclei line up along the surface of the egg.
   c). Imaginal discs are groups of cells set aside that will give rise to key parts of the adult fly.
   d). Maternal, rather than zygotic, genes govern early *Drosophila* development.

The correct answer is a--*Drosophila* go through four larval instar stages before undergoing metamorphosis.
A. *Drosophila* have only three larval instar stages.

The correct answer is a...
B. Answer b is incorrect because all of the nuclei within a syncytial blastoderm space themselves evenly and line up along the inside surface. Cells are formed as membranes grow between the nuclei.

The correct answer is a...
C. Answer c is incorrect because while imaginal discs formed during larval development, they do not play a role in the life of a larva. Rather, the imaginal discs are committed to from specific parts of the adult fly.

The correct answer is a...
D. Answer d is incorrect because maternal mRNAs are loaded by the mother into the unfertilized egg. As the egg divides, maternal mRNAs are distributed unevenly into different daughter cells. It is the maternal mRNAs that determine the initial events of development.

3). If a plant embryo failed to form enough ground tissue, what function(s) would likely be directly affected in the corresponding mature plant?
      a). seed formation
      b). meristem development
      c). cotyledon formation
      d). food and water storage

The correct answer is d...
A. Answer a is Incorrect because, while seed formation may be indirectly affected by inadequate food and water, the primary defect would be in food and water storage.

The correct answer is d...
B. Answer b is incorrect because, while meristem development may be indirectly affected by inadequate food and water, the primary defect would be in food and water storage.

The correct answer is d...
C. Answer c is incorrect because, while cotyledon formation may be indirectly affected by inadequate food and water, the primary defect would be in food and water storage.

The correct answer is d--food and water storage
D. The majority of the embryonic interior consists of ground tissue cells that eventually function in food and water storage. If the amount of ground tissue were inadequate, the plant would likely be unable to store enough food and water.

4). *C. elegans* is a powerful developmental model because
      a). these nematodes are very small, so it is easy to maintain a large population in a laboratory.
      b). the fate of every cell has been mapped.
      c). the fate of cells that will become eggs and sperm are predetermined.
      d). these nematodes have the same amount of DNA as *Drosophila*.

The correct answer is b...
A. Answer a is incorrect because, while *C. elegans* are small, this fact is not the primary reason they have become a model for development.

The correct answer is b--the fate of every cell has been mapped.
B. The fate of every cell in *C. elegans* has been determined from the single egg cell. This information is extremely using in study cell fate and therefore this organism has become a powerful developmental model.

The correct answer is b...
C. Answer c is incorrect because the fate of cells that will become eggs and sperm is not predetermined.

The correct answer is b...
D. Answer d is incorrect because, while it is true that these nematodes have the same amount of DNA as *Drosophila*, it is not the reason *C. elegans* is a powerful developmental model.

5). Which of the following best describes a morphogen?
      a). a cell that secretes diffusible signaling molecules that play a role in specifying cell fate
      b). a diffusible signaling molecule that plays a role in specifying cell fate
      c). a protein that helps mediate direct cell–cell interaction
      d). a protein that enables cells to become totipotent

The correct answer is b...
A. Answer a is incorrect because morphogens are not cells. Rather, morphogens are diffusible signaling molecules that play a role in specifying cell fate.

The correct answer is b--a diffusible signaling molecule that plays a role in specifying cell fate
B. Morphogens often form concentration gradients. Varying concentrations of these signaling molecules induces different cell fates.

The correct answer is b...
C. Answer c is incorrect because morphogens do not directly mediate cell–cell interactions. However because morphogens influence cell fate, they may indirectly lead to particular cell–cell interactions or communications.

The correct answer is b...
D. Answer d is incorrect because totipotent cells are potentially capable of expressing all of the genes of their genome. Thus, these cells are capable of acquiring any possible cell fate of the organism from which they arose. By comparison, morphogens are involved in specifying cell fate.

6). What would happen as a result of a transplantation experiment in a chick embryo in which cells determined to become a forelimb were replaced by some cells determined to become a hindlimb?
      a). A hindlimb would form in the region where the forelimb should be.
      b). A forelimb would form in the region where the hindlimb should be.
      c). Nothing; the forelimb would form normally.
      d). Neither a forelimb nor a hindlimb would form because the cells were already determined.

The correct answer is a--A hindlimb would form in the region where the forelimb should be.
A. The new cells would form a hindlimb because their fate had already been determined.

The correct answer is a...
B. Answer b is incorrect because a forelimb would not form. The cells determined to become a forelimb were removed.

The correct answer is a...
C. Answer c is incorrect because a forelimb would not form. The cells determined to become a forelimb were removed.

The correct answer is a...
D. Answer d is incorrect because the determined cells would form a hindlimb in the region where the forelimb should be.

7). Which group of genes, identified by Nusslein-Volhard and Caroll, is responsible for the final stages of segmentation in *Drosophila* embryos?
        a). morphogen gradient genes
        b). gap genes
        c). segment-polarity genes
        d). pair-rule genes

The correct answer is c...
A. Answer a is incorrect because although morphogens are involved in establishing polarity at various stages of embryonic development, morphogen gradient genes are not an official group of genes.

The correct answer is c...
B. Answer b is incorrect because gap genes are involved in the early stages of segmentation.

The correct answer is c--segment-polarity genes
C. This group of genes divides seven regions of the *Drosophila* embryo into 14 segments. It is the final stage of segmentation.

The correct answer is c...
D. Answer d is incorrect because pair-rule genes are involved in the middle stages of segmentation when large blocks of the embryo are divided into seven regions.

8). Suppose that during a mutagenesis screen to isolate mutations in *Drosophila*, you came across a fly with legs growing out of its head. What gene cluster is likely affected?
        a). *Bicoid*
        b). *Hunchback*
        c). *Bithorax*
        d). *Antennapedia*

The correct answer is d...
A. Answer a is incorrect because, while the segmentation gene *Bicoid* contains a homeobox consensus sequence, a mutation in *Bicoid* would not result in the specified mutation.

The correct answer is d...
B. Answer b is incorrect because *Hunchback* is a gap gene involved in the early stages of segmentation. Mutations in *Hunchback* result in embryos that lack a thorax region, but no not affect antenna development.

The correct answer is d...
C. Answer c is incorrect because mutations in the *Bithorax* complex affect development of body parts in the thorax and abdominal regions, not the anterior regions where the antenna are located.

The correct answer is d--*Antennapedia*
D. The *Antennapedia* complex controls the development of body parts in the anterior region of the embryo.

9). What would be the likely result of a mutation of the *bcl-2* gene on the level of apoptosis?
a). no change
b). a decrease in apoptosis
c). an increase in apoptosis
d). First it would increase, but later it would decrease.

The correct answer is c...
A. Answer a is incorrect because *bcl-2* is normally involved in preventing cell death. If this gene is defective, apoptosis would not be well controlled and likely result in increased cell death.

The correct answer is c...
B. Answer b is incorrect because *bcl-2* is normally involved in preventing cell death. If this gene is defective, apoptosis would not be well controlled and likely result in increased cell death.

The correct answer is c--an increase in apoptosis
C. The *bcl-2* gene is normally involved in blocking apoptosis. Without *bcl-2*, the level of apoptosis is likely to increase.

The correct answer is c...
D. Answer d is incorrect because *bcl-2* is normally involved in preventing cell death. If this gene is defective, apoptosis would not be well controlled and likely result in increased cell death.

10). The gene clock hypothesis is best described by which of the following explanations?
a). Mutations accumulate partially through the addition of an –OH group to the base guanine.
b). Specific genes exist to promote longevity.
c). Free radicals can cause genetic mutations, particularly when we are sleeping.
d). Calorie restriction leads to an increased life span.

The correct answer is b...
A. Answer a is incorrect because, while mutations have been demonstrated to accumulate partially through the addition of an –OH group to the base guanine, this description does not match that Gene Clock hypothesis.

The correct answer is b--Specific genes exist to promote longevity.
B. A number of genes and mutations have been linked to either longevity or a shortened life span. Thus, in addition to control of development, genes appear to influence many aspects of the aging process.

The correct answer is b...
C. Answer c is incorrect because, while calorie restriction has been hypothesized to lead to increased longevity, this description does not match that Gene Clock hypothesis.

The correct answer is b...
D. Answer d is incorrect because, while free radicals can cause genetic mutations, this description does not match that Gene Clock hypothesis. Further, the effects of free radicals do not only occur during periods of sleep.

Test Your Visual Understanding

1). Hayflick's experiment revealed that noncancerous cells have a definitive life span, whereas cancer cells do not have the same restrictions. Draw in curves that represent the growth patterns of each cell type.
Answer: The curves should resemble those depicted in figure 19.23.

Apply Your Knowledge

1). You have generated a cell line that expresses an altered form of cadherin. This mutant cadherin has the 110-amino-acid extracellular domain that is required for interaction with other cadherins, but lacks a transmembrane domain. If you were to mix this cell population with other cells expressing a wild-type, or normal, form of cadherin, would you expect these two cell populations aggregate with each other? Why or why not? Would the mutant cells be able to aggregate with other mutant cells?

Answer: Although the mutant cells express the cadherin interaction domain, this altered form of the protein would not be present on the cell surface because it lacks a transmembrane domain. Therefore, the mutant cells would be unable to interact and aggregate with each other or with wild-type cells.

Self Test

1). Tumor-suppressor genes includes *p53* and *Rb*. How would a "gain-of-function" mutation likely affect the cell?
  a). The cell would divide constantly because of the loss of cell cycle repression.
  b). The cell would divide much less frequently because of the extra cell cycle repression.
  c). The cell would divide normally because these genes have no effect on cell cycle control.
  d). The cell would commit suicide by apoptosis.

The correct answer is b...
A. Answer a is incorrect because tumor-suppressor genes normally function to repress the cell cycle, so a gain of function would increase this normal activity causing excess cell cycle repression.

The correct answer is b--The cell would divide much less frequently because of the extra cell cycle repression.
B. Answer b is correct because tumor suppressor genes normally function to repress the cell cycle, so a gain of function would increase this normal activity causing excess cell cycle repression.

The correct answer is b...
C. Answer c is incorrect because tumor-suppressor genes are critical in regulating entry into the S phase of the cell cycle.

The correct answer is b...
D. Answer d is incorrect because not all tumor suppressors affect apoptosis. *p53* is involved in the decision to enter apoptosis, but this is not a general feature of this class of protein.

2). In lab, you are studying cell cycle control in the fission yeast, *S. pombe*. A student finds a new mutant that she wants to call "giant" because the cells are much larger than normal (suggesting that it is not dividing normally). What type of mutation do you think your student has isolated?
  a). a loss-of-function mutation in a tumor-suppressor gene
  b). a loss-of-function mutation in a cellular proto-oncogene
  c). a gain-of-function mutation in a tumor-suppressor gene
  d). a gain-of-function mutation in a cellular proto-oncogene
  e). Both *a* and *d* are possible.
  f). Both *b* and *c* are possible.

The correct answer is f...
A. Answer a is incorrect because losing the function of a tumor-suppressor gene would remove the repression in cell cycle control. This would result in smaller than normal cells because they would divide prematurely.

The correct answer is f...
B. Answer b is incorrect because while proto-oncogenes normally function to stimulate cell cycle progression, this is not the only answer. Losing this function would result in larger than normal cells because cell division would not occur properly.

The correct answer is f...
C. Answer c is incorrect because this is not the only answer. Tumor-suppressor genes normally function to repress the cell cycle, so a gain of function would increase this normal activity causing

excess cell cycle repression. This would delay cell division and result in cells that were larger than normal.

The correct answer is f...
D. Answer d is incorrect because proto-oncogenes normally function to stimulate cell cycle progression. A gain of function in these genes would result in premature entry into the cell cycle. This would result in smaller than normal cells because cell division would occur too often.

The correct answer is f...
E. E is incorrect because both A and D are incorrect. A is incorrect because losing the function of a tumor suppressor gene would remove the repression in cell cycle control. This would result in smaller than normal cells because they would divide prematurely. D is incorrect because protooncogenes normally function to stimulate cell cycle progression. A gain of function in these genes would result in premature entry into the cell cycle. This would result in smaller than normal cells because cell division would occur too often.

The correct answer is f...
F. F is the correct answer because both B and C are correct. B is correct because protooncogenes normally function to stimulate cell cycle progression. Losing this function would result in larger than normal cells because cell division would not occur properly. C is correct because tumor suppressor genes normally function to repress the cell cycle, so a gain of function would increase this normal activity causing excess cell cycle repression. This would delay cell division and result in cells that were larger than normal.

3). Which of the following would be an effective approach to a new cancer therapy?
   a). finding a way to stabilize *p53* specifically in tumor cells
   b). preventing nucleotide synthesis in tumor cells
   c). inactivating the HER2 receptor on tumor cells
   d). inhibiting growth of new blood vessels with endostatin
   e). All of the above would help to fight cancer.

The correct answer is e...
A. Answer a is incorrect because while *p53* activity will lead to both cell cycle arrest and sometimes programmed cell death, this is not the only answer. Therefore, stabilizing *p53* protein in tumor cells will arrest tumor cell growth.

The correct answer is e...
B. Answer b is incorrect because while nucleotides are the building blocks of DNA, this is not the only answer. If a cell cannot replicate its DNA, it cannot divide. Blocking nucleotide biosynthesis will lead to a deficiency in these building blocks that will prevent cell division. One of the first chemotherapy drugs, methotrexate, functions by inhibiting nucleotide biosynthesis.

The correct answer is e...
C. Answer c is incorrect because while HER2 is a cell surface receptor that functions in growth factor signaling, a pathway that stimulates cell division, this is not the only answer. Inactivating this receptor will prevent growth factor signaling in tumor cells and thereby slow the growth of a tumor.

The correct answer is e...
D. Answer d is incorrect because this is not the only answer. Blood vessels are critical for keeping tissue alive; blood carries oxygen and signaling molecules into tissue as well as carbon dioxide and waste products away from tissue. Without this life-giving source of blood, tumors will die.

The correct answer is e--All of the above would help to fight cancer.
E. All of the above would help to fight cancer: finding a way to stabilize *p53* specifically in tumor cells, preventing nucleotide synthesis in tumor cells, inactivating the HER2 receptor on tumor cells, and inhibiting growth of new blood vessels with endostatin.

4). How would the cell cycle be affected if you removed the phosphorylation sites in the Rb protein?

      a). The cell cycle would not be affected because pRb is not phosphorylated normally.
      b). The cell cycle would be blocked in G_1.
      c). The cell cycle would be blocked in G_2.
      d). The cell cycle would be shorter.

The correct answer is b...
A. Answer a is not correct because the phosphorylation of pRb prevents it from inhibiting the E2F transcription factor thereby stimulating genes required for entry into the synthesis phase of the cell cycle.

The correct answer is b--The cell cycle would be blocked in G_1.
B. Answer b is correct because if pRb cannot be phosphorylated, it will continue to inhibit the E2F transcription factor. Without E2F activity, the genes required for entry to the synthesis phase of the cell cycle will not be expressed.

The correct answer is b...
C. Answer c is not correct because pRb functions at the G_1/S cell cycle checkpoint. It is not involved in the entry into mitosis.

The correct answer is b...
D. Answer d is not correct because pRb functions to prevent cell cycle progression. If it cannot be phosphorylated, it will continue to repress the cell cycle making it longer than normal.

5). Embryonic stem (ES) cells are an attractive source of material for therapeutic cloning because

      a). they can be induced to assume any cell fate.
      b). ES cells are not targets for the host immune response, so tissue rejection is not an issue.
      c). there are no other sources of stem cells to use for therapeutic cloning, so ES cells are the only solution.
      d). ES cells will not work as a source of tissue for cloning.

The correct answer is a--they can be induced to assume any cell fate.
A. Answer a is correct because ES cells are totipotent; that is they are as yet undifferentiated cells. Because of this, they can be induced to assume any developmental fate without the need to "deprogram" them first.

The correct answer is a...
B. Answer b is incorrect because any foreign tissue becomes a target for the host immune response.

The correct answer is a...
C. Answer c is incorrect because there are sources of stem cells in adults. For example, stem cells are present in gonads, muscle, and nervous tissue.

The correct answer is a...
D. Answer d is incorrect because ES cells have been used as the source of material for therapeutic cloning in nonhuman models.

6). How would growing cells in the presence of methyladenosine affect the mismatch repair system?

        a). The repair system would only repair half of the errors introduced by DNA polymerase.
        b). There would be no repair of mismatched DNA.
        c). Mismatch repair would be normal, but excision repair would fail.
        d). Methyladenosine would prevent DNA replication, so there would be no need for mismatch repair.

The correct answer is a--The repair system would only repair half of the errors introduced by DNA polymerase.
A. Answer a is correct because the repair enzymes would still recognize a mismatch, but would be unable to determine which DNA strand was the parent strand, and which was the newly synthesized daughter strand. Under these conditions, the repair enzyme would randomly select a strand for repair so it would only select the correct strand half of the time.

The correct answer is a...
B. Answer b is incorrect because there would still be a mismatch in the DNA that would be recognized by the mismatch repair enzymes.

The correct answer is a...
C. Answer c is incorrect because excision repair does not use methyladenosine to mark the parental strand of DNA.

The correct answer is a...
D. Answer d is incorrect because methyladenosine can be incorporated into growing DNA strands without ill effects.

7). Too much time in a tanning booth probably causes DNA damage to epithelial cells. The most likely effect would be
        a). depurination.
        b). pyrimidine dimers.
        c). deamination.
        d). single-stranded nicks in the phosphodiester backbone.

The correct answer is b...
A. Answer a is incorrect because depurination occurs spontaneously with DNA in solution, but UV light does not have this effect.

The correct answer is b--pyrimidine dimers.
B is correct because UV light does cause adjacent pyrimidines (usually thymine) to dimerize. This disrupts DNA structure and can cause mutations.

The correct answer is b...
C is incorrect because deamination is a spontaneous mutation and often affects cytosine. When this occurs, deaminated cytosine can base-pair like thymine.

The correct answer is b...
D is incorrect because single-stranded nicks in the phosphodiester backbone do not occur as a result of UV light.

8). Using a "car and driver" analogy, which of the following accurately describes the role of tumor-suppressor genes and proto-oncogenes in normal cells?

      a). Tumor-suppressor genes are the gas pedal, while proto-oncogenes are the brakes.

      b). Tumor-suppressor genes are the brakes while proto-oncogenes are the gas.

      c). Both tumor-suppressor genes and proto-oncogenes are like the gas, but tumor-suppressors are like turbo and proto-oncogenes are like a regular carburetor.

      d). Tumor-suppressor genes are like the steering wheel, and proto-oncogenes are like the turn signals.

The correct answer is b…

A. Answer a is incorrect because tumor suppressors suppress cell cycle progression while proto-oncogenes stimulate cell cycle progression.

The correct answer is b--Tumor-suppressor genes are the brakes while proto-oncogenes are the gas.

B. Answer b is correct because tumor suppressors suppress cell cycle progression while proto-oncogenes stimulate cell cycle progression.

The correct answer is b…

C. Answer c is incorrect because tumor suppressors and proto-oncogenes have the opposite affect on cell cycle progression.

The correct answer is b…

D. Answer d is incorrect because tumor-suppressor genes do not affect the fate of cells. Some proto-oncogenes, however, do play roles in development of cell fates!

9). During the early years of cancer research, there were two schools of thought regarding the causes of cancer: 1) that cancer was caused entirely by environmental factors, and 2) that cancer was caused by genetic factors. Which was correct?

      a). #1 because we have identified many potential carcinogens

      b). #2 because we know of many proto-oncogenes

      c). #2 because we know of many tumor-suppressor genes

      d). Both were correct; most chemical carcinogens function by altering genes.

The correct answer is d…

A. Answer a is incorrect because while there are many chemicals that are known to induce mutations, this is not the only answer.

The correct answer is d…

B. Answer b is incorrect because while there are many known proto-oncogenes whose normal function is to promote cell growth and division, this is not the only answer.

The correct answer is d…

C. Answer c is incorrect because while there are many known tumor-suppressor genes whose normal function is to inhibit cell growth and division, this is not the only answer.

The correct answer is d--Both were correct; most chemical carcinogens function by altering genes.

D. Answer d is correct because all of the above are true.

10. If you found a specific chromosomal deletion in the genome from a tumor, what could be the cause of this specific cancer?

       a). The deletion likely affected a tumor-suppressor gene, leading to a loss of function in the tumor cells.

       b). The deletion likely affected a proto-oncogene, leading to a loss of function in the tumor cells.

       c). The deletion likely affected a tumor-suppressor gene, leading to a gain of function in the tumor cells.

       d). The deletion likely affected a proto-oncogene, leading to a gain of function in the tumor cells.

The correct answer is a--The deletion likely affected a tumor-suppressor gene, leading to a loss of function in the tumor cells.

A. Answer a is correct because removing a tumor-suppressor gene will release the inhibition on cell cycle progression and result in over proliferation in these cells.

The correct answer is a...

B. Answer b is incorrect because removing a proto-oncogene will result in failure of cell division since proto-oncogenes normally promote cell growth and division.

The correct answer is a...

C. Answer c is incorrect because removing a gene will not cause a gain of function.

The correct answer is a...

D. Answer d is incorrect because removing a gene will not cause a gain of function.

Test Your Visual Understanding

1). If you were to observe two bacterial cells as shown here, what would you suggest is happening?

Answer: The two bacterial cells are exchanging genetic material in a process called conjugation. One cell extends a pilus to the other, forming a bridge between the two cells. The cells are drawn close together and the DNA in the plasmid of one cell is copied and sent through the conjugation bridge to the other cell.

Apply Your Knowledge

1). The data in table 20.3 show the incidence of specific cancers following exposure to environmental carcinogens. Discuss how this type of chemical exposure leads to such a high proportion of skin and lung tumors.

Answer: The skin is the outside barrier between the body and the environment, as is the mucous membrane that lines the respiratory tract to the lungs. Because of this, chemicals in the environment come into contact with these areas first and most frequently. As a result, cells of the skin and lungs are more prone to genetic damage from these chemicals, which can lead to cancer.

2). Pretend that you are preparing for a debate about the use of embryonic stem cells for therapeutic cloning, and list three pros and cons of this technology.

Answer: There are many pros and cons that could be included in this answer. Here are but a few. The pros: 1). Using pluripotent embryonic stem cells holds the possibility of curing chronic diseases such as Parkinson disease and type I diabetes which would improve the quality of life for so many. 2). Curing these and other chronic diseases would reduce healthcare costs, both the cost of medical treatments and long-term care that many of these patients require as they age. 3). This technology would reduce the number of organ transplants that are performed each year and reduce the wait of patients on lists waiting for organ transplants. Also, would eliminate the need for organ transplant patients to use immunosuppressant drugs, which reduces rejection of transplanted tissues but also make the person susceptible to infections.

The cons: 1). This technology involves the killing of an embryo, which is deemed immoral by many. Even in therapeutic cloning that uses the nucleus of the patient (needed to reduce rejection by the body), an embryo is still formed and killed in the process. 2). Many of these chronic diseases are genetic disorders and by using the patient's nucleus, the DNA of the embryonic stem cells still carries the mutations that caused the genetic disorder and so the transplanted cells may ultimately produce the same disorder in the replaced tissue. 3). This opens the door for abuses of the technology to be carried over into reproductive cloning that is banned in most countries.

Inquiry Questions

FIGURE 21.4
The Hardy–Weinberg equilibrium. In the absence of factors that alter them, the frequencies of gametes, genotypes, and phenotypes remain constant generation after generation.
If all white cats died, what proportion of the kittens in the next generation would be white?

Answer: This question can be answered in many ways. Here's one way: with the white cats dead, the new allele frequencies would be B: $p = 0.71$ and b: $q = 0.29$. Thus, the probability of getting a white kitten, whose genotype is bb, would be $q^2 = 0.08$.

Here's another way of looking at the same question: The only way that a white kitten could be born would be if two heterozygotes mated. The proportion of heterozygotes in the population would be $0.48 / (0.48 + .036 = 0.84) = 0.57$. Thus, the probability that two heterozygotes would mate is $0.57^2 = 0.32$. The probability that a kitten would be white if its parents are both heterozygotes is 1/4. Thus, $0.32 * 0.25 = 0.08$, the frequency of white kittens in the next generation.

FIGURE 21.8
Selection to match climatic conditions. Frequency of the cold-adapted allele for lactate dehydrogenase in a type of fish (the mummichog, *Fundulus heteroclitus*) decreases at lower latitudes, which are warmer.
Why does the allele frequency change from north to south?

Answer: Mean water temperature increases with latitude. Thus, the further north, the more advantageous is the cold-adapted allele.

FIGURE 21.10
Body size and egg-laying in water striders. Larger female water striders lay more eggs per day, but also survive for a shorter period of time. As a result, intermediate-sized females produce the most offspring over the course of their entire lives and thus have the highest fitness.
What evolutionary change in body size might you expect? If the number of eggs laid per day was not affected by body size, would your prediction change?

Answer: Yes. In that case, selection on longevity would favor small individuals. In the absence of any selective pressure in the opposite direction, this directional selection would be expected to lead to the evolution of smaller body size.

FIGURE 21.11
Degree of copper tolerance in grass plants on and near ancient mine sites. Individuals with tolerant alleles have decreased growth rates on unpolluted soil. Thus, we would expect copper tolerance to be 100% on mine sites and 0% on non-mine sites. However, prevailing winds blow pollen containing nontolerant alleles onto the mine site and tolerant alleles beyond the site's borders.
Would you expect the frequency of copper tolerance to be affected by distance from the mine site? How would your answer change depending on whether you were upwind or downwind from the mine site?

Answer: The frequency of copper tolerance should decrease with distance from the mine site because the further from the mine, the less pollen from the mine will be blown in. Copper tolerance should decline with distance both up- and downwind from the mine, but, for a given distance, the frequency should be considerably lower upwind (occasionally, pollen will move in that direction due to wind shifts and other reasons).

FIGURE 21.16
Directional selection for negative phototropism in *Drosophila*. Flies that moved toward light were discarded, and only flies that moved away from light were used as parents for the next generation. This procedure was repeated for 20 generations, producing substantial evolutionary change.
What would happen if after 20 generations, experimenters started keeping flies that moved *toward* the light and discarded the others?

Answer: Evolution would change directions and the trend would be toward increased tendency to fly toward light.

FIGURE 21.17
Stabilizing selection for birth weight in human beings. The death rate among babies (*red curve; right y-axis*) is lowest at an intermediate birth weight; both smaller and larger babies have a greater tendency to die than those around the most frequent weight (*blue area; left y-axis*) of between 7 and 8 pounds.
As improved medical technology leads to decreased infant mortality rates, how would you expect the distribution of birthrates in the population to change?

Answer: If babies far from the mean (either large or small) have higher survival rates, then selection against alleles for small or large size would not be as strong, and the expected results would be a broadening of the frequency distribution of birth weight in newborns.

FIGURE 21.19
Evolutionary change in spot number. Guppies raised in low-predation or no-predation environments in laboratory greenhouses had a greater number of spots, whereas selection in more dangerous environments, such as the pools with the highly predatory pike cichlid, led to less conspicuous fish. The same results are seen in field experiments conducted in pools above and below waterfalls (*photo*).
How do these results depend on the manner by which the guppy predators locate their prey?

Answer: If predators detect fish by smell or by feeling water currents (or any other non-visual sensory mode), then brightly colored fish would not be at a selective disadvantage. Other traits (odor, ability to move without creating much disturbance in the water) would, instead, be the target of selection.

FIGURE 21.20
Selection for increased speed in racehorses is no longer effective. Kentucky Derby winning speeds have not improved significantly since 1950.
What might explain the lack of change in winning speeds?

Answer: No genetic variation exists anymore, so winning speeds cannot be increased.

Self Test

1). Which of the following is *not* an assumption of the Hardy–Weinberg equilibrium?
      a). Mating occurs preferentially.
      b). The size of the population is large.
      c). There is no migration.
      d). There are no mutations.

The correct answer is a--Mating occurs preferentially.
A. The Hardy–Weinberg equilibrium assumes that mating is random, that there are no preferences exerted when it comes to selecting a mate. To say that mating occurs preferentially is in direct opposition to this condition of the Hardy–Weinberg equilibrium.

The correct answer is a...
B. Answer b is incorrect because a large population is a condition of the Hardy–Weinberg equilibrium. Small populations affect the flow of genetic information from one generation to the next and can cause disruption of the Hardy–Weinberg equilibrium.

The correct answer is a...
C. Answer c is incorrect because no migration is a condition of the Hardy–Weinberg equilibrium. The movement of individuals into and out of populations affects the distribution of alleles in the population and can cause disruptions of the Hardy–Weinberg equilibrium.

The correct answer is a...
D. Answer d is incorrect because no mutations is a condition of the Hardy–Weinberg equilibrium. Mutations alter the genetic information and can cause disruptions of the Hardy–Weinberg equilibrium.

Hint: Hardy and Weinberg pointed out that the original proportions of the genotypes in a population will remain constant from generation to generation, as long as the following assumptions are met:
1. The population size is large.
2. Random mating is occurring.
3. No mutation takes place.
4. No genes are input from other sources (no immigration takes place).
5. No selection occurs.
Because their proportions do not change, the genotypes are said to be in Hardy–Weinberg equilibrium.

2). In a population of red (dominant allele) or white flowers, the frequency of red flowers is 91%. What is the frequency of the red allele?
a). 9%
b). 30%
c). 91%
d). 70%

The correct answer is d...
A. Answer a is incorrect because 9% is the frequency of white flowers in the population, not the frequency of the red allele.

The correct answer is d...
B. Answer b is incorrect because 30% is the frequency of the white allele in the population, not the frequency of the red allele.

The correct answer is d...
C. Answer c is incorrect because 91% is the frequency of red flowers in the population but this is not the same as the frequency of the red allele.

The correct answer is d--70%
D. The Hardy–Weinberg equilibrium can be calculated with the equation:
$(p + q)^2 = p^2 + 2pq + q^2$ such that $p + q = 1$
In this case: q^2 (the frequency of white flowers) = 9% or 0.09 and so $q = 0.3$, because $p + q = 1$ then 1 - 0.3 = 0.7, so p (the frequency of the red allele) = 0.7 or 70%.

Hint: According to the Hardy–Weinberg equilibrium the letter p designates the frequency of one allele and the letter q the frequency of the alternate allele. Because there are only two alleles, p plus q must always equal 1. The Hardy–Weinberg equation cannot be expressed in the form of what is known as a binomial expansion:

$$(p + q)^2 = p^2 + 2pq + q^2$$

If $q^2 = 0.16$, then $q = 0.4$. Therefore, p, the frequency of allele B, would be 0.6 (1.0 - 0.4 = 0.6). We can now easily calculate the genotype frequencies: $p^2 = (0.6)^2 = 0.36$ or 36% BB individuals. The heterozygous would have a frequency of $2pq$ or (2 x 0.6 x 0.4) = 0.48 or 48%.

3). Which of the following describes gene flow?
   a). random mating
   b). migration
   c). genetic drift
   d). selection

The correct answer is b...
A. Answer a is incorrect because random mating describes mating in the population with no preferences exhibited by members of the population. Random mating does not describe gene flow or the movement of alleles between populations.

The correct answer is b--migration
B. Migration is the movement of individuals from one population to another, otherwise known as gene flow. When individuals move between populations, they take their alleles with them and this can affect the frequency of alleles in the population they left, as well as the alleles in the population into which they moved.

The correct answer is b...
C. Answer c is incorrect because genetic drift is the establishment of a new population with a small number of individuals from a source population. This is not the same as moving alleles between populations by the movement of individuals, which is called gene flow. There are two types of genetic drift, the bottleneck effect and the founder effect.

The correct answer is b...
D. Answer d is incorrect because selection, the process whereby some individuals leave behind more offspring than others because their phenotype or behavior is more advantageous or preferred in the population, does not describe gene flow. Selection alters the frequencies of alleles in the population but does not describe the movement of alleles between populations, gene flow.

Hint: Gene flow is the movement of alleles from one population to another. Sometimes gene flow is obvious, as when an animal moves from one place to another. Other important kinds of gene flow are not as obvious, for example, the dispersion of pollen or seeds to into other populations.

4). Which of the following conditions is *not* needed for natural selection to occur in a population?
   a). Individuals must be able to move between populations.
   b). Variation must be genetically inherited.
   c). Certain variations allow an individual to produce more offspring that survive in the next generation.
   d). There must be variations in the phenotypes of individuals in the population.

The correct answer is a--Individuals must be able to move between populations.
A. Migration, which is the movement of individuals between populations, is an important factor for bringing variation into the population but it is *not* necessary for natural selection as long as the population already exhibits variation.

The correct answer is a...
B. Answer b is incorrect because this is a necessary condition of natural selection. In order for natural selection to occur, there must be variation and the variation must be genetically controlled. Natural selection can act on acquired characteristics, such as dyed hair, but that trait will not be passed onto the next generation. In order for natural selection to impact a population, the variation must be genetic.

The correct answer is a...
C. Answer c is incorrect because this is a necessary condition of natural selection. In fact, when people describe the process of natural selection they usually speak of the "survival of the fittest," which implies that those individuals that are endowed with certain traits survive to produce more offspring. This is the essence of natural selection.

The correct answer is a...
D. Answer d is incorrect because this is a necessary condition of natural selection. Natural selection works by favoring individuals with certain traits over individuals with alternative traits. If no variation exists, natural selection cannot operate.

Hint: As Darwin pointed out, some individuals leave behind more progeny than others, and the rate at which they do so is affected by phenotype and behavior. We describe the results of this process as selection and speak of both artificial and natural selection. For natural selection to occur and result in evolutionary change, three conditions must be met:
  1. Variation must exist among individuals in a population.
  2. Variation among individuals results in differences in number of offspring surviving in the next generation.
  3. Variation must be genetically determined.

5). Which of the following is the ultimate source of genetic variation in a population?
  a). gene flow
  b). assortive mating
  c). mutation
  d). selection

The correct answer is c...
A. Answer a is incorrect because gene flow is important for the introduction of new alleles into a population but it isn't the ultimate source of genetic variation. Gene flow doesn't create the variation; it merely moves the variation around.

The correct answer is c...
B. Answer b is incorrect because assortive mating is a form of nonrandom mating that results when phenotypically similar individuals mate, which is a type of selection. This can alter the frequencies of alleles in a population that can lead to evolutionary change but it is not a source of variation in a population.

The correct answer is c--mutation
C. While mutation can disrupt Hardy–Woinberg equilibrium, it is not a significant factor in altering allele frequencies but it is significant in introducing change into the population. Mutation is the ultimate source of genetic variation because all other factors act on the variation in the population that is introduced by mutation.

The correct answer is c...
D. Answer d is incorrect because selection is a means of altering allele frequencies in a population by making some phenotypes more prevalent in the population because they increase an individual's fitness. However, selection it is not a source for introducing new variations into a population.

Hint: Mutation from one allele to another can obviously change the proportions of particular alleles in a population but mutation rates are so low that they have little effect on the Hardy–Weinberg equilibrium. Nonetheless, mutation is the ultimate source of genetic variation and thus makes evolution possible.

6). Natural selection can be countered by which of the following?
    a). genetic drift
    b). gene flow
    c). mutation
    d). All of the above can counter natural selection in some way.

The correct answer is d...
A. Answer a is incorrect because this isn't the only correct answer. Like natural selection, genetic drift can act to eliminate variation in a population. However, genetic drift is random and can result in the elimination of favored alleles, which is opposite to what results from natural selection. But, it can also enhance the presence of a favored allele, which supports selection in the population. Therefore, genetic drift can counter the effects of natural selection in certain circumstances.

The correct answer is d...
B. Answer b is incorrect because this isn't the only correct answer. Gene flow can be either a constructive or a constraining force on natural selection. Gene flow can spread beneficial mutations that arise to other populations, thereby enhancing natural selection. However, it can also counter natural selection by consistently importing inferior alleles from other populations. Therefore, gene flow can counter the effects of natural selection in certain circumstances.

The correct answer is d...
C. Answer c is incorrect because this isn't the only correct answer. While mutation rates are rarely high enough to counter natural selection, it is possible that an environmental factor could increase the likelihood of a particular mutation reoccurring which would counter the effects of natural selection by maintaining a less favorable allele in the population.

The correct answer is d--All of the above can counter natural selection in some way.
D. While some of the factors, such as gene flow, can have a more substantial effect of countering natural selection by continually bringing unfavorable alleles into a population, genetic drift and mutations can also counter natural selection. Mutations can reintroduce new, possibly unfavorable alleles into a population, although at very low levels, and genetic drift can counter the effects of natural selection by eliminating favorable alleles from a population.

Hint: Natural selection tends to reduce variation in a population but levels of variation that are retained in a population may be determined by the relative strength of different evolutionary processes. In theory, natural selection can be countered by maintaining variability in the population with the introduction of new alleles through mutations, although mutation rates are very low. Variability can also be maintained through gene flow, with new alleles being brought into a population from another population. Natural selection can further be countered by genetic drift, where favorable alleles may be eliminated by reducing the size of the population.

7). The maintenance of the sickle cell allele in human populations in central Africa is an example of
    a). gene flow.
    b). heterozygote advantage.
    c). genetic drift.
    d). nonrandom mating.

The correct answer is b...
A. Answer a is incorrect because gene flow is the process whereby alleles move from one population to another through migration. This is not the situation with the sickle cell allele in

central Africa. The sickle cell allele is not brought in from another population, but rather is selected for through natural selection, favoring heterozygous individuals.

The correct answer is b--heterozygote advantage.
B. Individuals that are heterozygous for the sickle cell allele are usually not greatly affected by sickle cell anemia but those who are homozygous usually die as children. In most circumstances, the sickle cell allele would be eliminated from the population through natural selection. However, the sickle cell allele is maintained at significant levels in central Africa because the heterozygous condition offers a certain level of "immunity" against another fatal disease, malaria. This is called heterozygote advantage, when the heterozygous condition is favored in the population.

The correct answer is b...
C. Answer c is incorrect because genetic drift, where a new population emerges from a small number of individuals that separated from a source population, does not explain the maintenance of the sickle cell allele in central Africa.

The correct answer is b...
D. Answer d is incorrect because nonrandom mating does not explain the maintenance of the sickle cell allele in central Africa. In this case, individuals that are heterozygous for the sickle cell allele have no outward, identifiable characteristics to show that they are immune to malaria, therefore it is a phenotype that cannot be selected for through nonrandom mating.

Hint: If heterozygotes are favored over homozygotes, then natural selection actually will tend to maintain variation in the population. Such heterozygous advantage will favor individuals with copies of both alleles and will maintain both alleles in the population. The best-documented example of heterozygote advantage is sickle cell anemia.

8). What would happen in the U.S. if malaria once again became a widespread disease?
    a). Over time, the sickle cell allele would become more prevalent in the population.
    b). Many individuals in the population would die of malaria.
    c). Individuals who were heterozygous for the sickle cell allele would be less susceptible to malaria.
    d). All of these events would occur.

The correct answer is d...
A. Answer a is incorrect because while it is true that the sickle cell allele would become more prevalent in the U.S. population, just as it is in central Africa, this is not the only correct answer.

The correct answer is d...
B. Answer b is incorrect because while it is true that many individuals who are not heterozygous for the sickle cell allele would contract malaria and would die, this is not the only correct answer.

The correct answer is d...
C. Answer c is incorrect because while it is true that the few individuals in the U.S. that are heterozygous for the sickle cell allele would be less susceptible to malaria just as those heterozygotes in central Africa are, this is not the only correct answer.

The correct answer is d--All of these events would occur.
D. Because similar selective pressures often result in the appearance of similar characteristics, a process called convergent evolution, it is reasonable to assume that similar selective pressures of two diseases, sickle cell anemia and malaria, will result in the same heterozygote advantage in the U.S. as it appears in central Africa.

Hint: The average incidence of the sickle cell allele in the central African population is about 0.12, far higher than that found among African Americans. Why is this? Even though most homozygous recessive individuals die before they have children, the sickle cell allele is maintained at high levels in these populations (it is selected for) because of its association with resistance to malaria in heterozygotes.

9). _____ operates to eliminate intermediate phenotypes.
    a). Directional selection
    b). Disruptive selection
    c). Stabilizing selection
    d). Random chance

The correct answer is b...
A. Answer a is incorrect because although one extreme phenotypic trait is selected for, it does not select against the intermediate phenotypes and so some individuals of intermediate phenotypes remain in the population.

The correct answer is b--Disruptive selection
B. In disruptive selection, the extreme forms of a phenotype are selected for but the intermediate phenotypes are selected against. In this particular situation, the intermediate phenotypes are eventually eliminated from the population.

The correct answer is b...
C. Answer c is incorrect because stabilizing selection actually selects for the intermediate phenotypes and the extreme phenotypes are usually eliminated from the population.

The correct answer is b...
D. Answer d is incorrect because random chance will usually not lead to the elimination of any particular phenotype. One phenotype is just as likely to be selected for or against as any other phenotype.

Hint: In some situations, selection acts to eliminate rather than to favor intermediate types. When this occurs, selection is in effect partitioning the population into two phenotypically distinct groups. This form of selection is called disruptive selection.

10). When transplanted to streams above waterfalls, guppy populations evolved more spots because
    a). predators are not present.
    b). they consumed different sources of food.
    c). spots make guppies harder to see against their background.
    d). all of the above

The correct answer is a--predators are not present.
A. Bright colored spots are a feature used in sexual selection of a mate in guppies. When under the threat of predation, brightly colored spots makes a male guppy easier to see and so there exists a balancing act between being brightly colored to attract mates but also to be nonconspicuous as to avoid predation. Pools above waterfalls lack the guppy predator, the pike cichlid and so under these conditions, a male can be more brightly colored to attract mates without the threat of being eaten. Therefore guppies that are moved to pools above waterfalls become more colorful because selection for mating is greater than selection against predation.

The correct answer is a…
B. Answer b is incorrect because although the studies didn't evaluation the food sources, the guppy is not a predator of other fish (like the pike cichlid) dependent upon a limited food source and so their diet probably isn't much different in pools above waterfalls compared to pools below waterfalls.

The correct answer is a…
C. Answer c is incorrect because the color spots actually make them more conspicuous against their backgrounds, which is why more brightly colored guppies are more prone to predation in waterfalls below the waterfall. Therefore guppies transplanted above waterfalls evolve more spots to make them more conspicuous for mating.

The correct answer is a…
D. Answer d is incorrect because only a is correct. The food sources above and below the waterfall, while not examined by researchers, probably doesn't vary much. Also spots make them more conspicuous so that they are easier to see against their background. This would be detrimental if there were predators but better for sexual selection.

Hint: In high-predation pools, guppies exhibit drab coloration. In low-predation environments, males display gaudy colors and spots that they use to court females.

Test Your Visual Understanding

1). Match the following descriptions with the correct panels in the figure.
    a). Phenotypically similar individuals mate.
    b). Individuals migrate.
    c). Space exploration expands with the settlement of a population of 100 individuals on Mars.
    d). A nuclear power plant dumps boiling water into a reservoir, killing all bacteria except those that contain a heat shock gene.

Answer:
    a)—(b) Nonrandom mating
    b)—(a) Gene flow
    c)—(c) Genetic drift
    d)—(d) Selection

Applying Your Knowledge

1). Consider a human population that is similar to the ideal Hardy–Weinberg population in that it is very large and generally random-mating. Although mutations occur, they alone do not lead to great changes in allele frequencies. However, migration occurs at relatively high levels—perhaps 1% per year. The following data describe relative numbers of individuals bearing the two alleles of the MN blood group:

	MM	MN	NN	Total
Individuals	1787	3037	1305	6129

Do these data suggest that some factor is disrupting the Hardy–Weinberg proportions of the three genotypes? What are the allele frequencies of M and N?

Answer:
The frequencies of the phenotypes are:
p^2 = 1787 / 6129 = 0.29 or 29%
q^2 = 1305 / 6129 = 0.21 or 21%
$2pq$ = 3037 / 6129 = 0.5 or 50%

Using a Punnett square you would expect a population of 25% homozygous dominant, 25% homozygous recessive, and 50% heterozygous. The frequencies found in this population are close to the expected values that would suggest that the population is in Hardy–Weinberg equilibrium.

The allele frequencies of M (p) and N (q) are:

p^2 = 0.29 so p equals the square root of 0.29 or p = 0.54
q^2 = 0.21 so q equals the square root of 0.21 or q = 0.46

According to the Hardy–Weinberg equilibrium ($p + q$) = 1 and using a Punnett square, the expected allele frequencies should be .50 for each allele and in this example: 0.54 + 0.46 = 1 This supports the conclusion that the population is in Hardy–Weinberg equilibrium such that there is no migration or selection is disrupting this equilibrium.

Inquiry Questions

FIGURE 22.3
Evidence that natural selection alters beak size in *Geospiza fortis*. (*a*) In dry years, when only large, tough seeds are available, the mean beak size increases. In wet years, when many small seeds are available, smaller beaks become more common. (*b*) Beak depth is inherited from parents to offspring.
Suppose a bird with a large bill mates with a bird with a small bill. Would the bills of the pair's offspring tend to be larger or smaller than the bills of offspring from a pair of birds with medium-sized bills?

Answer: The figure demonstrates that the beak depth of offspring can be predicted by the average beak depth of the parent's bills. Thus, one would expect the offspring to have the same beak depth if their parents' mean beak depth is the same. This is only correct if males and females do not differ in beak depth. In species for which the sexes differ (such as height in humans), then one would need to know both the depth and the sex of the parents and the calculation would be more complicated.

FIGURE 22.5
Selection against melanism. The circles indicate the frequency of melanic *Biston betularia* moths at Caldy Common in England, sampled continuously from 1959 to 1995. Diamonds indicate frequencies of melanic *B. betularia* in Michigan from 1959 to 1962 and from 1994 to 1995.
What can you conclude from the fact that the frequency of melanic moths decreased to the same degree in the two locations?

Answer: Such a parallel trend would suggest that similar processes are operating in both localities. Thus, one would conduct a study to identify similarities. In this case, both areas have experienced coincident reductions in air pollution, which most likely is the cause of the parallel evolutionary trends.

FIGURE 22.6
Artificial selection in the laboratory. In this experiment, one population of *Drosophila* was selected for low numbers of bristles and the other for high numbers. Note that not only did the means of the populations change greatly in 35 generations, but also all individuals in both experimental populations lie outside the range of the initial population.
What would happen if, within a population, both small and large individuals were allowed to breed, but middle-sized ones were not?

Answer: Assuming that small and large individuals would breed with each other, then middle-sized offspring would still be born (the result of matings between small and large flies). Nonetheless, there would also be many small and large individuals (the result of small x small and large x large matings). Thus, the frequency distribution of body sizes would be much broader than the distributions in the figures.

FIGURE 22.15
Evolutionary change in body size of horses. Lines indicate evolutionary relationships and reveal that although most change involved increases in size, some decreases also occurred.
Why might the evolutionary line leading to *Nannippus* have experienced an evolutionary decrease in body size?

Answer: This evolutionary decrease could occur for many reasons. For example, maybe *Nannippus* adapted to forested habitats and thus selection favored smaller size, as it had in the ancestral horses, before horses moved into open, grassland habitats. Another possibility is that there were many species of horses present at that time, and different sized horses ate different types of food. By evolving small size, *Nannippus* may have been able to eat a type of food not eaten by the others.

Self Test

1). Which of the following best describes the correlation between beak size and the amount of rain that fell on Daphne Major?
       a). Birds with small beaks are favored in dry years.
       b). All birds are favored equally in wet years.
       c). Birds with large beaks are favored during wet years.
       d). Birds with large beaks are favored during dry years.

The correct answer is d...
A. Answer a is incorrect because during dry years plants produce fewer small seeds, the preferred food of the ground finch, and so the finches have to survive on larger seed. Birds with larger beaks can eat the larger seeds more easily and therefore survive better in dry years.

The correct answer is d...
B. Answer b is incorrect because during wet years, the small seeds preferred by of the ground finch are more plentiful and birds with small beaks are more favored when the small seeds are abundant. Therefore, birds with smaller beaks are favored during wet years.

The correct answer is d...
C. Answer c is incorrect because during wet years, the small seeds preferred by the ground finch are more plentiful and birds with small beaks are more favored when the small seeds are abundant. Therefore, birds with smaller beaks are favored during wet years.

The correct answer is d--Birds with large beaks are favored during dry years.
D. During dry years, the plants produce fewer small seeds and so once the smaller seeds are consumed, only larger seeds are available. Birds with smaller beaks cannot crack open the larger seeds but birds with larger beaks can, therefore birds with larger beaks are favored during dry years when larger seeds are more plentiful.

Hint: The Grants found that not only did a great deal of variation in beak depth exist among members of the population, but the average beak depth changed from one year to the next in a predictable fashion. During droughts, plants produced few seeds and all available small seeds quickly were eaten, leaving large seeds as the major remaining source of food. As a result, birds with large beaks survived better because they were better able to break open these large seeds.

2). In peppered moths, the black coloration is selected when soot covers tree bark; this is a phenomena called
       a). artificial selection.
       b). convergent evolution.
       c). industrial melanism.
       d). none of these.

The correct answer is c...
A. Answer a is incorrect because artificial selection is a method whereby a certain trait can be made more pronounced in offspring by mating individuals that carry the trait. This is not the case with the peppered moths because the black coloration is selected for naturally by predation, not artificially by selected matings.

The correct answer is c...
B. Answer b is incorrect because convergent evolution is where similar traits appear in distantly related organisms that adapted in similar ways to similar environments. The selection of a dark coloration, as demonstrated with the peppered moths, could occur in other species, which might

be considered convergent evolution, but this question is only referring to the case of the peppered moth, no other cases.

The correct answer is c--industrial melanism.
C. Industrial melanism is the term given to a specific process whereby pollution, the result of expanded industrialism, causes a shift in variants within a population, from more light-colored individuals to more dark-colored individuals. The case of the peppered moths is one of several examples of industrial melanism.

The correct answer is c...
D. Answer d is incorrect because a correct answer is provided. Answer c, industrial melanism is correct.

Hint: The term industrial melanism refers to the process by which darker individuals come to predominate over lighter individuals. Dozens of other species of moths have changed in the same way as the peppered moth, in industrialized areas throughout Eurasia and North America.

3). Evolutionary change through artificial selection has been demonstrated in all but which of the following?
      a). Galápagos finches
      b). *Drosophila*
      c). corn
      d). dog breeding

The correct answer is a--Galápagos finches
A. The differences in the size and shape of the beak in Galápagos finches identified by Darwin were the result of natural selection, not artificial selection. The size and shape of the beak is determined by the type of food the bird eats and was not artificially selected for by humans.

The correct answer is a...
B. Answer b is incorrect because *Drosophila* is an organism used extensively in artificial selection experiments. Traits such as eye color, number of bristles on the body, etc. are traits that researchers were able to manipulate by crossing individuals that exhibited the desired variant.

The correct answer is a...
C. Answer c is incorrect because experiments performed on corn using artificial selection produced major changes quite quickly in the size and shape of the male and female portions of the plant.

The correct answer is a...
D. Answer d is incorrect because the breeding of dogs using artificial selection has produced the wide variety of dog breeds that exist today. In some cases, dog breeding has been very specific, breeding for traits that improve a dog's performance, such as breeding greyhound for speed and agility. Other traits that contributed to the domestication of dogs, such as a docile nature, have also resulted.

Hint: Artificial selection, imposed in laboratory experiments, agriculture, and the domestication process, has produced substantial change in almost every case in which it has been applied.

4). Darwin's examinations of fossils relied on _____ dating to determine the evolution of species.
      a). absolute
      b). carbon
      c). relative
      d). radioactive isotope

The correct answer is c...
A. Answer a is incorrect because absolute dating relies on measuring the amount of decay of naturally occurring radioactive isotopes that are present in the rocks that hold the fossils. Absolute dating is very accurate but wasn't a method used during Darwin's time.

The correct answer is c...
B. Answer b is incorrect because carbon dating is a form of absolute dating that was not used during Darwin's time. It measures the amount of decay of carbon 14, a radioactive isotope. Carbon 14 is an isotope of carbon that can be used to determine the age of substances less than 50,000 years old.

The correct answer is c--relative
C. Relative dating is a method of determining the age of a fossil by determining the age of the rock in which it was found using the relative position of the rock. Rocks in deeper strata are generally older, while rocks found nearer to the surface are younger. Relative dating provides a fairly accurate estimate of a rock's age but it isn't nearly as accurate as absolute dating using radioactive isotopes.

The correct answer is c...
D. Answer d is incorrect because radioactive isotopes are used in absolute dating which was not used during Darwin's time. Radioactive isotopes occur naturally in rock and over time, the atoms of the isotopes give up neutrons to become more stable. By measuring the amount of unstable and stable isotopes present in the rock, scientists can determine with certainty the age of the rock.

Hint: By dating the rocks in which fossils occur, we can get an accurate idea of how old the fossils are. In Darwin's day, rocks were dated by their position with respect to one another (relative dating); rocks in deeper strata are generally older. Knowing the relative positions of sedimentary rocks and the rates of erosion of different kinds of sedimentary rocks in different environments, geologists of the nineteenth century derived a fairly accurate idea of the relative ages of rocks.

5). The missing links between whales and their hoofed ancestors include
        a). *Pakicetus.*
        b). *Archaeopteryx.*
        c). *Equus.*
        d). all of these.

The correct answer is a--*Pakicetus*
A. The fossil of *Pakicetus* showed that it was a four-legged mammal that may have lived on land, also spending time in the sea, but had already evolved a whale-like skull.

The correct answer is a...
B. Answer b is incorrect because *Archaeopteryx* is believed to be the missing link between dinosaur and bird, not an ancestor of the whale.

The correct answer is a...
C. Answer c is incorrect because although *Equus* is a four-legged animal, it is the genus of current and ancestral species of horses, not an ancestor of the whale.

The correct answer is a...
D. Answer d is incorrect because only one answer is correct, answer a. Both *Archaeopteryx* and *Equus* are not ancestors of the whale. *Archaeopteryx* is believed to be the missing link between dinosaur and bird, not an ancestor of the whale. Although *Equus* is a four-legged animal, it is the genus of current and ancestral species of horses, not an ancestor of the whale.

Hint: Paleontologists continue to fill in the gaps in the fossil record. While many gaps interrupted the fossil record in Darwin's era, even then, scientists knew of the *Archaeopteryx* fossil transitional between dinosaurs and bird. Today the fossil record is far more complete. For example, recently a four-legged aquatic mammal, *Pakicetus*, was discovered that provides important insights concerning the evolution of whales and dolphins from land-living, hoofed ancestors.

6). Evolution has occurred in the horse as seen by
        a). a reduction in body size.
        b). an increase in complexity of ridges on teeth.
        c). an increase in the number of toes.
        d). all of these.

The correct answer is b...
A. Answer a is incorrect because although some branches of the horse's evolutionary tree showed a reduction in size, the overall trend has been an increase in body size.

The correct answer is b--an increase in complexity of ridges on teeth.
B. The teeth of the modern-day horse's ancestors were small and relatively simple in shape. However, as the diet of the ancestral horse changed so did the shape of the teeth. The fossil record reveals an ever-increasing complexity in the ridge patterns on molar and premolars, making the teeth better able to grind up and chew tough vegetation.

The correct answer is b...
C. Answer c is incorrect because the fossil record reveals a reduction in the number of toes, not an increase. The feet of the ancestor of the modern-day horse, *Hyracotherium*, had four toes on its front feet and three toes on its back feet. These toes were more like that of modern-day dogs and cats. The fossil record shows the transition: increase in length of the central toe, development of the bony hoof, and a reduction and loss of the other toes.

The correct answer is b...
D. Answer d is incorrect because answer b is the only correct answer. The fossil record of the evolution of the horse reveals a trend of increasing body size, not decreasing size, and a reduction in the number of toes, not an increase in the number. However, there has been an increase in the complexity of the ridge pattern on the teeth.

Hint: One of the best-studied cases in the fossil record concerns the evolution of horses. Examination of these fossils has provided a particularly well-documented case of how evolution has proceeded by adaptation to changing environments. The teeth of the horse ancestor *Hyracotherium* were small and relatively simple in shape. Through time, horse teeth have increased greatly in length and have developed a complex pattern of ridges on their molars and premolars. The effect of these changes is to produce teeth better capable of chewing tough and gritty vegetation.

7). Over time, the same bones in different vertebrates were put to different uses. This falls under the category of
        a). missing links.
        b). vestigial structures.
        c). analogous structures.
        d). homologous structures.

The correct answer is d...
A. Answer a is incorrect because missing links are organisms that create links between two different classification groups (i.e., *Archaeopteryx* as the missing link between dinosaurs and birds). Now, some missing link organisms may have similar bones to one of the groups it links but this isn't to say that the structures are the missing links.

The correct answer is d...
B. Answer b is incorrect because vestigial structures are structures or organs that have no apparent function in an organism but resemble structures that their presumed ancestors had.

The correct answer is d...
C. Answer c is incorrect because analogous structures are structures in unrelated or very distantly related organisms that look the same and serve the same function but arise from different origins (i.e., the wings of a bird and the wings of a butterfly).

The correct answer is d--homologous structures.
D. Homologous structures are structures that may look different and function different but arise from the same origins in an ancestor (i.e., the arm of a human and the wing of a bat).

Hint: As vertebrates evolved, the same bones were sometimes put to different uses. Yet the bones are still seen, their presence betraying their evolutionary past. For example, the forelimbs of vertebrates are all homologous structures, that is, structures with different appearances and functions that all derived from the same body part in the common ancestor.

8). After examining the evidence related to the evolution of hemoglobin, you might conclude that
       a). bird hemoglobin evolved prior to lamprey hemoglobin.
       b). frogs are more closely related to lampreys than to birds.
       c). evolutionary changes occur at the molecular level.
       d). only DNA can be examined for establishing evolutionary differences.

The correct answer is c...
A. Answer a is incorrect because knowing that human hemoglobin evolved most recently, the hemoglobin that is closest to human hemoglobin evolved more recently. Bird hemoglobin is closer in structure to human hemoglobin, which means it evolved after the lamprey hemoglobin, not prior to it.

The correct answer is c...
B. Answer b is incorrect because frog hemoglobin differs from bird hemoglobin in approximately 22 amino acids but differs from lamprey hemoglobin in approximately 58 amino acids. The more similar the structures of hemoglobin, the more closely related are the organisms, therefore frogs are more closely related to birds than they are to lampreys.

The correct answer is c--evolutionary changes occur at the molecular level.
C. This makes sense when you consider that genetics underlies evolutionary changes. For species to adapt to changes in their environments, they must first experience changes at the molecular level. Genes are altered which in turn alter proteins. These proteins may ultimately evolve different functions.

The correct answer is c...
D. Answer d is incorrect because evolution can be established by examining proteins as well as DNA.

Hint: Traces of our evolutionary past are also evident at the molecular level. When an ancestral species gives rise to two or more descendants, those descendants will initially exhibit fairly high overall similarity in their DNA. However, as the descendants evolve independently, they will accumulate more and more differences in their DNA. Consequently, organisms that are more distantly related would be expected to accumulate a greater number of evolutionary differences, whereas two species that are more closely related should share a greater portion of their DNA.

9). An example of convergent evolution is
        a). Australian marsupials and placental mammals.
        b). the flippers in fish, penguins, and dolphins.
        c). the wings in birds, bats, and insects.
        d). all of these.

The correct answer is d...
A. Answer a is incorrect because although the development of similar characteristics in Australian marsupials and placental mammals is an example of convergent evolution, this is not the only example provided.

The correct answer is d...
B. Answer b is incorrect because although the development of flippers in fish, penguins, and dolphins is an example of convergent evolution, this is not the only example provided.

The correct answer is d...
C. Answer c is incorrect because although the development of wings in birds, bats, and insects is an example of convergent evolution, this is not the only example provided.

The correct answer is d--all of these.
D. Convergent evolution can be viewed as two different species adapting to similar environments in similar ways. All of the examples listed exhibit parallel evolutionary adaptations in similar environments.

Hint: Different geographical areas sometimes exhibit groups of plants and animals of strikingly similar appearance, even though the organisms may be only distantly related. It is difficult to explain so many similarities as the result of coincidence. Instead, natural selection appears to have favored parallel evolutionary adaptations in similar environments. Because selection in these instances has tended to favor change that made the two groups more alike, their phenotypes have converged. This form of evolutionary change is referred to as convergent evolution.

10). The shape of the beaks of Darwin's finches, industrial melanism, and the changes in horse teeth are all examples of
        a). artificial selection.
        b). natural selection.
        c). convergent evolution.
        d). homologous structures.

The correct answer is b...
A. Answer a is incorrect because artificial selection is the process whereby humans impose selection on plants and animals through selective mating to enhance characteristics desirable for human uses. Artificial selection has produced substantial change in the phenotypes of organisms throughout human history. The changes, which occurred in Darwin's finches, moths, and horse teeth, were not controlled by human intervention, rather by natural alterations of their environments.

The correct answer is b--natural selection.
B. Natural selection is the selection of specific genetically controlled traits in organisms over time based on the contributions of those traits to survival. The shape of the beaks of Darwin's finches, the coloration of moths in industrialized areas, and the changes in horse teeth were all traits selected for by changes in the organism's environment.

The correct answer is b...
C. Answer c is incorrect because convergent evolution is the appearance of similar characteristics in distantly related organisms that are adaptations to similar environments. Finch beaks, moth coloration, and horse teeth are not examples of convergent evolution. These traits did not evolve as a result of similar environmental conditions.

The correct answer is b...
D. Answer d is incorrect because homologous structures are structures that evolved from a structure or organ in an ancestral species that adapted to different environments. Homologous structures look different and may have different functions in different species but all have the same evolutionary origin.

Hint: A variety of processes produce evolutionary change but most evolutionary biologists believe that natural selection is the primary process responsible for major evolutionary changes. Although we cannot travel back through time, a variety of modern-day evidence confirms the power of natural selection as an agent of evolutionary change. These data come from both the field and the laboratory and from natural and human-altered situations.

Test Your Visual Understanding

1). The graph illustrates how a radioactive isotope decays over time. Some isotopes decay more quickly than others do (they have shorter half-lives), but all isotope decay follows this same scale—that is, half of the isotope atoms decay with each half-life. For each of the isotopes in the following list, calculate how long it will take each parent sample to decay to 12.5% of the original amount. Also, graph three of the isotopes, plotting the proportion of parent isotope remaining to the number of half-lives, and compare these three graphs with the figure. Are they similar, or are they different?

Isotope	Half-life
a). beryllium-11	13.81 seconds
b). oxygen-15	2 minutes
c). sodium-24	15 hours
d). phosphorus-32	14.3 days
e). carbon-14	5,730 years
f). plutonium-239	24,110 years

Answer: It takes 3 half-lives of any isotope to reduce the original amount of parent isotope down to 12.5%, therefore the time it takes for each isotope is their half-life times 3:

    a). Beryllium-11 would take 41.43 seconds to reach 12.5%
    b). Oxygen-15 would take 6 minutes to reach 12.5%
    c). Sodium-24 would take 45 hours to reach 12.5%
    d). Phosphorus-32 would take 42.9 days to reach 12.5%
    e). Carbon-14 would take 17,190 years to reach 12.5%
    f). Plutonium-239 would take 72,330 years to reach 12.5%

All three graphs, regardless of the isotope's rate of decay, would look the same as the graph pictured.

Apply Your Knowledge

1). In a laboratory experiment, researchers selected for an increase and a decrease in protein content of corn seeds. The initial population contained an average of 9.5% protein by weight. As with the artificial selection experiments described in this chapter, corn seeds with the top 20% protein content were crossed and corn seeds with the lowest 20% protein contents were crossed. After 50 generations, the high-protein offspring averaged 19.2% protein, and the low-protein offspring averaged 5.4% protein.

    a). What percentage of change was recorded for the high-protein and low-protein populations?

b). Which trait, the high- or the low-protein level, was modified more because of selection? Can you explain why one trait was modified more?

Answer:

1a). The high-protein population increased by
(19.2 - 9.5) / 9.5 = 1.02 or a 102% increase in protein content
The low-protein population decreased by
(9.5 - 5.4) / 9.5 = 0.43 or a 43% decrease in protein content
1b).The high-protein population was modified more by selection. One reason why this may have occurred is that the plant requires protein to grow and there may be a lower limit of protein content, under which growth ceases. Corn seed with less than this lower limit (maybe around 5.4%) may not grow and reproduce and so there would be no corn seeds with less than 5.4% protein.

2). Why is it incorrect to think of evolution as progressive (i.e., proceeding from lowest or simplest to highest or most complex)?
Answer: Although many evolutionary trends noted thus far have been examples of increasing complexity this is not to say that evolution is progressive, pushing in a single direction. When we examine horse evolution, there is a general trend to larger, more complex animals but throughout the fossil record, there are also examples where the animals became smaller, less complex. The evolution of the hemoglobin molecule doesn't show directionality in its evolution; rather just a modification of what is there (i.e., the amino acid sequence). Another example discussed in this chapter is the evolution of the vertebrate eye. Creatures that may be considered "lower" on the evolutionary tree such as mollusks actually have eyes that are more optimally designed for sensing light. Evolution through natural selection occurs more by the appearance of workable solutions rather than the appearance of optimal designs.

Inquiry Questions
None for this chapter.

Self Test

1). Prezygotic isolating mechanisms include all of the following except
   a). hybrid sterility.
   b). courtship rituals.
   c). habitat separation.
   d). seasonal reproduction.

The correct answer is a--hybrid sterility.
A. Hybrid sterility is what results when individuals from two different species are able to mate but their offspring is not fertile, meaning that their offspring are not able to reproduce. Because this occurs after the formation of the zygote, this is a postzygotic isolating mechanism, not a prezygotic mechanism.

The correct answer is a...
B. Answer b is incorrect because courtship rituals are mechanisms of prezygotic isolation called behavioral isolation. Individuals of different species will often display different courtship mating rituals that are identified by individuals of their same species but are not recognized by individuals of other species. By establishing different rituals, species are able to recognize individuals of their own species and not expend energy mating with individuals of other species.

The correct answer is a...
C. Answer c is incorrect because habitat separation, also called ecological isolation, is a mechanism of prezygotic isolation. If individuals of two different species are located in different areas, or occupy different niches, they will rarely come into contact with each other and so will not have the opportunities to mate, thereby preserving their species identity.

The correct answer is a...
D. Answer d is incorrect because seasonal reproduction, also called temporal isolation, is a mechanism of prezygotic isolation. If individuals of two different species mate at different times of the year (i.e., one species mates in spring and the other in summer), they will rarely mate because they are not ready to mate at the same time.

Hint: How do species keep their separate identities? Reproductive isolating mechanisms fall into two categories: prezygotic isolating mechanisms, which prevent the formation of zygotes; and postzygotic isolating mechanisms, which prevents the proper functioning of zygotes after they form, including fertility of offspring.

2). Which of the following is an example of mechanical isolation?
   a). Two species of birds live in the same habitat; one mates in spring and the other in summer.
   b). Two species of frogs have different mating calls.
   c). The flower structure of one species prevents the transfer of pollen from another species.
   d). One species of lizards inhabits the trees, and another species inhabits the ground cover.

The correct answer is c...
A. Answer a is incorrect because this is a mechanism of temporal isolation. Individuals of two species that inhabit the same area may come into contact with each other but if one species mates in the spring and the other in the summer, they will not mate because they are not ready to mate at the same time.

The correct answer is c...
B. Answer b is incorrect because this is a mechanism of behavioral isolation. Mating calls, mating rituals, pheromones, etc. are all examples of behavioral isolation. If an individual from one species does not recognize the mating call of another species, it will not respond and the two will not mate.

The correct answer is c--The flower structure of one species prevents the transfer of pollen from another species.
C. Some species are restricted from mating by physical limitations. Differences in size or differences in the structure of copulatory organs can result in the inability of two individuals from mating. This is called mechanical isolation. As in this example, the structure of a flower can restrict the fertilization of the flower by another species' pollen.

The correct answer is c...
D. Answer d is incorrect because this is a mechanism of ecological isolation. Individuals from two different species that inhabit different niches may never come into contact with each other and therefore, will never have the opportunity to mate.

Hint: Structural differences prevent mating between some related species of animals. Flowers of related species of plants often differ significantly in their proportions and structures and these differences can limit the transfer of pollen from one plant species to another. This is an example of mechanical isolation.

3). _____ isolating mechanisms include improper development of hybrids and failure of hybrids to become established in nature.
      a). Prezygotic
      b). Postzygotic
      c). Temporal
      d). Mechanical

The correct answer is b...
A. Answer a is incorrect because prezygotic isolating mechanisms are those mechanisms that occur prior to the formation of the zygote. They include mechanisms such as ecological isolation, behavioral isolation, temporal isolation, mechanical isolation, and prevention of gamete fusion.

The correct answer is b--Postzygotic
B. Postzygotic isolating mechanisms are those mechanisms that occur after the formation of the zygote but prevent viable embryos or, if hybrids are born, prevent the viability or the reproductive abilities of the hybrid.

The correct answer is b...
C. Answer c is incorrect because temporal isolating mechanisms are prezygotic mechanisms that restrict mating between different species. Temporal isolation occurs when species have different breeding seasons and so they don't produce hybrids because they are not mating at the same time.

The correct answer is b...
D. Answer d is incorrect because mechanical isolation mechanisms are prezygotic mechanisms that restrict mating between different species. Mechanical isolation occurs when species have different copulatory organs that are not compatible. Therefore, they are not able to mate and produce offspring.

Hint: Prezygotic isolation mechanisms prevent hybridization. If hybrid matings do occur and zygotes are produced, many factors known as postzygotic isolating mechanisms may still prevent those zygotes from developing into normally functioning, fertile individuals.

4). Reproductive isolation and the evolution of species could occur through which of the following?
  a). founder effect
  b). reinforcement
  c). adaptation
  d). all of these

The correct answer is d...
A. Answer a is incorrect because although the founder effect, where a new population arises from a very few number of individuals, is a mechanism by which reproductive isolation and species can evolve, this is not the only correct answer.

The correct answer is d...
B. Answer b is incorrect because although reinforcement, where natural selection "weeds out" hybrids and selection is against hybridization, is a mechanism by which reproductive isolation and species can evolve, this is not the only correct answer.

The correct answer is d...
C. Answer c is incorrect because although adaptation, where individuals of a population adapt to different niches in the same habitat, is a mechanism by which reproductive isolation and species can evolve, this is not the only correct answer.

The correct answer is d--all of these
D. There are several different mechanisms of reproductive isolation, any of which can result in speciation. Therefore, it is reasonable to assume that these mechanisms evolved themselves in several different ways. The founder effect, reinforcement, and adaptation can all be used to explain the evolution of reproductive isolation and speciation.

Hint: Most reproductive isolating mechanisms initially arise for some reason other than to provide reproductive isolation. For example, a population that colonizes a new habitat may evolve adaptations for living in that habitat. As a result, individuals from that population might never encounter individuals from the ancestral population. Even if they do meet, the population in the new habitat may have evolved new phenotypes or behaviors so that they don't recognize each other as potential mates. Or, if they do mate, their offspring are less viable so they tend not to mate, further reinforcing their differences.

5). Speciation occurs most frequently in populations that are
  a). sympatric.
  b). undergoing disruptive selection.
  c). allopatric.
  d). not geographically separated.

The correct answer is c...
A. Answer a is incorrect because a sympatric population, a population where all individuals live in a single locality without any geographic separation of individuals, is not a common circumstance for the evolution of new species. Gene flow in sympatric populations tends to erase any phenotypic differences that arise from genetic drift or selection.

The correct answer is c...
B. Answer b is incorrect because a population that is undergoing disruptive selection can result in speciation but this is less likely than other processes of speciation and in fact is believed to be a rare event.

The correct answer is c--allopatric.

C. Allopatric populations are populations that experience geographic separation. Individuals within the population become separated or isolated and it is under these conditions that reproductive isolation and speciation are most likely to occur.

The correct answer is c...

D. Answer d is incorrect because populations that are not geographically isolated will experience gene flow. Gene flow tends to make the population more homogeneous and less likely to undergo speciation.

Hint: Speciation is a two-part process. First, initially identical populations must diverge and, second, reproductive isolation must evolve to maintain these differences. The difficulty with this process, as we have seen, is that the homogenizing effect of gene flow between populations will constantly be acting to erase any differences that may arise, either by genetic drift or natural selection. Consequently, speciation is much more likely in geographically isolated populations.

6). The large number of Hawaiian *Drosophila* species has likely resulted from
    a). adaptive radiation.
    b). a single common ancestor.
    c). geographic isolation.
    d). all of these

The correct answer is d...

A. Answer a is incorrect because although adaptive radiation, which is the evolution of closely related species all from a common ancestor by adapting to different habitats, contributed to the formation of the large number of *Drosophila* species in Hawaii, this isn't the only correct answer.

The correct answer is d...

B. Answer b is incorrect because although the large number of Hawaiian *Drosophila* species most likely evolved from a single common ancestor, this isn't the only correct answer.

The correct answer is d...

C. Answer c is incorrect because although geographic isolation led to allopatric speciation that then expanded to other islands, this isn't the only correct answer.

The correct answer is d--all of these

D. The large number of *Drosophila* species that inhabit the Hawaiian Islands evolved through adaptive radiation, that is, the emergence of groups of closely related species that have recently evolved from a common ancestor by adapting to different habitats. The separation of the islands and the open and varied habitats on each island provided the geographic isolation that is key to allopatric speciation.

Hint: One of the most visible manifestations of evolution is the existence of groups of closely related species that have recently evolved from a common ancestor by adapting to different habitats. Such adaptive radiation is particularly common on oceanic islands, where the original colonist probably encountered an environment with few species and many available resources. Adaptive radiation requires both speciation and adaptation to different habitats. Speciation occurs allopatrically, and then the newly arisen species colonize other islands.

7). The finch species of the Galápagos Islands are grouped according to their food sources; which of the following is *not* a finch food source?
    a). seeds
    b). carrion
    c). insects
    d). tree buds

The correct answer is b...
A. Answer a is incorrect because the ground finches are seed eaters. The size and shape of the bill reflects the type of seeds on which the species feeds.

The correct answer is b--carrion
B. The finch species contain birds that eat seeds, insects, cactus flowers, fruit, and buds but none of the species feeds on carrion, which is the carcass of dead animals.

The correct answer is b...
C. Answer c is incorrect because the tree finches and warbler finches feed on insects. The tree finches eat insects that are found in trees and the warbler finches eat insects that crawl on the ground.

The correct answer is b...
D. Answer d is incorrect because the vegetarian tree finch feeds on tree buds. The bill of this species is very heavy in order to wrench buds from the branches.

Hint: There are six species of ground finches, most of them feeding on seeds. There are five species of insect-eating tree finches. The warbler finches have slender, warbler-like beaks that they use to feed on insects that crawl on the ground. The vegetarian finch has a heavy bill used to wrench buds from branches.

8). Cichlid diversity can be attributed to
      a). adaptive radiation.
      b). new habitats and geographic isolation.
      c). a second set of jaws in the throat of the fish.
      d). All of the above contributed to cichlid diversity.

The correct answer is d...
A. Answer a is incorrect because although adaptive radiation aided in the explosion of cichlid diversity after the introduction of the first group of cichlids about 200,000 years ago, this is not the only correct answer.

The correct answer is d...
B. Answer b is incorrect because although the rising and falling of the water level in the lake caused the formation of new habitats and geographic isolation of some populations, which contributed to cichlid diversity, this is not the only correct answer.

The correct answer is d...
C. Answer c is incorrect because although the evolution of a second set of jaws in the throat, that aided in eating, allowed for a large amount of variation of the mouthparts that led to the evolution of many species of cichlids, this is not the only correct answer.

The correct answer is d--All of the above contributed to cichlid diversity.
D. The first cichlids were only introduced into Lake Victoria some 200,000 years ago (not long ago in terms of evolutionary change), but had undergone a great amount of evolutionary change in that time. Adaptive radiation is when a large amount of variation evolves from a small population, which occurred with the cichlids. The adaptation to new habitats and the occasional geographic isolation that occurred helped speciation along, as well as the evolution of a second set of jaws that allowed the other mouthparts to adapt in other ways.

Hint: Lake Victoria is an immense shallow freshwater sea in East Africa that until recently was home to an incredibly diverse collection of over 300 species of cichlid fishes. The cluster of species appears to have evolved recently and quite rapidly. Scientists estimate that the first cichlids entered the lake about 200,000 years ago. Dramatic changes in water level encouraged species formation. Cichlid fish have a remarkable trait that may have been instrumental in this evolutionary radiation: a second set of functioning jaws in the throats of the fish which freed the oral jaws to evolve for other purposes, creating great diversity.

9). The hypothesis that evolution occurs in spurts, with great amounts of evolutionary change followed by periods of stasis, is
        a). punctuated equilibrium.
        b). allopatric speciation.
        c). gradualism.
        d). Hardy–Weinberg equilibrium.

The correct answer is a--punctuated equilibrium.
A. Niles Eldredge and Stephen Jay Gould proposed the hypothesis of punctuated equilibrium, which challenged the then widely accepted evolutionary model, gradualism. According to the model of gradualism, evolutionary changes occur very slowly, over long periods of time. Punctuated equilibrium states instead that evolutionary changes occur in short time intervals separated by long periods of little or no evolutionary change.

The correct answer is a...
B. Answer b is incorrect because allopatric speciation is the evolution of species in populations that are isolated from each other. While evolutionary change in these populations could occur in spurts, they could also occur gradually. Allopatric speciation is not the hypothesis referred to in this question.

The correct answer is a...
C. Answer c is incorrect because gradualism was the widely accepted model of evolution before this hypothesis was presented. This hypothesis challenged the gradualism model, which stated that evolutionary change occurred slowly, and gradually, over long periods of time.

D. Answer d is incorrect because the Hardy–Weinberg equilibrium describes populations that are static, undergoing no evolutionary change. This is not the hypothesis referred to in this question.

Hint: Gradualism was challenged in 1972 by paleontologists Niles Eldredge and Stephen Jay Gould who argued that species experience long periods of little or no evolutionary change (termed stasis), punctuated by bursts of evolutionary change occurring over geologically short time intervals. Moreover, they argued that these periods of rapid change occurred only during the speciation process.

10). Biological diversity through time has
        a). gradually increased.
        b). been constant.
        c). increased overall despite periodic drops.
        d). both increased and decreased with no overall change.

The correct answer is c...
A. Answer a is incorrect because although diversity has increased overall with some periods showing gradual increases, there have been periods of great losses (i.e. mass extinctions) and periods of stasis, where species numbers plateau. The increase in diversity has not been gradual.

The correct answer is c...
B. Answer b is incorrect because biological diversity has not remained constant through time. There have been periods of species loss (i.e. mass extinctions) and periods of gradual and abrupt species formation.

The correct answer is c--increased overall despite periodic drops.
C. The overall number of species has increased through time, a trend that started in the early Cambrian. There have been periods of species loss due to mass extinctions, but the overall trend in an increase in the number of species.

The correct answer is c...
D. Answer d is incorrect because although there has been periods where biodiversity increased and periods where it decreased, the overall trend is an increase in the number of species.

Hint: Biological diversity has increased vastly since the Cambrian period. However, the trend has been far from consistent. After a rapid rise, diversity reached a plateau for about 200 million years, but since then has risen steadily. Nonetheless, speciation has not always outpaced extinction. In particular, interspersed in the long-term increase in species diversity have been a number of sharp declines, termed mass extinctions.

Test Your Visual Understanding

1). In all of the examples in the figure, one interbreeding population has been divided, which results in two or more geographically isolated populations. Over time, these isolated populations can undergo little or no evolutionary change, can undergo speciation, or can become extinct. Explain under what conditions each scenario can occur:
    a). Population undergoes little or no evolutionary change.
    b). Population undergoes speciation.
    c). Population becomes extinct.
Answer:
    1a). The populations that become geographically isolated may not necessarily undergo speciation. If there is no significant change in the environmental conditions to which each population is exposed, there will be no selection pressure driving evolutionary change. Except for random mutations, there may not be a change in the gene pools of these populations and unless the mutations are selected for, they will not become significant sources of variation in the populations.
    1b). Allopatric divergence is the primary means of speciation. Populations that are geographically isolated often experience different environmental conditions that select for different phenotypes in the two populations. As selection and reproductive isolation increases in the two populations, speciation can result.
    1c). When a population becomes divided, it is possible that the newly formed sub-populations have more limited gene pools than the parent population and have less genetic variability. Genetic drift becomes a significant factor in these populations. If the environmental conditions remain stable, these populations may survive but if the populations are exposed to shifting environmental conditions and they don't have the genetic variability in the population to response to selection pressures, the populations could become extinct.

Applying Your Knowledge

1). Adaptive radiation results when an ancestral species gives rise to many descendants which are adapted to many different parts of the environment. How would scenarios for adaptive radiation differ if speciation occurred allopatrically versus sympatrically?
Answer: Adaptive radiation results when an ancestral species gives rise to many descendants, which are adapted to many different parts of the environment. How would scenarios for adaptive radiation differ if speciation occurred allopatrically versus sympatrically?
    Allopatric speciation results when descendants are separated geographically and are not able to interbreed. Under these circumstances, the two populations experience different selection pressures and can evolve into two separate species through reproductive isolation.
    Sympatric speciation results when descendants remain in the same area where selective pressures would presumably be the same for all descendants. However, speciation can occur in

this type of population if some descendants are barred from interbreeding because of genetic incompatibility, such as polyploidy. This can result from an error in meiosis or as a result of hybridization. Sympatric speciation, when it occurs, is usually more immediate than allopatric speciation, where the new species forms within one or two generations.

2). Polyploid animals are far less common than polyploid plants. Why do you think this might be so?

Answer: Plants contain "male" and "female" structures but very few plant species contain individuals of opposite sexes. Many animal species, on the other hand, contain male and female individuals that are determined by sex chromosomes. Animals are less viable under conditions of polyploidy because the doubling of the chromosomes, including the sex chromosome, can be very damaging and in most cases lethal. Plants can be viable with twice the number of chromosomes but the viability of animal cells is influenced by a genetic balance in the cells. Too many chromosomes can be just as damaging as too few chromosomes.

Self Test

1). Humans and pufferfish have a similar number of genes, yet the human genome is approximately nine time larger than the pufferfish genome. In what form is much of this extra DNA?
   a). introns
   b). exons
   c). retrotransposons
   d). RNA

The correct answer is a...introns
A. Much of the extra DNA appears to be in the form of introns, which are noncoding regions of DNA that separate exons, which contain DNA sequence that is expressed.

The correct answer is a...
B. Answer b is incorrect because exons contain the DNA coding regions of a gene. Exons do not account for the extra DNA sequence.

The correct answer is a...
C. Answer c is incorrect because retrotransposons are stretches of repetitive, transposable DNA sequences. These elements can be copied and then integrated into another region of the chromosome. However, they do not account for the extra DNA.

The correct answer is a...
D. Answer d is incorrect because RNA is distinct from DNA. RNA is made from DNA with the help of enzymes called RNA polymerases. RNA does not account for the extra DNA.

2). Genome comparisons have suggested that mouse DNA has mutated about twice as fast as human DNA. What is a possible explanation for this discrepancy?
   a). Mice are much smaller than humans.
   b). Mice live in much less sanitary conditions than humans and are therefore exposed to a wider range of mutation-causing substances.
   c). Mice have a smaller genome size.
   d). Mice have a much shorter generation time.

The correct answer is d...
A. Answer a is incorrect because, while it is true that mice are much smaller than humans, this difference does not account for the higher mutational rate in mice.

The correct answer is d...
B. Answer b is incorrect because, while living conditions of humans and mice can influence mutations and natural selection, the difference in living conditions between the two does not account for the higher mutational rate in mice.

The correct answer is d...
C. Answer c is incorrect because, while mice do have a smaller genome size, this fact does not appear to impact the mutational rate in mice.

The correct answer is d...Mice have a much shorter generation time.
D. Mutations can occur at any given point in the lifespan of an organism, but only those that accumulate in germ cells will be passed on to future generations. Since mice have a much faster generation time than humans, it is thought that this difference may allow mutations to accumulate more quickly than in humans.

3). How many pairs of chromosomes do chimpanzees carry?
   a). 23
   b). 46
   c). 24
   d). 48

The correct answer is c...
A. Answer a is incorrect because chimpanzees have one more pair of chromosomes than humans, who have 23 pairs.

The correct answer is c...
B. Answer b is incorrect because chimpanzees have two more chromosomes than humans, who have 46 chromosomes.

The correct answer is c...24
C. It is believed that at some point during evolution, two mid-sized ape chromosomes fused to make what is now human chromosome 2, the second largest in our genome. Therefore chimpanzees have one more pair of chromosomes than humans.

The correct answer is c...
D. Answer d is incorrect because while chimpanzees do have 48 chromosomes, they only have 24 *pairs* of chromosomes.

4). Why was the genome of the protist *P. falciparum* difficult to sequence?
   a). This protist has a large genome.
   b). This organism hides inside red blood cells, making it difficult to obtain enough DNA for the sequencing project.
   c). The apicoplast structures in this protist inhibit sequencing reactions.
   d). The genome contains a high proportion of adenine and thymine.

The correct answer is d...
A. Answer a is incorrect because *P. falciparum* has a relatively small genome and its size did not contribute to the difficulty of the project.

The correct answer is d...
B. Answer b is incorrect because, while this organism is capable of hiding inside red blood cells, this localization did not affect DNA isolation and sequencing.

The correct answer is d...
C. Answer c is incorrect because DNA to be used for sequencing is first isolated away from other cellular components. Thus, the apicoplast structures would not interfere with sequencing reactions.

The correct answer is d...The genome contains a high proportion of adenine and thymine.
D. The high proportion of adenine and thymine made it very difficult for researchers to distinguish different parts of the genome and align sequences into a linear map.

5). All of the following are believed to contribute to genomic diversity among various species, *except*
   a). gene duplication.
   b). gene transcription.
   c). lateral gene transfer.
   d). chromosomal rearrangements.

The correct answer is b...
A. Answer a is incorrect because gene duplication can, in fact, contribute to genomic changes and diversity.

The correct answer is b...gene transcription.
B. Gene transcription is the process by which genomic information is converted to mRNA, which is then translated to form a protein, the final gene product. Thus, gene transcription does not, in itself, contribute to genomic diversity.

The correct answer is b...
C. Answer c is incorrect because lateral gene transfer refers the process by which DNA from one species is transferred to another. This process does lead to increased genomic diversity.

The correct answer is b...
D. Answer d is incorrect because chromosomal rearrangements can contribute to increased genomic diversity.

6). What is the fate of *most* duplicated genes?
    a). gene inactivation.
    b). gain of a novel function through subsequent mutation
    c). they are transferred to a new organism using lateral gene transfer
    d). they become orthologs

The correct answer is a...gene inactivation
A. When a gene duplicates it will most often eventually lose its function through subsequent mutation However, it can also gain a novel function through subsequent mutation.

The correct answer is a...
B. Answer b is incorrect because while a duplicated gene can gain a novel function through subsequent mutation, more often it will eventually be inactivated through subsequent mutation.

The correct answer is a...
C. Answer c is incorrect because, while lateral gene transfer can occur between organisms, it is not the usual fate of most duplicated genes.

The correct answer is a...
D. Answer d is incorrect because orthologs are related genes in different organisms. However, duplicated genes can result in paralogs, which are closely related genes within the same organism.

7). Which of the following best describes pseudogenes?
    a). two functional genes within an organism that arose from the duplication of one gene
    b). genes that share the same ancestral sequence, but are found in different organisms
    c). sequences of DNA that are very similar to functional genes, but do not produce a functional product
    d). sequences of DNA that are very similar to inactive genes, but do produce a functional product

The correct answer is c...
A. Answer a is incorrect because two functional genes within an organism that arose from the duplication of one gene are considered paralogs, not psuedogenes.

The correct answer is c...
B. Answer b is incorrect because genes that share the same ancestral sequence, but found in different organisms, are considered orthologs, not psuedogenes.

The correct answer is c...sequences of DNA that are very similar to functional genes, but do not produce a functional product.

C. Psuedogenes are inactive and do not produce a functional gene product.

The correct answer is c...

D. Answer d is incorrect because psuedogenes do not produce a functional product.

8). The *Tbx5* gene is known to play a role in which process?
     a). notochord development
     b). limb formation
     c). eye formation
     d). sexual reproduction

The correct answer is b...

A. Answer a is incorrect because *Tbx5* is a transcription factor that is expressed in developing limb buds. There is no evidence of direct involvement of *Tbx5* in notochord development.

The correct answer is b...limb formation

B. *Tbx5* encodes a T-box-containing transcription factor that regulates genes involved in limb formation.

The correct answer is b...

C. Answer c is incorrect because *Tbx5* is a transcription factor that is expressed in developing limb buds. There is no evidence of direct involvement of *Tbx5* in eye formation.

The correct answer is b...

D. Answer d is incorrect because *Tbx5* is a transcription factor that is expressed in developing limb buds. There is no evidence of direct involvement of *Tbx5* in sexual reproduction.

9). Which of the following organisms is not considered to be a model genetic system?
     a). mice
     b). fruit flies
     c). humans
     d). yeast

The correct answer is c...

A. Answer a is incorrect because mice are used as a model genetic system. Interestingly, since mice and humans are both mammals, many of the genes in mice have very similar functions as they do in humans.

The correct answer is c...

B. Answer b is incorrect because fruit flies are considered to be a quite powerful model genetic system. Many tools are available to manipulate fly DNA to study gene expression and function.

The correct answer is c...humans

C. Due to a variety of moral, ethical, and practical reasons, humans are not commonly used as a model genetic system. Instead, we use other organisms to learn about gene function and then use much of that information to further our understanding of the human body.

The correct answer is c...

D. Answer d is incorrect because yeast is a simple eukaryote and an excellent model to study many basic cellular processes.

10). Which of the following statements about *Pax6* is false?
   a). *Pax6* has a similar function in mice and flies.
   b). *Pax6* is involved in eyespot formation in ribbon worms.
   c). *Pax6* is required for eye formation in *Drosophila*.
   d). *Pax6* is required for eyespot formation in planaria.

The correct answer is d...
A. Answer a is incorrect because *Pax6* is a mouse gene that can initiate eye development when it is introduced into a fly.

The correct answer is d...
B. Answer b is incorrect because when the head of a ribbon worm is removed, it regenerates. *Pax6* genes are expressed in the region of the regenerating head where the new eyespots will form.

The correct answer is d...
C. Answer c is incorrect because *Pax6* is the mouse gene that is functionally equivalent to the *eyeless* gene in flies. When the fly has a mutation in *eyeless* (*Pax6*), no eyes form.

The correct answer is d--*Pax6* is required for eyespot formation in planaria.
D. Planaria can regenerate eyespots whether or not the *Pax6* gene is expressed. This result shows Pax6 is not required for eyespot formation in *Pax6*.

Test Your Visual Understanding

1). *Pax6* is known to play a role in the formation of eyespots during regeneration of the ribbon worm. Beginning with the removal of the head in the above diagram, outline the regeneration process and eyespot formation of a normal, wild-type ribbon worm and in one that lacks *Pax6* expression. How are they different?
Answer: Refer to figure 24.16 for regeneration of a normal, wild-type ribbon worm. By contrast, in ribbon worms that lack *Pax6* expression, regeneration of the head region should proceed relatively normally, except that no eyespots would form.

Apply Your Knowledge

1. How might knowledge of the *Oryza sativa* genome help combat world hunger?
Answer: Along with wheat and a few other similar crops, rice comprises a large portion of the world's food and animal feed. As we learn more about the rice genome we may be able to generate a larger variety of genetically modified rice strains to help combat world hunger and malnutrition. Recently, strains of rice have been developed to increase yields by 35%, as well as to provide vitamins and minerals to improve the health of the people in third-world countries. For example, one newly developed strain of genetically modified rice is IR68144, with artificially high levels of iron, zinc (to prevent anemia), and Vitamin A (to prevent blindness).

2). Can a human embryo that exhibits polyploidy survive until birth? What is the difference between polyploidy and trisomy?
Answer: A polyploidy human embryo that is $3n$ would not be expected to survive to birth. In contrast to polyploidy, trisomy involves the addition of a chromosome to a diploid genome ($2n +1$). Three forms of trisomy can lead to a viable infant, although the trisomy of chromosome 21, which results in Down syndrome, is the only condition in which a significant number of individuals live longer than a year past birth. The other two viable trisomies, Patau syndrome (trisomy 13) and Edward's syndrome (trisomy 18) have severe birth defects and often die within the first three or four months of birth. It is believed that other forms of trisomy result in spontaneous abortion of the embryo or fetus early in pregnancy. These observations suggest that normal human embryonic development requires a precise diploid number of chromosomes.

3). In a paper by Halder et al., 1995, the authors use the inducible GAL4-UAS expression system to artificially overexpress the *eyeless* (*Pax6*) gene in tissues where it is not normally expressed. Why does this system use the yeast transcriptional activator, GAL4, which is not normally present in *Drosophila*?

Answer: The GAL4-UAS system was developed in 1993 by Andrea Brand and Nobert Perrimon. It is based on the yeast transcriptional activator, GAL4, and its upstream activation sequence (UAS). *Drosophila* does not have any endogenous GAL4 or GAL4 binding sites and therefore allows relatively tight spatial and temporal control over transcriptional activity of the gene of interest.

FIGURE 25.15
A new hypothesis for land plant evolution. Kingdom Plantae has been reduced to a clade within the green algal branch Streptophyta, and a new kingdom, Viridplantae, which includes the green algal branches Chlorophyta and Streptophyta, has been proposed. Within the Streptophyta, the relatively complex Charales are believed to be the sister clade to the land plants.
Contrast this phylogeny with the one predicted by the six-kingdom system in figure 25.9.

Answer: In the six-kingdom system (figure 25.9), only the land plants would be predicted to be members of the kingdom Plantae. The green algae would be classified as protists, not as members of the Viridplantae (green plant kingdom). The red algae would not be considered to be members of the Viridplantae in either scheme. A fundamental problem with the six-kingdom system is that the protists are a catchall group and many protists have only the most distant phylogenetic relationships to each other.

Self Test

1) There are over 300 different species of fiddler crabs. In all of these species, the adult males possess an enlarged front claw. Based on this feature, biologists group these different species together in the same genus, *Uca*. Therefore, the large claw is
  a). an outgroup.
  b). an analogous trait.
  c). a homoplasy.
  d). a synapomorphy.

The correct answer is d…
A. Answer a is incorrect because an outgroup refers to a group that is closely related to, but not a member of, the group being classified.

The correct answer is d…
B. Answer b is incorrect because an analogous trait is one that is derived from different ancestral structures.

The correct answer is d…
C. Answer c is incorrect because a homoplasy refers to a character that is similar but not homologous.

The correct answer is d--a synapomorphy.
D. Answer d is correct because a synapomorphy is a derived character that is shared by the members of a clade. The large claw is shared by all members with the clade *Uca*.

Hint: A synapomorphy is a derived character that is shared by all the members of a clade. All adult male fiddler crabs of the genus *Uca* have an enlarged claw and this feature is a synapomorphy for the group.

2). The domestic dog, *Canis familiaris*, is related to wild dog species such as the gray wolf, *Canis lupus*. To which most exclusive category do the wolf and dog both belong?
  a). order
  b). family
  c). genus
  d). species

The correct answer is c...
A. Answer a is incorrect because both the dog and the wolf do belong to the same Order (*Carnivora*) but this is not the most exclusive category to which they both belong.

The correct answer is c...
B. Answer b is incorrect because both the dog and the wolf do belong to the same family (*Canidae*) but this is not the most exclusive category to which they both belong.

The correct answer is c--genus
C. Answer c is correct because the genus *Canis* is the most exclusive category to which they both belong.

The correct answer is c...
D. Answer d is incorrect because the dog and the wolf do not belong to the same species.

Hint: The most exclusive group is the group to which the fewest groups of individuals belong. In this example, the genus is the most exclusive group to which both species belong.

3). The simplest animals, the sponges (Parazoa), lack true tissues. All other animals (Eumetazoa) have distinct tissues. The presence of true tissues is a
      a). useful character for distinguishing amongst the eumetazoans.
      b). shared ancestral state.
      c). shared derived state.
      d). plesiomorphy.

The correct answer is c...
A. Answer a is incorrect because a trait that is shared by all members of a group is not useful in determining relationships amongst the members of that group.

The correct answer is c...
B. Answer b is incorrect because the presence of true tissues is a derived trait.

The correct answer is c--shared derived state.
C. Answer c is correct because the presence of true tissues is a derived state that is shared by all members of the Eumetazoans.

The correct answer is c...
D. Answer d is incorrect because the presence of true tissues is a shared derived trait whereas a plesiomorphy is an ancestral state.

Hint: The Parazoa are ancestral to the Eumetazoa. Therefore, the presence of true tissues is a derived trait that is shared by all members of the Eumetazoa. To be useful to distinguish amongst the members of a trait a character must vary amongst the individuals in that group. All eumetazoans have true tissues so it is not a useful character for distinguishing among the eumetazoans.

4). Originally, organisms were classified according to a two-domain system that consisted of the bacteria and the eukaryotes. Recently, a three-domain system of classification has been proposed in which domain Bacteria was divided into domain Archaea and domain Bacteria. This is because
      a). there are so many different species of prokaryotes.
      b). of the large genetic differences between the archaebacteria and the bacteria.
      c). the archaebacteria have a nucleus like that of eukaryotes.
      d). the archaebacteria live in inhospitable environments, so they should be put In a different domain.

The correct answer is b...
A. Answer a is incorrect because classification systems are determined by evolutionary relatedness, not the number of species.

The correct answer is b--of the large genetic differences between the archaebacteria and the bacteria.
B. Answer b is correct because the prokaryotes were divided into bacteria and archaebacteria after the large genetic differences between the groups were realized.

The correct answer is b...
C. Answer c is incorrect because the archaebacteria do not have a nucleus.

The correct answer is b...
D. Answer d is incorrect because classification systems are determined by evolutionary relatedness, not the environment in which species live. Additionally, archaebacteria have been found to live in diverse environments, not only extreme environments.

Hint: Recent genetic analyses have indicated that the archaebacteria and the bacteria are genetically quite distinct. Analyses also indicate that the archaebacteria are more closely related to eukaryotes than to the bacteria.

5). Which of the following is the most abundant group of organisms on earth?
  a). archaebacteria
  b). bacteria
  c). protists
  d). fungi

The correct answer is b...
A. Answer a is incorrect because although the archaebacteria are able to live in extreme environments, they are not the most abundant organisms on earth.

The correct answer is b--bacteria
B. Answer b is correct. The bacteria are the most abundant organisms on earth.

The correct answer is b...
C. Answer c is incorrect because although the protists are abundant, they are not the most abundant organisms on earth.

The correct answer is b...
D. Answer d is incorrect because the fungi are not the most abundant organisms on earth.

Hint: There are more bacteria on earth than any other type of organism.

6). Biologists do not consider viruses to be alive. This is because viruses
  a). are unable to reproduce on their own.
  b). do not contain genetic material.
  c). do not contain proteins.
  d). are smaller than living organisms.

The correct answer is a--are unable to reproduce on their own.
A. Answer a is correct. Viruses cannot replicate outside of a host cell and so are not considered to be alive.

The correct answer is a...
B. Answer b is incorrect. Viruses contain either DNA or RNA.

The correct answer is a…
C. Answer c is incorrect. Viruses are comprised of genetic material inside a protein coat.

The correct answer is a…
D. Answer d is incorrect. Viruses are usually smaller than the cells of living organisms but this is not the reason they are not considered living organisms.

Hint: Viruses are unable to reproduce outside of a host cell. Therefore, biologists do not consider them to be living organisms.

7). As more is learned about the molecular and genetic aspects of organisms, taxonomic groupings are changing. Which group of eukaryotes is the focus of most controversy related to their taxonomic groupings?
>   a). bacteria
>   b). protists
>   c). animals
>   d). fungi

The correct answer is b…
A. Answer a is incorrect because bacteria are not eukaryotic.

The correct answer is b--protists
B. Answer b is correct. The protists are a paraphyletic group whose evolutionary relationships are unclear.

The correct answer is b…
C. Answer c is incorrect. The classification of the animals is not as controversial as the classification of the protists.

The correct answer is b…
D. Answer d is incorrect. The classification of the fungi is not as controversial as the classification of the protists.

Hint: The protists are all single-celled eukaryotic organisms. Beyond those similarities, they are a very diverse group and their classification system is highly controversial.

8). According to new molecular and biochemical information, should the plants still be recognized as a distinct kingdom?
>   a). Yes, the green algae are now considered to be in the kingdom Plantae.
>   b). Yes, the green algae and the plants are now recognized to be unrelated.
>   c). No, the plants and the green algae are now classified together in the kingdom Virdiplantae.
>   d). No, the plants are now classified together within the Chlorophyta.

The correct answer is c…
A. Answer a is incorrect because the data suggests that plants should not be recognized as a distinct kingdom and the green algae are not classified as plants.

The correct answer is c…
B. Answer b is incorrect because the data suggests that plants should not be recognized as a distinct kingdom and the green algae and plants are known to be related.

The correct answer is c--No, the plants and the green algae are now classified together in the kingdom Viridiplantae.
C. Answer c is correct because the data suggests that plants should not be recognized as a distinct kingdom and should be classified with the green algae in the kingdom Viridiplantae.

The correct answer is c...
D. Answer d is incorrect because the plants are not classified within the Chlorophyta.

Hint: Molecular evidence indicates that the land plants belong within the group Streptophyta rather than as a separate kingdom. It has been suggested that the plants and the green algae (Chlorophyta and Streptophyta) be combined into kingdom Viridiplantae.

9). The relationship between the annelids and the arthropods is now thought to be
        a). monophyletic.
        b). polyphyletic.
        c). paraphyletic.
        d). unrelated.

The correct answer is b...
A. Answer a is incorrect because segmentation has arisen twice and is not a shared derived characteristic for these two groups. Therefore, annelids and arthropods do not share a most recent common ancestor and are not monophyletic.

The correct answer is b--polyphyletic.
B. Answer b is correct because segmentation has arisen twice and is not a shared derived characteristic for these two groups. Therefore, annelids and arthropods do not share a most recent common ancestor and are polyphyletic.

The correct answer is b...
C. Answer c is incorrect because segmentation has arisen twice and is not a shared derived characteristic for these two groups. Therefore, annelids and arthropods do not share a most recent common ancestor and are not paraphyletic.

The correct answer is b...
D. Answer d is incorrect because arthropods are annelids are related. However, they do not constitute a monophyletic grouping.

Hint: The annelids and the arthropods were originally considered a clade under the assumption that body segmentation arose only once. It is now recognized that segmentation arose independently in the annelids and the arthropods and they are of polyphyletic origins.

Test Your Visual Understanding

1). Using the image from figure 25.8, fill in the following table to indicate the presence or absence of the derived character.

	Light bones	Breastbone	Downy feathers	Feathers with vanes, shafts, and barbs	Aerodyna mic feathers	Arms longer than legs
Other Dinosau rs						
Coeloph ysis						
Tyranno saurus						
Sinosau ropteryx						
Velocira ptor						
Caudipt eryx						
Archaeo pteryx						
Modern Birds						

Answer:

	Light bones	Breastbone	Downy feathers	Feathers with vanes, shafts, and barbs	Aerodyna mic feathers	Arms longer than legs
Other Dinosau rs	0	0	0	0	0	0
Coeloph ysis	1	0	0	0	0	0
Tyranno saurus	1	1	0	0	0	0
Sinosau ropteryx	1	1	1	0	0	0
Velocira ptor	1	1	1	1	0	0
Caudipt eryx	1	1	1	1	1	0
Archaeo pteryx	1	1	1	1	1	1
Modern Birds	1	1	1	1	1	1

Apply Your Knowledge

1). Most biologists consider viruses to be nonliving because they are unable to replicate outside of a host cell. How might you argue against this position? What characteristics do viruses have them make them lifelike?
Answer: Viruses contain genetic material and thus are subject to natural selection as are all living organisms.

2). Phylogenetic relationships are established based on assumptions about evolutionary relatedness. It is assumed that the more similar two organisms are, the more closely they are related. What problems does the process of convergent evolution cause for systematists?
Answer: Convergent evolution is a process by which two unrelated species evolve to become more similar. This is due to the species use of similar habitats, which results in selection for similar adaptations. As a result of convergent evolution, systematists may classify two species as being closely related when in fact they are not.

3). Ethnobotanical research involves the exploration of plants that may have uses, particularly medical, for humans. Of what value is knowledge of systematics to an ethnobotanist?
Answer: Related species share biochemical similarities. If a certain species of plant is found to contain medicinal compounds, it would be worthwhile to examine related species to determine if they have similar compounds.

None for this chapter.

Self Test

1). Viruses consist of a _____ core surrounded by a protein coat.
     a). RNA
     b). DNA
     c). chromosome
     d). nucleic acid

The correct answer is d...
A. Answer a is incorrect because although some viruses contain a core of RNA, called retroviruses, some viruses contain DNA instead. It is most accurate to say that viruses contain a core of nucleic acids.

The correct answer is d...
B. Answer b is incorrect because although some viruses contain a core of DNA, some other viruses contain an RNA core. It is most accurate to say that viruses contain a core of nucleic acids.

The correct answer is d...
C. Answer c is incorrect because although viruses have a genome, the genome is not organized into structured chromosomes. The genome can be linear or circular but is not associated with histones in a chromosome.

The correct answer is d--nucleic acid
D. Although viruses have very different shapes and sizes, all viruses have the same basic structure consisting of a nucleic acid core surrounded by a protein coat.

Hint: All viruses have the same basic structure: a core of nucleic acid surrounded by protein. Individual viruses contain only a single type of nucleic acid, either DNA or RNA. The DNA or RNA genome may be linear or circular, and single stranded or double stranded.

2). Phages infect bacterial cells by
     a). poking holes in the cell and injecting their DNA.
     b). destroying the bacterial cell wall.
     c). receptor-mediated endocytosis.
     d). exocytosis.

The correct answer is a--poking holes in the cell and injecting their DNA.
A. Phages do not enter the bacterial cell, rather they dock on the outside of the cell and use their tail to puncture a small hole in the cell wall and plasma membrane and inject their DNA inside. Once inside the DNA is used to manufacture new phages.

The correct answer is a...
B. Answer b is incorrect because if the bacterial cell wall is destroyed, the phage would be killing the bacterium before it had an opportunity to infect it and use its cellular machinery to make more phages.

The correct answer is a...
C. Answer c is incorrect because receptor-mediated endocytosis would involve engulfing the phage and bringing it into the host cell. This occurs with some animal viruses but not with bacteriophages.

The correct answer is a...
D. Answer d is incorrect because exocytosis is the process whereby materials are expelled from a cell, not taken into a cell. A phage could not infect a bacterial cell by exocytosis.

Hint: During the process of bacterial infection by T4 phage, at least one of the tail fibers of the phage contacts the lipoproteins of the host bacterial cell wall. The tail contracts, and the tail tube passes through an opening piercing the cell wall. The contents of the head, mostly DNA, are then injected into the host cytoplasm.

3). The end result of the viral lytic cycle is
        a). the release of new viruses.
        b). the incorporation of viral genome into the host genome.
        c). the conversion of the virus into a prophage.
        d). Both b and c are correct.

The correct answer is a--the release of new viruses.
A. The lytic cycle results in the reproduction of the virus by the replication and translation of the viral genome that produces the nucleic acid and proteins. The new viruses are assembled and released by the lysis of the host cell.

The correct answer is a...
B. Answer b is incorrect because the incorporation of the viral genome into the host genome occurs in the lysogenic cycle, not in the lytic cycle.

The correct answer is a...
C. Answer c is incorrect because the conversion of the virus into a prophage occurs during the lysogenic cycle, not in the lytic cycle. Once the viral genome is incorporated into the host genome, it is no longer called a virus because the virus is no longer present. The viral genome is called a prophage. At some point the prophage is activated and the host cell enters a lytic cycle.

The correct answer is a...
D. Answer d is incorrect because answers b and c are not correct. The incorporation of viral genome into the host genome and the conversion of the virus into a prophage occurs in the lysogenic cycle, not in the lytic cycle.

Hint: When a virus kills the infected host cell in which it is replicating, the reproductive cycle is referred to as a lytic cycle. The T-series bacteriophages are all virulent viruses, multiplying within infected cells and eventually rupturing them and releasing new viruses.

4). The alteration of a cell's genome by the incorporation of foreign DNA is called
        a). genetic conversion.
        b). mutation.
        c). transformation.
        d). reverse transcription.

The correct answer is c...
A. Answer a is incorrect because genetic conversion is not the term used to describe this process. Phage conversion is the term used to describe the process whereby a bacterial virus is the source of foreign DNA, but in general, the term transformation is used to describe the alteration of a cell's genome in this way.

The correct answer is c...
B. Answer b is incorrect because mutations are a way of altering a cell's genome but this occurs through damage to the DNA, not by the incorporation of foreign DNA.

The correct answer is c--transformation.
C. Transformation is the process whereby a cell's genome is changed by the incorporation of foreign DNA, usually from a virus. The term phage conversion is used in the specific situation where the foreign DNA comes from a bacterial virus.

The correct answer is c...
D. Answer d is incorrect because reverse transcription is the process whereby an RNA virus is able to convert into a molecule of DNA so that it can become incorporated into the host's genome. This occurs only with the infection by an RNA virus.

Hint: During the integration portion of a lysogenic reproductive cycle, virus genes are often expressed. The RNA polymerase of the host cell reads the viral genes just as if they were host genes. Sometimes, expression of these genes has an important effect on the host cell, altering it in novel ways. The genetic alteration of a cell's genome by the introduction of foreign DNA is called transformation. When a bacterial virus contributes the foreign DNA, the alteration is called phage conversion.

5). Which of the following is a viral glycoprotein that plays a role in the infection of human cells by HIV?
        a). gp120
        b). CD4
        c). CCR5
        d). Both b and c are correct.

The correct answer is a--gp120
A. gp120 is a glycoprotein that appears on the surface of the HIV virus. This glycoprotein binds to a cell-surface receptor on the human white blood cell and is eventually enveloped into the human cell.

The correct answer is a...
B. Answer b is incorrect because CD4 is a receptor on the human white blood cell; it is not a viral glycoprotein. The CD4 receptor binds the glycoprotein gp120 present on the surface of HIV.

The correct answer is a...
C. Answer c is incorrect because the CCR5 is a receptor on the human white blood cell; it is not a viral glycoprotein. The CCR5 receptor joins with the CD4 receptor that is attached to the HIV virus and brings the virus into the cell.

The correct answer is a...
D. Answer d is incorrect because neither answers b nor c are correct. CD4 is a receptor on the human white blood cell; it is not a viral glycoprotein. The CD4 receptor binds the glycoprotein gp120 present on the surface of HIV. CCR5 is a receptor on the human white blood cell; it is not a viral glycoprotein. The CCR5 receptor joins with the CD4 receptor that is attached to the HIV virus and brings the virus into the cell.

Hint: How does a virus such as HIV recognize a specific kind of target cell? Each HIV particle possesses a glycoprotein (called gp120) on its surface that precisely fits a cell-surface marker protein called CD4 on the surfaces of immune system cells called macrophages and T cells. Macrophages are infected first.

6). The HIV enzyme, _____, produces a DNA copy of the viral genome once it is inside the host cell.
        a). DNA polymerase
        b). reverse transcriptase
        c). RNA polymerase
        d). helicase

The correct answer is b...
A. Answer a is incorrect because DNA polymerase is the host cell enzyme that is used to replicate DNA in the nucleus; it is not a viral enzyme.

The correct answer is b--reverse transcriptase
B. Reverse transcriptase is an enzyme used by RNA viruses to make a double-stranded DNA copy of their RNA. The host cell does not directly use the viral RNA. First, the RNA is transcribed in the reverse direction to produce a complementary strand of DNA that forms a second strand through complementary base-pairing. The enzyme, reverse transcriptase, carries out this process.

The correct answer is b...
C. Answer c is incorrect because RNA polymerase is the host cell enzyme that is used to make a strand of RNA that is complementary to the gene sequence found on the DNA molecule; it is not a viral enzyme.

The correct answer is b...
D. Answer d is incorrect because helicase is the host cell enzyme that is used to unwind the DNA during DNA replication or transcription; it is not a viral enzyme.

Hint: Once inside the macrophage, the HIV particle sheds its protective coat. This leaves the virus RNA floating in the cytoplasm, along with a virus enzyme that was also within the virus shell. This enzyme, called reverse transcriptase, synthesizes a double strand of DNA complementary to the virus RNA, often making mistakes and so introducing new mutations.

7). The drug AZT and its analogs functions by
        a). inhibiting the replication of viral nucleic acid.
        b). blocking the production of envelope proteins.
        c). blocking the production of capsid proteins.
        d). blocking the binding of the virus to human cell receptors.

The correct answer is a--inhibiting the replication of viral nucleic acid.
A. AZT and its analogs have been effective when used in combination with protease inhibitors at eliminating HIV from patients' bloodstreams. AZT inhibits the replication of viral nucleic acid thereby inhibiting the replication of the virus.

The correct answer is a...
B. Answer b is incorrect because AZT does not block the production of envelope proteins; protease inhibitors used in conjunction with AZT inhibit the production of viral proteins including envelope proteins.

The correct answer is a...
C. Answer c is incorrect because AZT does not block the production of capsid proteins; protease inhibitors used in conjunction with AZT inhibit the production of viral proteins including capsid proteins.

The correct answer is a...
D. Answer d is incorrect because AZT does not block human cell receptors. Proteins found in humans, such as chemokine and CD8+ cell antiviral factor (CAF) function by blocking cell receptors so that HIV cannot bind to the host cells.

Hint: A variety of drugs inhibit HIV in the test tube. These include AZT and its analogs (which inhibit virus nucleic acid replication) and protease inhibitors (which inhibit the cleavage of the large polyproteins encoded by *gag*, *pol*, and *env* genes into functional capsid, enzyme, and envelope segments). When combinations of these drugs were administered to people with HIV in controlled studies, their conditions improved.

8). What is the function of the CD8$^+$ cell antiviral factor (CAF) in human white blood cells?
  a). disables the CD4 receptor
  b). blocks replication of the HIV virus
  c). interferes with the production of viral proteins
  d). blocks the CCR5 or CXCR4 receptors

The correct answer is b...
A. Answer a is incorrect because CAF does not disable the CD4 receptor. Research on treatments for AIDS is looking at the possibility of producing mutations that will disable receptors for HIV, but CAF is not being used in these studies.

The correct answer is b--blocks replication of the HIV virus
B. CAF is a protein found in human white blood cells but its levels are elevated in HIV-positive people who have not developed AIDS. This suggests that CAF may inhibit the onset of AIDS. CAF has not yet been isolated but it seems to function by stopping the replication of the HIV virus once it has infected a cell.

The correct answer is b...
C. Answer c is incorrect because CAF does not interfere with the production of viral proteins. Protease inhibitors that are used in conjunction with AZT disrupt the production of proteins needed by the virus to make new viruses.

The correct answer is b...
D. Answer d is incorrect because chemokines, not CAF, function in white blood cells to block the CCR5 and CXCR4 receptors.

Hint: Researchers report that in their tests, the levels of chemokines were not different between HIV-positive patients who develop AIDS and those who do not. More promising, levels of another factor called CAF (CD8$^+$ cell antiviral factor) are different between these two groups. Researchers have not yet succeeded in isolating CAF, which seems not to block receptors that HIV uses to gain entry to cells, but instead, to prevent replication of the virus once it has infected the cells.

9). New strains of flu viruses are most likely to arise in the Far East because
  a). of overpopulation in these areas.
  b). adequate sanitation is lacking.
  c). common hosts (ducks, chickens, pigs) live in close proximity to humans.
  d). of environmental mutagens that cause changes in viral RNA.

The correct answer is c...
A. Answer a is incorrect because overpopulation is not limited to areas in the Far East. Many areas, including here in the U.S. experience conditions of overpopulation. Also, overpopulation may contribute to the rapid spreading of a new strain but not necessarily with the development of a new strain.

The correct answer is c...
B. Answer b is incorrect because lack of adequate sanitation may be a problem in some areas of the Far East, but other areas also experience poor sanitation. Also, while some diseases are a result of poor sanitation, other factors influence the emergence of flu in a population.

The correct answer is c--common hosts (ducks, chickens, pigs) live in close proximity to humans.
C. The influenza virus is an animal retrovirus that passed to humans from birds. Common hosts of the flu virus are farm animals such as ducks, chickens, and pigs. In the Far East, humans live in close proximity with these types of animals allowing more opportunity for viruses to spread between these animals and humans.

The correct answer is c...
D. Answer d is incorrect because although new strains arise from changes to viral RNA, these changes result from recombinations as well as mutations. Also, other areas outside of the Far East have problems with environmental mutagens.

Hint: It is no accident that the new strains of flu usually originate in the Far East. The most common hosts of influenza viruses are ducks, chickens, and pigs, which in Asia often live in close proximity to each other and to humans. This creates conditions favoring genetic recombinations between strains, producing new combinations of H and N subtypes.

10). Which of the following infectious agents does *not* contain protein?
     a). viruses
     b). viroids
     c). prions
     d). none of these

The correct answer is b...
A. Answer a is incorrect because viruses are infectious agents that are a nucleic acid core surrounded by a protein coat, so viruses do contain protein.

The correct answer is b--viroids
B. Viroids are small, naked molecules of RNA that cause infectious diseases in plants. They contain no protein. It is not clear how viroids cause disease but they may be catalysts that disrupt the integrity of chromosomes.

The correct answer is b...
C. Answer c is incorrect because prions are infectious protein particles—they are all protein. Prions are proteins with abnormal conformations. When these abnormal proteins are injected (or ingested) by healthy individuals, they begin appearing in the healthy person.

The correct answer is b...
D. Answer d is incorrect because there is a correct answer, answer b. Viruses and prions both contain protein but a viroid is merely a naked molecule of RNA.

Hint: Viroids are tiny, naked molecules of RNA, only a few hundred nucleotides long, that are important infectious disease agents in plants. It is not clear how viroids cause disease. One clue is that viroid nucleotide sequences resemble the sequences of introns within ribosomal RNA genes. These sequences are capable of catalyzing excision from DNA—perhaps the viroids are catalyzing the destruction of chromosomal integrity.

Test Your Visual Understanding

1). Describe the overall shape of each of the viruses in the figure, either as helical, isometric, or icosahedral.
Answer: (a) This bacteriophage has a spherical head so it is isometric but the head is made up of triangular facets and so the head is also icosahedral in shape. The tail region is helical. (b) This tobacco mosaic virus is helical in shape. (c) This HIV virus is isometric and although not visible, it is most likely composed of triangular facets (as most viruses are) and is therefore also icosahedral.

2). List which of these viruses attacks:
     a). animals
     b). plants
     c). bacteria

Answer:

        a). animals—(c) Human immunodeficiency virus (HIV)

        b). plants— (b) Tobacco mosaic virus (TMV)

        c). bacteria— (a) Bacteriophage

Apply Your Knowledge

1). AIDS was first identified in 1981 in the United States, and in 2002, an estimated 495,000 cases of AIDS and/or HIV had been reported. The total U.S. population at the end of 2002 was approximately 290 million. What percent of the population was living with AIDS and/or HIV?

Answer: To find the percent of individuals with AIDS in the total population, divide the number of individuals with AIDS and/or HIV by the total population and multiply by 100 or:

(495,000 / 290,000,000) x 100 = 0.17%

2). In what ways might the early, self-replicating particles that gave rise to the first organisms have resembled, or differed from, viruses?

Answer: In order to be self-replicating, these early precursors to organisms had to contain a molecule that could be replicated, most likely RNA- or DNA-like viruses. Unlike viruses, these early precursors to organisms most likely encased their nucleic acid in a lipid membrane rather than a protein coat as viruses do. The temperatures of early earth were very hot and would most likely have denatured proteins. In the hot, aquatic environment a lipid membrane would offer more protection for the nucleic acid than protein.

3). If a viral disease such as influenza could kill 22 million people over 18 months in 1918–1919, why do you suppose the killing ever stopped? What prevented the flu virus from continuing its lethal assault on humanity?

Answer: Just as mutation and recombination gives rise to new, more lethal strains of flu viruses, they can also make the virus more easily attacked by the human immune system. Point mutations of the surface proteins occur in 1 in every 100,000 viruses and although a strain of viruses may be particularly lethal, the viruses of that strain continue to mutate and undergo recombinations. Eventually, the virus may change in a way that the human immune system can now kill it, making the virus less lethal. After 18 months, the viruses most likely mutated and underwent recombination to the point where they were less lethal and the infected individuals could fight off the disease.

FIGURE 27.9
Trends in sexually transmitted diseases in the United States.
How is it possible for the incidence of one STD (chlamydia) to rise as another (gonorrhea) falls?

Answer: The simplest explanation is that the two STDs are occurring in different populations, and one population has rising levels of sexual activity, while the other has falling levels. However, the rise in incidence of an STD can reflect many parameters other than level of sexual activity. The virulence or infectivity of one or both disease agents may be changing, for example, or some aspect of exposed people may be changing in such a way as to alter susceptibility. Only a thorough public health study can sort this out.

Self Test

1). Once they evolved, _____ forever changed the atmosphere on earth.
     a). bacteria
     b). archaebacteria
     c). cyanobacteria
     d). eukaryotes

The correct answer is c...
A. Answer a is incorrect because the atmosphere wasn't altered until the evolution of a particular type of bacteria called cyanobacteria. Therefore, to say that bacteria changed the atmosphere is a statement that is too general.

The correct answer is c...
B. Answer b is incorrect because the archaebacteria lived very well in the atmosphere of early earth and continue to inhabit environments that are too harsh for most organisms. They were not responsible for the alterations to the earth's atmosphere.

The correct answer is c--cyanobacteria
C. Cyanobacteria are photosynthetic bacteria that began pumping oxygen into the atmosphere as a byproduct of their photosynthetic activity. As they became more and more abundant on the earth, the atmosphere changed to contain more and more oxygen. Aerobic organisms then appeared, using the oxygen in the atmosphere to power respiration.

The correct answer is c...
D. Answer d is incorrect because the eukaryotes didn't appear on the earth until after oxygen was present in the atmosphere. Cyanobacteria first appeared and created an oxygen-rich atmosphere and then the eukaryotes appeared.

Hint: Bacteria are the oldest, structurally simplest, and the most abundant forms of the life on earth. They are also the only organisms with prokaryotic cellular organization. Represented in the oldest rocks, from which fossils have been obtained, 3.5 to 3.8 billion years old, bacteria were abundant for over 2 billion years before eukaryotes appeared in the world. Early photosynthetic bacteria (cyanobacteria) altered the earth's atmosphere with the production of oxygen, which led to extreme bacterial and eukaryotic diversity.

2). Which of the following statements is *not* true of prokaryotic cells?
     a). Prokaryotic cells are multicellular.
     b). Prokaryotic cells do not have a nucleus.
     c). Prokaryotic cells have circular DNA.
     d). Prokaryotic cells have flagella.
The correct answer is a--Prokaryotic cells are multicellular.

A. Prokaryotic cells do not form multicellular structures. Some prokaryotic cells associate with each other, forming clusters or strands of cells, but these are not true multicellular structures. Only eukaryotes form multicellular structures.

The correct answer is a...
B. Answer b is incorrect because this statement is true. Prokaryotic cells do not have internal membrane-bounded organelles including a nucleus. Prokaryotic DNA localizes in an area of the cell called the nucleoid but this isn't a membrane-bound nucleus.

The correct answer is a...
C. Answer c is incorrect because this statement is true. The DNA in prokaryotic cells in not linear, organized into chromosomes as it is in eukaryotes. Prokaryotic DNA is circular, although the circular DNA may twist upon itself but it is not associated with proteins as in chromosomes. The DNA is localized to an area in the cell called the nucleoid.

The correct answer is a...
D. Answer d is incorrect because this statement is true. Some but not all prokaryotes have flagella. Flagella are whiplike structures that project out from the cell and propel the cell through its environment. Eukaryotic cells may also have flagella but the flagella are structurally different in prokaryotes. The flagella in prokaryotes are made of the protein flagellin and spin like a propeller. In eukaryotes, flagella are made of microtubules that move in a whiplike motion.

Hint: All prokaryotes are fundamentally single-celled. In some types, individual cells adhere to each other within a matrix and form filaments, however the cells retain their individuality. The activities of a prokaryotic colony are less integrated and coordinated than those in multicellular eukaryotes.

3). When bacterial cell walls are covered with an outer membrane of lipopolysaccharide, they are
   a). gram-positive.
   b). gram-negative.
   c). encapsulated.
   d). endospores.

The correct answer is b...
A. Answer a is incorrect because gram-positive bacteria have cell walls containing several layers of peptidoglycan but no outer membrane of lipopolysaccharide.

The correct answer is b--gram-negative.
B. Gram-negative bacteria have a thinner layer of peptidoglycan compared to gram-positive bacteria but they also have an outer membrane composed of lipopolysaccharides. This outer membrane provides a certain level of defense against some antibiotics that act on the peptidoglycan layer.

The correct answer is b...
C. Answer c is incorrect because bacteria that are encapsulated have an outer layer or covering of protein called the capsule but this is different from an outer membrane of lipopolysaccharide.

The correct answer is b...
D. Answer d is incorrect because endospores are the dormancy state that some bacteria enter during times of environmental stress. The endospore is formed by a thick cell wall surrounding the bacterial DNA and some surrounding cytoplasm.

Hint: There are two major types of bacteria identified using a staining process called a Gram stain. Gram-positive bacteria have the thicker peptidoglycan wall and stain a purple color. The more common gram-negative bacteria contain less peptidoglycan and do not retain the purple-colored dye. Gram-negative bacteria stain red. The outer membrane layer makes gram-negative bacteria resistant to many antibiotics that interfere with cell wall synthesis in gram-positive bacteria.

4). The prokaryotic genome is contained in the
        a). plasmid.
        b). endospore.
        c). pilus.
        d). nucleoid region.

The correct answer is d...
A. Answer a is incorrect because the plasmid is a small circle of DNA that is separate from the prokaryotic genome. The plasmid contains only a few genes that are usually not essential for cell survival.

The correct answer is d...
B. Answer b is incorrect because the endospore is a structure formed by the prokaryote during times of environmental stress. A thick wall forms around the bacterial DNA protecting it from desiccation or extreme temperatures.

The correct answer is d...
C. Answer c is incorrect because the pilus is a hairlike structure projecting out from the prokaryotic cell surface. The pilus (plural—pili) helps the prokaryote attach to appropriate substrates and exchange genetic information.

The correct is d--nucleoid region.
D. The prokaryotic cell does not contain a nucleus as eukaryotic cells do, but the prokaryotic genome is sequestered in a particular region of the cell called the nucleoid region.

Hint: Prokaryotes lack nuclei and do not possess the complex chromosomes characteristic of eukaryotes. Instead, their genes are encoded within a single double-stranded ring of DNA that is crammed into one region of the cell known as the nucleoid region.

5). Archaebacteria and bacteria differ in all of the following ways except
        a). the structure of the cell wall.
        b). their presence in nonextreme environments.
        c). the structure of the plasma membrane.
        d). the kinds of ribosomal proteins they possess.

The correct answer is b...
A. Answer a is incorrect because archaebacteria and bacteria do differ in the structure of their cell walls. The cell wall of bacteria contains peptidoglycan and that of archaebacteria does not.

The correct answer is b--their presence in nonextreme environments.
B. Archaebacteria were first isolated from extreme environments such as very salty waters, very acidic or alkaline environments, or extremely hot or cold conditions. At first, scientists thought that archaebacteria were confined to these extreme environments but species of archaebacteria have been found in nonextreme environments, such as soil.

The correct answer is b...
C. Answer c is incorrect because archaebacteria and bacteria do differ in the structure of their plasma membranes. All bacteria have plasma membranes of a lipid bilayer but the membranes of archaebacteria and bacteria differ in the types of lipids that make up the bilayer.

The correct answer is b...
D. Answer d is incorrect because archaebacteria and bacteria do differ in the kinds of proteins found within the ribosomes. Bacteria ribosomal proteins are distinctly different from eukaryotic ribosomes but archaebacterial ribosomes more closely resemble eukaryotic ribosomes.

Hint: Bacteria split into two lines early in the history of life. The differences between these groups are so fundamental that biologists assign the two groups of bacteria to separate domains. One domain, the Archae, consists of the archaebacteria. It was once thought that survivors of this group were confined to extreme environments that may resemble habitats on the early earth. However, the use of genetic screening has revealed that these "ancient" bacteria live in nonextreme environments as well.

6). Genetic recombination has led to antibiotic resistance through the transfer of
      a). pili.
      b). endospores.
      c). plasmids.
      d). bacterial chromosomes.

The correct answer is c...
A. Answer a is incorrect because pili are the hairlike structures that project out from the bacterial surface that can function in the transfer of genetic material between bacteria. Pili are the passageways through which the antibiotic resistance genes are transferred.

The correct answer is c...
B. Answer b is incorrect because endospores are structures created by bacteria during stressful environmental conditions. During times of stress, a cell wall forms around the bacterial genome and goes into a state of dormancy until the environmental conditions are more favorable for survival.

The correct answer is c--plasmids.
C. Many bacteria possess small, independent replicating circles of DNA called plasmids. Plasmids contain only a few genes, usually not essential for cell's survival but in some instances, these genes may provide the bacterium with environmental advantages, such as antibiotic resistance. The transfer of plasmids carrying antibiotic resistance genes allows antibiotic resistance to spread to other bacteria.

The correct answer is c...
D. Answer d is incorrect because the genes for antibiotic resistance are found on plasmids, not as part of the bacterial chromosome. Through conjugation, plasmids are transferred between bacterial cells and result in genetic recombination.

Hint: Bacterial recombination occurs by the transfer of genes from one cell to another by viruses, or through conjugation. The rapid transfer of newly produced, antibiotic resistant genes by plasmids has been an important factor in the appearance of the resistant strains of *Staphylococcus aureus*.

7). Prokaryotic organisms that obtain their energy by oxidizing inorganic substances are called
      a). chemoautotrophs.
      b). photoautotrophs.
      c). chemoheterotrophs.
      d). photoheterotrophs.

The correct answer is a--chemoautotrophs.
A. Autotrophs are organisms that acquire energy to produce their own nutrients from inorganic substances. Those that harvest energy from inorganic chemicals are called chemoautotrophs.

The correct answer is a...
B. Answer b is incorrect because photoautotrophs are organisms that acquire energy to produce their own nutrients but they acquire their energy from the sun, not by oxidizing inorganic substances.

The correct answer is a...
C. Answer c is incorrect because chemoheterotrophs are organisms that obtain energy and nutrients from the oxidation of organic molecules such as glucose.

The correct answer is a...
D. Answer d is incorrect because photoheterotrophs are organisms that obtain their energy from the sun but then obtain nutrients from organic molecules such as carbohydrates or alcohol.

Hint: Autotrophs are organisms that obtain their carbon from inorganic CO_2. Autotrophs that harvest energy from inorganic chemicals are called chemoautotrophs.

8). What disease is experiencing new outbreaks because of antibiotic resistance?
      a). smallpox
      b). cholera
      c). tuberculosis
      d). diphtheria

The correct answer is c...
A. Answer a is incorrect because smallpox is a disease which has essentially been eliminated worldwide.

The correct answer is c...
B. Answer b is incorrect because although cholera is a potentially fatal disease, outbreaks of cholera are usually caused by overcrowding and poor sanitation rather than by antibiotic resistance.

The correct answer is c--tuberculosis
C. Tuberculosis (TB) has been one of the great killer diseases for thousands of years. The U.S. has been experiencing a dramatic resurgence of TB since the mid-1980s. The causes of this current resurgence include social factors but also the appearance of multidrug-resistant strains. These strains are resistant to most prescribed medications and can spread fairly easily from one person to another.

The correct answer is c...
D. Answer d is incorrect because although diphtheria spreads through contact, the development of a vaccine has greatly reduced the numbers of infected individuals.

Hint: In addition to the increased number of cases of TB—more than 25,000 nationally as of March 1995—there have been alarming outbreaks of multidrug-resistant strains—strains resistant to the best available anti-TB medications. Multidrug-resistant TB is particularly concerning because it requires much more time to treat, is more expensive to treat, and may prove to be fatal.

9). The disease sometimes referred to as the "silent STD" because it is usually asymptomatic in women early on is
      a). chlamydia.
      b). gonorrhea.
      c). syphilis.
      d). pelvic inflammatory disease.

The correct answer is a--chlamydia.
A. Chlamydia is caused by an unusual bacterium, *Chlamydia trachomatis*, that has both bacterial and viral characteristics. Although chlamydia can be treated with antibiotics, it often goes undiagnosed as women do not present symptoms until the infection has become established. For this reason, it is sometimes referred to as the "silent STD."

The correct answer is a...
B. Answer b is incorrect because a person with gonorrhea does present symptoms and the infection is curable. The incidence of gonorrhea has been on the decline but still remains a serious threat.

The correct answer is a...
C. Answer c is incorrect because a person with syphilis does present symptoms in four distinct stages. Syphilis is a very destructive STD but is less common now than in the past due in part to the advent of blood-screening procedures and antibiotics.

The correct answer is a...
D. Answer d is incorrect because pelvic inflammatory disease is a secondary condition that occurs in women affected by a STD but left untreated. PID, a condition in which the fallopian tubes become scarred and blocked, can eventually lead to sterility. PID can occur in women untreated for gonorrhea or chlamydia.

Hint: Chlamydia is called the "silent STD" because women usually experience no symptoms until after the infection has become established. In part, because of this symptomless nature, the incidence of chlamydia has skyrocketed, increasing by more than seven-fold nationally since 1984.

10). Which of the following can be attributed to bacteria?
      a). decomposition of dead organic matter
      b). increasing oxygen levels in the atmosphere
      c). production of antibiotics
      d). all of these

The correct answer is d...
A. Answer a is incorrect because although bacteria do help the environment by decomposing dead organic matter, this is not the only attribute of bacteria.

The correct answer is d...
B. Answer b is incorrect because although bacteria, specifically cyanobacteria, did change the earth's atmosphere by increasing the oxygen levels in the atmosphere, this is not the only attribute of bacteria.

The correct answer is d...
C. Answer c is incorrect because although certain bacteria have been useful in producing antibiotics, usually substances that they produce to reduce competition from other bacteria, this is not the only attribute of bacteria.

The correct answer Is d--all of these
D. All of these are attributes of bacteria. Bacteria hold a vital place in the food web by decomposing dead organic matter and recycles organic and inorganic substances back into the environment. Cyanobacteria altered the earth's environment by releasing oxygen into the atmosphere as a byproduct of photosynthesis. Certain bacteria have been helpful in the production of antibiotics that they in fact use to decrease competition from other bacteria.

Hint: Bacteria were largely responsible for creating the properties of the atmosphere and soil over billions of years. Heterotrophic bacteria play a key role in the world ecology by breaking down organic compounds. Many of the most widely used antibiotics, including streptomycin, aureomycin, erythromycin, and chloromycetin, are derived from bacteria.

Test Your Visual Understanding

1). This figure shows two kinds of bacterial cell walls. Match the following labels with the appropriate numbered structures.
>   lipopolysaccharides
>   outer membrane
>   peptidoglycan
>   plasma membrane
>   protein

Answer:
>   lipopolysaccharides—4
>   outer membrane—5
>   peptidoglycan—1, 6
>   plasma membrane—2, 7
>   protein—3

2). What type of bacteria would have the cell wall structure shown in the upper figure? What type of bacteria would have the cell wall structure shown in the lower figure?
Answer: Upper figure depicts a Gram-positive bacteria because of the thicker peptidoglycan layer and the purple stain. The lower figure depicts a Gram-negative bacteria because there is less peptidoglycan and a red stain.

Apply Your Knowledge

1). Bacterial populations grow through binary fission, which means the bacterium divide in half such that each bacterium gives rise to two bacteria. Assume that a bacterium is placed in culture and undergoes binary fission every 30 minutes. The addition of a competing bacterium reduces the population size by 25%. How many bacteria from the original culture will be present after 24 hours?
Answer: Each division of the bacterium results in two individuals. If the bacterium divides every 30 minutes, they will undergo 48 division cycles in 24 hours. So after 24 hours the number of bacteria equals:

2^{48} or 281,474,976,710,656 bacteria or 2.81×10^{14}
But, the population has been reduced by 25% so:

281,474,976,710,656 x 0.75 = 211,106,232,532,992 bacteria or
2.11×10^{14}

2). Justify the assertion that life on earth could not exist without prokaryotes.
Answer: Prokaryotes are essential to all aspects of life on earth. Without bacteria, oxygen levels would not have increased in the atmosphere and although bacterial life would have still existed, we would not see the great diversity that currently inhabits the earth. Also, without prokaryotes, there would be little nitrogen in the soil for plants to use for growth. Prokaryotes decompose dead organic matter so that it recycles back into the environment.

3). What are the functions of antibiotics are in the prokaryotes that produce them?
Answer: Prokaryotes produce chemicals that protect their environment from competition. In order to reduce the number of competitors for resources, a prokaryote produces a chemical that harms other strains of prokaryotes but not itself. We use these chemicals as antibiotics to treat certain, primarily bacterial, infections. Although effective against some bacteria, these antibiotics

are not effective against all prokaryotes, particularly the type of prokaryotes that produced the chemical.

4). What are endospores? Why would they be an advantage? Would a bacterium with the ability to form endospores have a greater or lesser chance of extinction? Why?
Answer: Endospores are thick-walled spores produced by certain bacteria that protect its genome and a small amount of cytoplasm. The bacteria produce these spores under conditions that are harmful to the bacteria, for example extreme heat or cold or arid conditions that could lead to desiccation. Endospores offer an advantage to bacteria that are able to produce them because it protects them from destruction. Bacteria that produce endospores would have a lesser chance of becoming extinct because of this advantage. The endospores are in a state of dormancy and when conditions improve, the endospores germinate and produce live bacteria that can continue to grow and reproduce. Bacteria that cannot form endospores would die off in the extremely harsh environmental conditions.

Inquiry Questions
None for this chapter.

Self Test

1). The mitochondria of eukaryotic cells most likely arose as a result of endosymbiosis between a eukaryotic cell and a
      a). blue-green alga.
      b). nonsulfur purple bacterium.
      c). red alga.
      d). cyanobacterium.

The correct answer is b…
A. Answer a is incorrect because modern mitochondria most closely resemble a nonsulfur purple bacterium.

The correct answer is b--nonsulfur purple bacterium.
B. Answer b is correct because modern mitochondria most closely resemble a nonsulfur purple bacterium.

The correct answer is b…
C. Answer c is incorrect because modern mitochondria most closely a resemble nonsulfur purple bacterium.

The correct answer is b…
D. Answer d is incorrect because modern mitochondria most closely a resemble nonsulfur purple bacterium.

Hint: The most similar prokaryote to modern mitochondria is the nonsulfur purple bacterium, which is able to carry out oxidative metabolism.

2). The protists are a paraphyletic group that have traditionally been grouped together because
      a). they are all genetically similar to each other.
      b). they all have very similar morphological characters.
      c). they are not fungi, animals, or plants.
      d). they all have similar nutritional modes and live in similar environments.

The correct answer is c…
A. Answer a is incorrect because the protists are only distantly related to each other and many are genetically dissimilar.

The correct answer is c…
B. Answer b is incorrect because there is a great deal of morphological variation in the protists.

The correct answer is c--they are not fungi, animals, or plants.
C. Answer c is correct because the protists have been grouped together because they do not fit in any of the other kingdoms (fungi, plants, or animals).

The correct answer is c…
D. Answer d is incorrect because the protists are nutritionally diverse and live in diverse environments.

Hint: The protists are a paraphyletic group that should not be grouped together in a single kingdom. Traditionally, they have been grouped together because the different species that make up this kingdom could not be placed in any other kingdom. Modern analyses are attempting to sort the protists out into more evolutionary meaningful groups.

3). Many protists are able to resist harsh environmental conditions by
    a). forming a cyst and slowing metabolism during times of stress.
    b). utilizing a wide variety of nutritional modes.
    c). reproducing asexually through the process of budding.
    d). moving away from a harsh environment by using pseudopodia.

The correct answer is a--forming a cyst and slowing metabolism during times of stress.
A. Answer a is correct because many types of protists are able to form protective cysts which help protect the organism from extreme environmental conditions. While inside the cyst, metabolism usually slows which also helps the organism avoid harsh conditions.

The correct answer is a…
B. Answer b is incorrect because most protist species use only a single nutritional mode. While there is diversity in nutritional mode throughout the protists, each species usually only has one mode. An exception is the euglenoids—some species are able to be both phototrophic and autotrophic.

The correct answer is a…
C. Answer c is incorrect. Many species of protists do reproduce asexually via budding but this does not necessarily help protect them from a harsh environment.

The correct answer is a…
D. Answer d is incorrect. Most protists are motile however they are not usually able to move away from harsh environmental conditions.

Hint: Many protists are able to form cysts during harsh environmental conditions. During this time, their metabolism slows down and they are able to survive in this condition until environmental conditions improve.

4). The light-sensing organ in the *Euglena* is a
    a). flagellum.
    b). contractile vacuole.
    c). pellicle.
    d). stigma.

The correct answer is d…
A. Answer a is incorrect because a flagellum is a hairlike structure used in locomotion.

The correct answer is d…
B. Answer b is incorrect because a contractile vacuole is an organelle used by protists to maintain osmotic pressure.

The correct answer is d…
C. Answer c is incorrect because a pellicle is a flexible structure found within the membrane of euglenoids that gives the organism flexible support.

The correct answer is d--stigma.
D. Answer d is correct because a stigma is a light-sensitive organ found in some photosynthetic protists.

Hint: A stigma is a light-sensitive organ that allows photosynthetic organisms to orient toward a light source.

5). The parasitic kinetoplast that causes leishmaniasis must spend part of its life cycle in a nonhuman host. What organism(s) serve(s) as the vector for this life cycle?
        a). small mammals
        b). a sand fly
        c). a mosquito
        d). a tse-tse fly

The correct answer is b…
A. Answer a is incorrect because small mammals are responsible for the spread of Chagas disease.

The correct answer is b--a sand fly
B. Answer b is correct because sand flies are responsible for the spread of leishmaniasis.

The correct answer is b…
C. Answer c is incorrect because mosquitoes do not spread leishmaniasis.

The correct answer is b…
D. Answer d is incorrect because tse-tse flies help to spread African sleeping sickness.

Hint: Leishmaniasis is spread by sand flies. This disease causes skin sores and possible death if internal organs are affected.

6). You are examining cells from an unknown organism under the microscope. You note that the cells have a membrane-bounded nucleus and that there are small cavities in the membranes along the internal cell surface. Based upon this information alone, you conclude that these most likely are _____ cells.
        a). bacterial
        b). diatom
        c). dinoflagellate
        d). kinetoplastid

The correct answer is c…
A. Answer a is incorrect because bacteria do not have a membrane-bounded nucleus.

The correct answer is c…
B. Answer b is incorrect because the diatoms are recognized by their unique double shells made of silica.

The correct answer is c--dinoflagellate
C. Answer c is correct because the dinoflagellates are members of the Alveolata, which are distinguished by the presence of alveoli—small cavities below their plasma membranes.

The correct answer is c…
D. Answer d is incorrect because the kinetoplastids are recognized by the presence of a kinetoplast.

7). The parasitic protist that causes malaria, *Plasmodium*, must spend part of its life cycle in a nonhuman host. What organism(s) serve(s) as the vector for this life cycle?
        a). small mammals
        b). a sand fly
        c). a mosquito
        d). a tse-tse fly

The correct answer is c…
A. Answer a is incorrect. Mosquitoes are the vector for the malarial parasite *Plasmodium*.

The correct answer is c…
B. Answer b is incorrect. Mosquitoes are the vector for the malarial parasite *Plasmodium*.

The correct answer is c--a mosquito
C. Answer c is correct. Mosquitoes are the vector for the malarial parasite *Plasmodium*.

The correct answer is c…
D. Answer d is incorrect. Mosquitoes are the vector for the malarial parasite *Plasmodium*.

Hint: Mosquitoes are the vector for the malarial parasite *Plasmodium*. Efforts to eradicate malaria center on controlling the populations of mosquitoes and developing effective vaccines against the disease.

8). *Phytopthora infestans* is the oomycete that causes
      a). Chagas disease.
      b). potato blight.
      c). red tides.
      d). African sleeping sickness.

The correct answer is b…
A. Answer a is incorrect because Chagas disease is caused by a kinetoplastid.

The correct answer is b--potato blight.
B. Answer b is correct. Potato blight is caused by the oomycetes *Phytopthora infestans*.

The correct answer is b…
C. Answer c is incorrect. Red tides are caused by dinoflagellates.

The correct answer is b…
D. Answer d is incorrect. African sleeping sickness is caused by a kinetoplastid.

Hint: *Phytopthora infestans* is the causative agent of potato blight. It is this organism that caused the Irish potato famine that killed 400,000 people in Ireland and caused millions of Irish to emigrate to the United States during the 1840s.

9). A biologist discovers an alga that is marine, multicellular, lacks flagella and centrioles, and contains phycobilisomes. It probably belongs to which group?
      a). Rhodophyta
      b). Brown algae
      c). Chlorophyta
      d). Foraminifera

The correct answer is a--Rhodophyta
A. Answer a is correct. The Rhodophyta are mainly multicellular algae that lack flagella and centrioles and contain accessory photosynthetic pigments inslde phycobilisomes.

The correct answer is a…
B. Answer b is incorrect. The brown algae do not contain phycobilisomes.

The correct answer is a…
C. Answer c is incorrect. The Chlorophyta do not contain phycobilisomes.

The correct answer is a...
D. Answer d is incorrect. The Foraminifera is a heterotrophic group that does not contain photosynthetic pigments.

Hint: The Rhodophyta, or red algae, are mainly multicellular marine algae that contain red accessory photosynthetic pigments. These accessory pigments are contained inside structures known as phycobilisomes. The red algae also lack flagella and centrioles.

10). The green algae gave rise to which modern group of organisms?
        a). photosynthetic bacteria
        b). plants
        c). photosynthetic euglenoids
        d). animals

The correct answer is b...
A. Answer a is incorrect because the green algae are ancestors to modern plants.

The correct answer is b--plants
B. Answer b is correct because the green algae are ancestors to modern plants.

The correct answer is b...
C. Answer c is incorrect because the green algae are ancestors to modern plants.

The correct answer is b...
D. Answer d is incorrect because the green algae are ancestors to modern plants.

Hint: The green algae gave rise to modern plants. The green algae are divided into two main lineages—the Chlorophyta and the Streptophyta. The Streptophyta gave rise to the modern land plants.

Test Your Visual Understanding

1). This image shows several different types of protists that are characterized by a rigid double wall of silica. To what group do these organisms belong?
Answer: These are diatoms in the kingdom Stramenopila.

Apply Your Knowledge

1). Protists typically reproduce asexually. However, some protists undergo sexual reproduction during times of environmental stress. What advantage does sexual reproduction give a protist during these times?
Answer: Sexual reproduction provides greater genetic variability in the next generation. New gene combinations that are adaptive under the specific environmental stress may enhance the survival and reproduction of offspring with the favorable genotype.

2). Scientists are working to develop a vaccine against African sleeping sickness. Use what you know about the trypanosome responsible for this disease to determine why it is so difficult to develop a vaccine.
Answer: The African sleeping sickness trypanosome has a glycoprotein coat that can trigger an immune response. Vaccines are designed to mimic the antigenic part of the glycoprotein coat and to trigger immunity without causing disease. The problem with trypanosomes is that they have a complex genetic mechanism that continually changes the structure of the glycoprotein coat. One vaccine cannot provide immunity against the constantly changing antigens.

Self Test

1). All plants exhibit alternation of generations. This means their life cycle
  a). includes both haploid and diploid gametes.
  b). shows only asexual reproduction.
  c). has both a multicellular haploid stage and a multicellular diploid stage.
  d). does not include meiosis.

The correct answer is c...
A. Answer a is incorrect because gametes are always haploid and never diploid.

The correct answer is c...
B. Answer b is incorrect because plants undergo sexual reproduction.

The correct answer is c--has both a multicellular haploid stage and a multicellular diploid stage.
C. Answer c is correct. Alternation of generations refers to the alternation between multicellular haploid and diploid stages during the life cycle.

The correct answer is c...
D. Answer d is incorrect because the plant life cycle does include meiosis.

Hint: Alternation of generations refers to a life cycle in which there is an alternation between multicellular haploid and diploid stages.

2). The plant life cycle has both a sporophyte and a gametophyte generation. In the sporophyte stage,
  a). gametes are produced.
  b). meiosis occurs.
  c). only mitosis takes place.
  d). gametophytes form.

The correct answer is b...
A. Answer a is incorrect because gametes are produced in the gametophyte generation.

The correct answer is b--meiosis occurs.
B. Answer b is correct because meiosis takes place in the sporophyte (diploid stage) of the plant life cycle.

The correct answer is b...
C. Answer c is incorrect because meiosis occurs in the sporophyte stage, not mitosis.

The correct answer is b...
D. Answer d is incorrect because the gametophyte forms from the spores that are produced in the sporophyte stage of the life cycle.

Hint: The diploid sporophyte stage gives rise to haploid spores. These spores are produced through meiosis and give rise to the haploid gametophyte generation.

3). In plants,
  a). gametes are produced directly after meiosis.
  b). gametes are produced directly after mitosis.
  c). no gametes are motile.
  d). seeds are always produced.

The correct answer is b...
A. Answer a is incorrect because in plants, gametes are produced after mitosis.

The correct answer is b--gametes are produced directly after mitosis.
B. Answer b is correct because in plants, gametes are produced after mitosis.

The correct answer is b...
C. Answer c is incorrect because motile gametes are found in some groups of plants.

The correct answer is b...
D. Answer d is incorrect because many plants do not produce seeds.

4). Which of the following is true of the bryophytes?
       a). It is the only group that shows an alternation of generations.
       b). Bryophytes exhibit extensive vascular tissue.
       c). The sporophyte (multicellular diploid) is the conspicuous stage.
       d). The gametophyte (multicellular haploid) is the conspicuous stage.

The correct answer is d...
A. Answer a is incorrect because all plants show alternation of generations.

The correct answer is d...
B. Answer b is incorrect because the bryophytes do not have vascular tissue.

The correct answer is d...
C. Answer c is incorrect because the gametophyte is the conspicuous stage in the bryophyte life cycle.

The correct answer is d--The gametophyte (multicellular haploid) is the conspicuous stage.
D. Answer d is correct because the gametophyte is the conspicuous stage in the bryophyte life cycle.

Hint: The life cycle of the bryophytes is characterized by a conspicuous gametophyte generation and an inconspicuous sporophyte generation.

5). A plant's vascular tissue is composed of xylem and phloem. The xylem generally transports _____, whereas the phloem transports _____.
       a). water/sugar
       b). sugar/water
       c). water/water
       d). sugar/sugar

The correct answer is a--water/sugar
A. Answer a is correct because xylem transports water and phloem transports sugars.

The correct answer is a...
B. Answer b is incorrect because xylem transports water and phloem transports sugars.

The correct answer is a...
C. Answer c is incorrect because xylem transports water and phloem transports sugars.

The correct answer is a...
D. Answer d is incorrect because xylem transports water and phloem transports sugars.

Hint: Vascular plants contain tissues which allow them to transport water and sugar around their bodies. Xylem transports water and phloem transports sugar.

6). In the conifers, the
      a). gametophyte is prominent, and the sporophyte is dependent upon the gametophyte.
      b). sporophyte is prominent, with the sporophyte and gametophyte living independently.
      c). sporophyte is prominent, and the gametophyte is dependent upon the sporophyte.
      d). gametophyte is prominent, and the sporophyte stage has disappeared.

The correct answer is c…
A. Answer a is incorrect. The sporophyte is the prominent generation in the conifers.

The correct answer is c…
B. Answer b is incorrect. The sporophyte and the gametophyte do not live independently in the conifers.

The correct answer is c--the sporophyte is prominent, and the gametophyte is dependent upon the sporophyte.
C. Answer c is correct. In the conifers, the sporophyte is prominent and the gametophyte is dependent upon the sporophyte for support and nutrition.

The correct answer is c…
D. Answer d is incorrect. The sporophyte is the prominent generation in the conifers.

Hint: In the conifers, the sporophyte is the prominent generation and the gametophyte generation is dependent upon the sporophyte tissue for support and nutrition.

7). Which of the following characters is seen in the gymnosperms, but is not seen in other seeded vascular plants?
      a). alternation of generations
      b). exposed seeds
      c). sporophyte stage
      d). pollen

The correct answer is b…
A. Answer a is incorrect because all plants have alternation of generations.

The correct answer is b--exposed seeds
B. Answer b is correct because exposed seeds are only found in the gymnosperms.

The correct answer is b…
C. Answer c is incorrect because all plants have a sporophyte stage.

The correct answer is b…
D. Answer d is incorrect. Pollen is found in both the gymnosperms and the angiosperms.

Hint: Exposed seeds is a distinguishing characteristic of the gymnosperms.

8). All flowering plants (angiosperms)
      a). produce exposed seeds.
      b). are nonvascular.
      c). have flagellated sperm.
      d). have fruit.

The correct answer is d…
A. Answer a is incorrect because the angiosperms produce protected seeds.
The correct answer is d…
B. Answer b is incorrect because the angiosperms are vascular.

The correct answer is d...
C. Answer c is incorrect. The angiosperms do not have flagellated sperm.

The correct answer is d--have fruit.
D. Answer d is correct. All angiosperms bear fruit.

Hint: The angiosperms are characterized by the production of fruit. Only the angiosperms bear true fruit.

9). In the angiosperms, the
   a). gametophyte is prominent, and the sporophyte is dependent upon the gametophyte.
   b). sporophyte is prominent, with the sporophyte and gametophyte living independently.
   c). sporophyte is prominent, and the gametophyte is dependent upon the sporophyte.
   d). gametophyte is prominent, and the sporophyte stage has disappeared.

The correct answer is c...
A. Answer a is incorrect. The sporophyte is the prominent generation in the angiosperms.

The correct answer is c...
B. Answer b is incorrect. The sporophyte and the gametophyte do not live independently in the angiosperms.

The correct answer is c--sporophyte is prominent, and the gametophyte is dependent upon the sporophyte.
C. Answer c is correct. In the angiosperms, the sporophyte is prominent and the gametophyte is dependent upon the sporophyte for support and nutrition.

The correct answer is c...
D. Answer d is incorrect. The sporophyte is the prominent generation in the angiosperms.

Hint: In the angiosperms, the sporophyte is the prominent generation and the gametophyte generation is dependent upon the sporophyte tissue for support and nutrition.

10). Which of the following is *not* characteristic of a monocot?
   a). leaves with parallel veins
   b). flower parts usually in threes or multiples of three
   c). lateral meristems occurring rarely
   d). seed with two cotyledons

The correct answer is d...
A. Answer a is incorrect. Monocots have leaves with parallel veins.

The correct answer is d...
B. Answer b is incorrect. Monocots have flowers with parts in threes.

The correct answer is d...
C. Answer c is incorrect. In the monocots, lateral meristems rarely occur.

The correct answer is d--seed with two cotyledons
D. Answer d is correct. Monocots have one cotyledon, not two.

Hint: The monocots are those angiosperms with one cotyledon (mono=one).

1). Label the diagram with the following terms: stigma, style, ovule, ovary, carpel, anther, filament, stamen.
Answer:

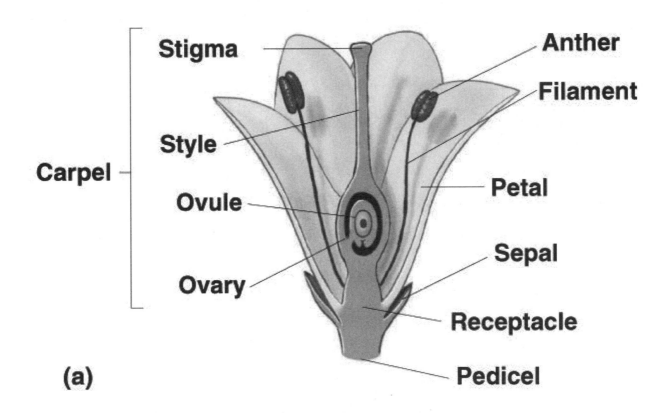

(a)

Apply Your Knowledge

1). A major factor in life on land is coping with ultraviolet radiation from the sun. Early in the evolution of land plants, there was a change from having a prominent haploid gametophyte to a prominent diploid sporophyte. Explain why this change may have occurred in reference to ultraviolet radiation.
Answer: A haploid organism has only one copy of each gene. If ultraviolet radiation mutates that single copy, the organism will most likely be severely damaged. Diploid organisms have two copies of each gene. If the ultraviolet radiation mutates one copy, there is another copy present to compensate.

2). Plants provide many vital products for humans. Make a list of all the plant-based products that you use in a single day.
Answer: Examples: food, clothing, wood, paper, gasoline.

3). Many flowering plants have adapted in response to a particular animal pollinator, and they rely on that animal for proper pollination to occur. What will happen to the plant population if the animal pollinator goes extinct?

Answer: Unless another animal can fill the role of pollinator, the plant species will probably go extinct along with its animal pollinator.

Self Test

1). How many species of fungi are thought to exist?
      a). 1500
      b). 150,000
      c). 1.5 million
      d). 1.5 billion

The correct answer is c...
A. Answer a is incorrect because there are an estimated 1.5 million species of fungi.

The correct answer is c...
B. Answer b is incorrect because there are an estimated 1.5 million species of fungi.

The correct answer is c--1.5 million
C. Answer c is correct because there are an estimated 1.5 million species of fungi.

The correct answer is c...
D. Answer d is incorrect because there are an estimated 1.5 million species of fungi.

Hint: Mycologists estimate there are 1.5 million species of fungi.

2). Which of the following is *not* a characteristic of the fungi?
      a). They are all absorptive heterotrophs.
      b). They have cell walls made of chitin.
      c). Mitosis takes place within the nuclear membrane.
      d). They are all motile.

The correct answer is d...
A. Answer a is incorrect because all fungi are absorptive heterotrophs.

The correct answer is d...
B. Answer b is incorrect because fungi have cell walls made of chitin.

The correct answer is d...
C. Answer c is incorrect mitosis takes place within the nuclear membrane in the fungi.

The correct answer is d--They are all motile.
D. Answer d is correct because most fungi are not motile. The Chytridiomycota are the only motile fungi.

3). A mycelium is
      a). a specialized reproductive structure of a fungus.
      b). a mass of connected fungal hyphae.
      c). a mutualistic relationship between a fungus and a plant.
      d). a partition between the cells of fungal hyphae.

The correct answer is b...
A. Answer a is incorrect because a mycelium is a mass of connected hyphae.

The correct answer is b--a mass of connected fungal hyphae.
B. Answer b is correct because a mycelium is a mass of connected hyphae.

The correct answer is b...
C. Answer c is incorrect because mycelium is a mass of connected hyphae.

The correct answer is b...
D. Answer d is incorrect because the partitions between the cells of fungal hyphae are known as septa.

Hint: A mycelium is a mass of fungal hyphae.

4). Which of the following statements best describes fungi?
        a). All are eukaryotic, multicellular autotrophs.
        b). All are eukaryotic heterotrophs that feed by absorption.
        c). All are prokaryotic, multicellular autotrophs.
        d). All are eukaryotic heterotrophs that feed by ingestion.

The correct answer is b...
A. Answer a is incorrect because all fungi are heterotrophs and there are some unicellular members of this kingdom.

The correct answer is b--All are eukaryotic heterotrophs that feed by absorption.
B. Answer b is correct because all fungi are eukaryotic, heterotrophic, and they feed by absorbing nutrients from the environment.

The correct answer is b...
C. Answer c is incorrect because fungi are eukaryotic heterotrophs and there are some unicellular members of this kingdom.

The correct answer is b...
D. Answer d is incorrect because fungi feed by absorption rather than ingestion.

Hint: All fungi are eukaryotic heterotrophs that feed by absorption. There are both unicellular (yeasts) and multicellular representatives of this kingdom.

5). A wildlife pathologist is examining some skin tissue from a dead frog. She notes the presence of a fungus. She cultures some of the fungal cells and notices that some of the cells are flagellated. She concludes that the frog has a fungal disease caused by
        a). an ascomycete.
        b). a zygomycete.
        c). a basdiomycete.
        d). a chytrid.

The correct answer is d...
A. Answer a is incorrect because ascomycetes do not have flagellated cells—chytrids are the only fungi with flagellated cells.

The correct answer is d...
B. Answer b is incorrect because zygomycetes do not have flagellated cells—chytrids are the only fungi with flagellated cells.

The correct answer is d...
C. Answer c is incorrect because basidiomycetes do not have flagellated cells—chytrids are the only fungi with flagellated cells.

The correct answer is d--a chytrid.
D. Answer d is correct. Chytrids are the only fungi with flagellated cells.

6). You are walking in the woods and see a fungus that is unfamiliar to you. You remove a reproductive structure, and take it home to examine further. When you look at it under the microscope, you find a zygosporangium. Based on this information alone, this fungus is a(n)
    a). zygomycete.
    b). chytrid.
    c). basidiomycete.
    d). ascomycete.

The correct answer is a--zygomycete.
A. Answer a is correct because the distinctive reproductive structure of the zygomycete is the zygosporangium.

The correct answer is a...
B. Answer b is incorrect because the chytrids do not form a zygosporangium during sexual reproduction.

The correct answer is a...
C. Answer c is incorrect because the basidiomycetes do not form a zygosporangium during sexual reproduction.

The correct answer is a...
D. Answer d is incorrect because the ascomycetes do not form a zygosporangium during sexual reproduction.

Hint: A distinguishing characteristic of the Zygomycota is the production of a zygosporangium during sexual reproduction.

7). A basidium is typically observed in the common
    a). bread mold.
    b). gilled mushroom.
    c). lichen.
    d). chytrid.

The correct answer is b...
A. Answer a is incorrect because bread molds are zygomycetes which form a zygosporangium, not a basidium.

The correct answer is b--gilled mushroom.
B. Answer b is correct because gilled mushrooms are representative of the Basidiomycota which form basidia during sexual reproduction.

The correct answer is b...
C. Answer c is incorrect because lichens are mutualistic symbioses between a fungus (usually an ascomycete) and a photosynthetic organism (often a green alga).

The correct answer is b...
D. Answer d is incorrect because chytrids do not form basidia during sexual reproduction.

Hint: The Basidiomycota produce a distinctive reproductive structure known as a basidium during sexual reproduction. The gilled mushrooms are representative of the basidiomycetes.

8). An ascomycete can be distinguished from other fungi
    a). because ascomycetes are mainly diploid.
    b). because ascomycetes lack a dikaryotic phase.
    c). by the presence of eight sexual spores in an ascus.
    d). by the presence of gills on the mycelium.

The correct answer is c…
A. Answer a is incorrect because fungi exist mainly in the haploid state.

The correct answer is c…
B. Answer b is incorrect because the ascomycetes do not lack a dikaryotic phase.

The correct answer is c--by the presence of eight sexual spores in an ascus.
C. Answer c is correct because the ascomycetes are distinguished by the presence of ascus during sexual reproduction.

The correct answer is c…
D. Answer d is incorrect because the gilled mushrooms belong to the Basidiomycota.

Hint: The Ascomycota are distinguished by the presence of eight sexual spores in an ascus during sexual reproduction.

9). A lichen can be described as a mutualistic symbiosis between an ascomycete and a(n)
      a). chytrid.
      b). archeabacterium.
      c). green alga.
      d). angiosperm root.

The correct answer is c…
A. Answer a is incorrect because lichens are a mutualistic relationship between a fungus, usually an ascomycete, and a photosynthetic organism such as a green alga.

The correct answer is c…
B. Answer b is incorrect because lichens are a mutualistic relationship between a fungus, usually an ascomycete, and a photosynthetic organism such as a green alga.

The correct answer is c--green alga.
C. Answer c is correct because lichens are a mutualistic relationship between a fungus, usually an ascomycete, and a photosynthetic organism such as a green alga.

The correct answer is c…
D. Answer d is incorrect because lichens are a mutualistic relationship between a fungus, usually an ascomycete, and a photosynthetic organism such as a green alga.

Test Your Visual Understanding

1). This is a diagram of the life cycle of a typical bread mold.
      a). Is this sexual or asexual reproduction?
      b). On this diagram, indicate where in the life cycle meiosis takes place.
      c). Label the reproductive structures of this fungus.
      d). To what group of fungi does this organism belong?
Answer:
      a). sexual
      b). –on diagram
      c). –on diagram
      d). Zygomycota

2). Two equal-sized plots of Italian ryegrass were grown, one with an done without endophytes. Each plot was exposed to aphids in the experiment shown above.
      a). What conclusion would you draw from the experimental results?
      b). What advantages and disadvantages does the ryegrass have in an endophytic relationship?

Answer: 2a).   There are fewer aphids on ryegrass plants that are grown with endophytes than without endophytes. The endophyte appears to protect the ryegrass from aphid infection.

        2b).   Advantage: The endophytic relationship appears to protect the ryegrass from aphids that drain plant nutrients and leave excrement on the leaves that can lead to fungal infection of the leads.

            Disadvantage: It is possible that the ryegrass provides endophytes with some nutrients in exchange for protection.

Self Test

1). Which feature is *not* characteristic of the animals?
        a). multicellular heterotrophs
        b). sexual reproduction
        c). embryonic development
        d). cell walls

The correct answer is d…
A. Answer a is incorrect because this is a characteristic of the animal phyla. All animals are multicellular heterotrophs, meaning that their bodies are cellular complexes and they have to obtain energy by consuming other organisms (i.e., plants, algae, other animals, etc.).

The correct answer is d…
B. Answer b is incorrect because this is a characteristic of the animal phyla. Most animals reproduce sexually, producing haploid gametes that fuse to form diploid zygotes.

The correct answer is d…
C. Answer c is incorrect because this is a characteristic of the animal phyla. Most animals have a similar pattern of embryonic development, where the zygote undergoes a series of mitotic divisions to form a multicellular embryo called a gastrula.

The correct answer is d--cell walls
D. Animal cells, unlike the cells of plants and fungi, lack rigid cell walls. The cell membranes are quite flexible and are held together by extracellular protein lattices.

Hint: Animals are heterotrophs and must ingest plants, algae, or other animals for nourishment. All animals are multicellular, and unlike plants, protists, and fungi, animal cells lack cell walls.

2). Most of the phyla of the animal kingdom are found
        a). on land.
        b). in the ocean.
        c). burrowing underground.
        d). in freshwater habitats.

The correct answer is b…
A. Answer a is incorrect because terrestrial habitats are home to the fewest number of animal phyla, behind freshwater phyla and marine phyla.

The correct answer is b--in the ocean.
B. Of the approximately 35 animal phyla identified, most contain animals that live in marine environments, followed by freshwater environments, and then terrestrial environments.

The correct answer is b…
C. Answer c is incorrect because the fewest number of phyla contain animals that burrow underground. These animals would fall within the group of terrestrial phyla whose numbers fall short of freshwater phyla and marine phyla.

The correct answer is b…
D. Answer d is incorrect because although freshwater habitats are home to more animal phyla than terrestrial environments, they are second in number to marine phyla.

Hint: The animal kingdom includes about 35 phyla, most of which occur in the sea. Far fewer phyla occur in freshwater and fewer still occur on land. Members of three successful marine phyla, Arthropoda (insects), Mollusca (snails), and Chordata (vertebrates) dominate animal life on land.

3). The subkingdom of animals that lack symmetry and have no true tissues or organs is the
        a). Eumetazoa.
        b). Radiata.
        c). Parazoa.
        d). Bilateria.

The correct answer is c…
A. Answer a is incorrect because the Eumetazoa is the name for the animal subkingdom that contains animals that have a definite shape and symmetry and, in most cases, tissues organized into organs and organ systems.

The correct answer is c…
B. Answer b is incorrect because the Radiata is a subgroup of the subkingdom Eumetazoa that contains animals with radial symmetry and cells divided into two layers of tissues, an ectoderm layer and an endoderm layer.

The correct answer is c--Parazoa.
C. The Parazoa subkingdom is quite limited as in the number of different kinds of animals placed into that subkingdom. The Parazoa contains animals that lack symmetry and have no true tissues or organs. The only animals that fit into this category are the sponges, the phylum Porifera.

The correct answer is c…
D. Answer d is incorrect because the Bilateria is a subgroup of the subkingdom Eumetazoa that contain animals with bilateral symmetry and cells divided into three layers of tissues: ectoderm, endoderm, and mesoderm.

Hint: The kingdom Animalia is traditionally divided by taxonomists into two main branches, one of which is Parazoa—animals that for the most part lack a definite symmetry and possess neither tissues nor organs, mostly comprised of the sponges, phylum Porifera.

4). Except for the Radiata, the eumetazoans
        a). lack true tissues and organs.
        b). are monoblastic.
        c). are diploblastic.
        d). are triploblastic.

The correct answer is d…
A. Answer a is incorrect because the eumetazoans, including the Radiata, have true tissues and organs. The parazoans lack true tissues and organs.

The correct answer is d…
B. Answer b is incorrect because the eumetazoans have three layers of tissue and monoblastic implies the presence of just one tissue layer.

The correct answer is d…
C. Answer c is incorrect because the Radiata are diploblastic, meaning that they have two tissue layers, the ectoderm and the endoderm. The other eumetazoans have three tissue layers.

The correct answer is d--are triploblastic.

D. The eumetazoans include two subgroups, the Radiata and the Bilateria. The two groups differ in their axes of symmetry (radial symmetry vs. bilateral symmetry) and their tissue layers. The Radiata have two tissue layers, ectoderm and endoderm, and so are referred to as diploblastic. The other eumetazoans, the Bilateria, have three tissue layers, ectoderm, endoderm, and mesoderm and so are referred to as triploblastic.

Hint: Eumetazoans of the subgroup Radiata have two layers, and outer ectoderm and an inner endoderm, and thus are called diploblastic. All other eumetazoans, the Bilateria, are triploblastic and produce a third layer, the mesoderm, between the ectoderm and the endoderm.

5). Cnidarians and ctenophorans differ from other eumetazoans by having
        a). radial symmetry.
        b). bilateral symmetry.
        c). major organ systems.
        d). three tissue layers.

The correct answer is a--radial symmetry.
A. The cnidarians and ctenophorans are members of the subgroup Radiata, which means that they have radial symmetry and two tissue layers, the ectoderm and the endoderm.

The correct answer is a…
B. Answer b is incorrect because the cnidarians and ctenophorans have radial symmetry, not bilateral symmetry.

The correct answer is a…
C. Answer c is incorrect because the cnidarians and ctenophorans are members of the subgroup Radiata, which means that they have two layers of tissues that form major organ systems, although the Bilateria have more complex organ systems because they have three layers of tissues.

The correct answer is a…
D. Answer d is incorrect because the cnidarians and ctenophorans are members of the subgroup Radiata, which means that they have two layers of tissues, not three.

Hint: Symmetrical bodies first evolved in marine animals belonging to two phyla: Cnidaria (jellyfish, sea anemones, and corals) and Ctenophora (comb jellies). The bodies of these two phyla, the Radiata, exhibit radial symmetry, a body design in which the parts of the body are arranged around a central axis.

6). The advantage of bilateral symmetry is that it allowed for the evolution of
        a). appendages.
        b). cephalization.
        c). reproductive structures.
        d). parasites.

The correct answer is b…
A. Answer a is incorrect because animals with radial symmetry also have appendages, such as tentacles on sea anemone.

The correct answer is b--cephalization.
B. Animals with radial symmetry have a nervous system but they are more in the form of dispersed nerve nets and not localized in a "head" region. With the evolution of bilateral symmetry, the nerves became grouped in the anterior end of the body.

The correct answer is b...
C. Answer c is incorrect because the evolution of a body cavity had much more of an effect on the evolution of larger, more specialized reproductive structures.

The correct answer is b...
D. Answer d is incorrect because parasites prey on essentially all animal types, not just on animals with bilateral symmetry.

Hint: Much of the nervous system in bilaterally symmetrical animals is in the form of major longitudinal nerve cords. In a very early evolutionary advance, nerve cells became grouped in the anterior end of the body. This trend ultimately led to the evolution of a definite head and brain area, a process called cephalization.

7). Members of which group are *not* deuterostomes?
   a). chordates
   b). echinoderms
   c). arthropods
   d). none of these, all are deuterostomes

The correct answer is c...
A. Answer a is incorrect because the chordates exhibit a form of embryonic development known as deuterostome. Deuterostomes have radial cleavage (as opposed to spiral cleavage) and the blastopore becomes the anus (as opposed to becoming the mouth).

The correct answer is c...
B. Answer b is incorrect because the echinoderms exhibit a form of embryonic development known as deuterostome. Deuterostomes have radial cleavage (as opposed to spiral cleavage) and the blastopore becomes the anus (as opposed to becoming the mouth).

The correct answer is c--arthropods
C. Arthropods, along with mollusks and annelids, exhibit a form of embryonic development known as protostome. Protostomes have spiral cleavage (as opposed to radial cleavage in deuterostomes) and the blastopore becomes the mouth (as opposed to becoming the anus in deuterostomes).

The correct answer is c...
D. Answer d is incorrect because arthropods are not deuterostomes, they are protostomes.

Hint: Coelomates can be divided into two groups based on differences in the basic pattern of development. One group, the protostomes includes the mollusks, annelids, and arthropods. Two outwardly dissimilar groups, the echinoderms and the chordates, together with a few other smaller related phyla comprise the second group, the deuterostomes.

8). The evolution of an internal body cavity offered an advantage in animal body design in all areas except
   a). circulation.
   b). digestion.
   c). freedom of movement.
   d). gamete storage.

The correct answer is a--circulation.
A. The evolution of a body cavity resulted in the isolation of different tissues and organs in the body. With tissues and organs separated from the surface and from each other, there needed to be a system by which molecules could pass between cells. The evolution of a circulatory system solved this problem in animals with body cavities.

The correct answer is a...
B. Answer b is incorrect because the evolution of a body cavity allowed for the lengthening of the digestive system and lead to specialization of digestive organs.

The correct answer is a...
C. Answer c is incorrect because the evolution of a body cavity, which is essentially a tube within the body cavity, was more flexible, allowing for a greater freedom of movement for animals.

The correct answer is a...
D. Answer d is incorrect because the evolution of a body cavity allowed for space within the body for the gonads to expand in size. With larger gonads (testes and ovaries), the animals could accumulate a larger number of eggs and sperm.

Hint: The development of the coelom poses a problem—circulation—solved in pseudocoelomates by churning the fluid within the body cavity. In coelomates, the gut is again surrounded by tissue that presents a barrier to diffusion. This problem is solved among coelomates by the development of a circulatory system.

9). The segments of annelids are
      a). apparent in the embryo but not in the adult.
      b). specialized for different functions.
      c). most obvious in the mesoderm (muscles) but not in the ectoderm.
      d). repetitive—each able to develop a complete set of adult organs.

The correct answer is d...
A. Answer a is incorrect because segmentation is apparent in the developing embryo but segments are also very apparent in the adult.

The correct answer is d...
B. Answer b is incorrect because the segments of annelids are repetitive units, each able to develop the organ systems and therefore are not specialized for different functions.

The correct answer is d...
C. Answer c is incorrect because the segments are very apparent in the ectoderm, which gives rise to the outer covering of the body and the nervous system.

The correct answer is d--repetitive—each able to develop a complete set of adult organs.
D. Segmentation in annelids occurs such that each segment may go on to develop a complete set of adult organs. This repetitiveness in the nature of the segments is advantageous in the event that some of the segments are damaged, the others can take over the functions of the lost segments.

Hint: In annelids and other highly segmented animals, each segment may go on to develop a more or less complete set of adult organ systems. Damage to any one segment need not be fatal to the individual, since the other segments duplicate that segment's function.

10). Which of the following hypotheses about the origin of metazoans is supported by ribosomal RNA analysis?
      a). the multinucleate hypothesis
      b). the colonial flagellate hypothesis
      c). the polyphyletic origin hypothesis
      d). None of these; rRNA analysis doesn't support any specific hypothesis.

The correct answer is b…
A. Answer a is incorrect because the multinucleate hypothesis that states that metazoans arose from a multinuclear protists like today's ciliates is not supported by molecular evidence because metazoans are closer to eukaryotic algae than they are to ciliates.

The correct answer is b--the colonial flagellate hypothesis
B. The colonial flagellate hypothesis states that the metazoans arose from colonial protists, which are hollow spherical colonies of flagellated cells. The rRNA analysis shows both parazoans and eumetazoans share a common ancestor and this ancestor is most like the colonial flagellated species.

The correct answer is b…
C. Answer c is incorrect because the polyphyletic origin hypothesis proposes that the sponges (parazoans) evolved independently from eumetazoans. The molecular evidence supports a monophyletic origin, the parazoans and eumetazoans evolving from a common ancestor.

The correct answer is b…
D. Answer d is incorrect because there is a correct answer. The molecular evidence using rRNA analysis clearly supports the colonial flagellate hypothesis, answer b.

Hint: Most taxonomists agree that the animal kingdom is monophyletic—that is, that parazoans and eumetazoans have a common ancestor. Molecular systematics based on ribosomal RNA sequences settles this argument clearly in favor of the colonial flagellate hypothesis.

Test Your Visual Understanding

1). Which of these drawings (a or b) depicts a radially symmetrical animal? Which depicts a bilaterally symmetrical animal? Although a radially symmetrical animal can be bisected into equal halves in any two-dimensional plane, can you describe a plane of orientation of a radially symmetrical animal that produces dissimilar halves (Refer to the planes of bisection in b.)?
Answer: The radially symmetrical is the sea anemone in a and the bilaterally symmetrical animal is the squirrel in b. A radially symmetrical animal can be bisected into equal halves in any two-dimensional plane in the *vertical* direction but not necessarily through a *horizontal* plane, like the frontal plane in b. Many radially symmetrical animals, like jellyfish or hydra, have a dorsal and ventral part of the body, such that a plane that bisects through the dorsal/ventral axis of the body would produce dissimilar halves.

Apply Your Knowledge

1). In what ways is an earthworm more complex than a flatworm?
Answer: An earthworm, in the Annelida phylum, is a coelomate and a flatworm; in the Platyhelminthes phylum, is an acoelomate. The presence of a body cavity in the earthworm allows for specialization of the internal organs, compared to the flatworm. The coelom also leads to the evolution of a circulatory system in the earthworm that is not present in the flatworm. The reproductive organs and gametes in the earthworm are also larger and more diverse, which expands the reproductive strategies used by earthworms compared to flatworms.

2). Why is it believed that echinoderms and chordates, which are so dissimilar, are members of the same evolutionary line?
Answer: Chordates and echinoderms shared a very key characterization of animal taxonomy—that of embryo growth pattern. These two groups comprise the deuterostomes whose embryological development differs greatly from the protostomes (mollusks, annelids, and arthropods). These embryological developmental patterns are guided by genetic differences in the expression of *Hox* genes, which suggests that echinoderms and chordates share a key characteristic very distinct from other animal groups. And, although the adult echinoderms look very different from the chordates, an earlier stage in their development looks more closely related to the chordates.

Self Test

1). The traditional animal family tree places more significance on body plan (the presence of a coelom) while the rRNA tree places more significance on
    a). embryological development patterns.
    b). whether or not the animal molts.
    c). symmetry.
    d). all of these.

The correct answer is b…
A. Answer a is incorrect because both classification schemes place significance on embryological development patterns; each breaking down the eumetazoans into protostomes or deuterostomes.

The correct answer is b--whether or not the animal molts.
B. The traditional animal family tree places significance on the body plan of the protostomes, indicating whether an animal is a noncoelomate, a pseudocoelomate, or a coelomate. The rRNA animal family tree places significance on the growth characteristics of the protostomes, indicating whether an animal molts or not. Molting protostomes are the ecdysozoans and the nonmolting protostomes are the lophotrochozoans.

The correct answer is b…
C. Answer c is incorrect because both classification schemes place significance on the symmetry of the animal, whether radially symmetrical or bilaterally symmetrical.

The correct answer is b…
D. Answer d is incorrect because there is only one correct answer, answer b. Both classification systems recognize the significance of embryological development patterns and the symmetry of the animal. The differences between the two classification systems is that the traditional system subdivides the protostomes by body plan and the rRNA system subdivides the protostomes by the ability to molt.

Hint: Phylogenies based on rRNA sequences suggest a very different lineage for the protostome phyla. Two major clades are recognized which have been evolving independently since ancient times: the lophotrochozoans and the ecdysozoans. Lophotrochozoan animals grow the same way you do, by adding additional mass to an existing body. Ecdysozoans are the molting animals. They increase in size by molting their external skeletons, an ability that seems to have evolved only once.

2). A key evolutionary development seen for the first time in the sponges is
    a). a complete digestive system.
    b). tissues.
    c). body symmetry.
    d). multicellularity.

The correct answer is d…
A. Answer a is incorrect because sponges do not have a complete digestive system. They have cellular digestion that is carried out by the choanocyte cells. These flagellated cells draw in water carrying nutrients. The nutrients are absorbed through endocytosis into the cell.

The correct answer is d…
B. Answer b is incorrect because sponges do not have tissues. They have specialized cells but they are not associated into discrete tissue layers.

The correct answer is d...
C. Answer c is incorrect because sponges do not exhibit body symmetry. A few small species of sponges appear to have radial symmetry, but most members of this phylum completely lack symmetry.

The correct answer is d--multicellularity.
D. The protists from which all animal phyla evolved were flagellated, colonial organisms, however they did not exhibit true multicellularity. Multicellularity, which is the presence of different cell types working in concert, first appears in the sponges, phylum Porifera.

Hint: The sponges are parazoans, animals that lack tissues and organs and a definite symmetry. However, sponges, like all animals, have true, complex multicellularity, unlike their protistan ancestors. The body of a sponge contains several distinctly different types of cells whose activities are loosely coordinated with one another.

3). All of the following are found in sponges except
      a). spicules.
      b). choanocytes.
      c). a digestive tract.
      d). sexual and/or asexual reproduction.

The correct answer is c...
A. Answer a is incorrect because sponges contain spicules which are needlelike structures made of calcium carbonate or silica. Spicules strengthen and add support to the sponge body.

The correct answer is c...
B. Answer b is incorrect because sponges contain choanocytes. Choanocytes are specialized flagellated cells that line the inside cavity of the sponge. The beating of the flagella draws water into the cavity through small pores. Plankton is filtered from the water as it flows through the choanocytes.

The correct answer is c--a digestive tract.
C. Sponges do not contain a digestive tract. Sponges feed by the filtering of plankton from water through specialized cells called choanocytes. They do not contain a specialized organ involved in digestion.

The correct answer is c...
D. Answer d is incorrect because sponges reproduce by both sexual and asexual reproduction methods. Sponges reproduce asexually by fragmentation. Small fragments break off and grow into new animals. Sexual reproduction occurs in some mature individuals producing eggs and sperm. Fertilization results in flagellated larva that swim to new locations, settle on the substrate, and transform into adults.

Hint: Sponges feed in a unique way. The beating of flagella that line the inside of the sponge draw water in through numerous small pores. Plankton and other small organisms are filtered from the water.

4). The first animal group to show extracellular digestion was the
      a). sponges
      b). cnidarians.
      c). flatworms.
      d). roundworms.

The correct answer is b…
A. Answer a is incorrect because sponges do not exhibit extracellular digestion, which requires a digestive tract, but rather intracellular digestion, where substances are brought into the choanocytes and digested within those cells.

The correct answer is b--cnidarians.
B. The cnidarians was the first animal group to have distinct tissues and with that came specialized structures and functions. In the cnidarians, digestion occurs in a gut cavity rather than in individual cells and is called extracellular digestion. Digestion in sponges occurs intracellularly, taking place within the choanocytes.

The correct answer is b…
C. Answer c is incorrect because although flatworms have extracellular digestion, they were not the first animal group to exhibit this characteristic.

The correct answer is b…
D. Answer d is incorrect because although roundworms have extracellular digestion, they were not the first animal group to exhibit this characteristic.

Hint: A major evolutionary innovation in cnidarians, compared with sponges, is the internal extracellular digestion of food. Digestion takes place within a gut cavity, rather than only within individual cells.

5). Cnidarians project a nematocyst to capture their prey by
    a). building up a high internal osmotic pressure.
    b). ejecting it with a jet of water.
    c). using a springlike apparatus.
    d). muscle contractions that "throw" the nematocyst.

The correct answer is a--building up a high internal osmotic pressure.
A. The nematocyst is contained within a cell called a cnidocyte. The interior of the cnidocyte builds up osmotic pressure by transporting in ions through active transport but maintains a water-impermeable plasma membrane. When the cnidocyte is stimulated, the plasma membrane becomes permeable to water and water rushes into the cell. This influx of water forces the nematocyst out of the cell.

The correct answer is a…
B. Answer b is incorrect because the nematocyst is ejected by the influx of water into the cell, not by the force of water out of the cell, such as a jet of water flowing out of the cell.

The correct answer is a…
C. Answer c is incorrect because the use of a springlike apparatus suggests a mechanical mechanism that thrusts the nematocyst out of the cell and this is not the case. The nematocysts are ejected by the force of water into the cell, pushing the nematocyst out of the cell.

The correct answer is a…
D. Answer d is incorrect because although cnidarians contain epitheliomuscular cells that contract allowing the animal to move through the water, muscular cells are not involved in the ejection of the nematocysts out of the cell.

Hint: To propel the harpoon, the cnidocyte uses water pressure. Before firing, the cnidocyte builds up a very high internal osmotic pressure. This is done by using active transport to build a high concentration of ions inside, while keeping its wall impermeable to water. When a flagellum-like trigger on the cnidocyte is stimulated to discharge, its walls become permeable to water, which rushes inside and violently pushes out the barbed filament.

6). Which of the following is an example of an organism with the medusa body form?
    a). a hydra
    b). a coral
    c). an anemone
    d). a jellyfish

The correct answer is d…
A. Answer a is incorrect because a hydra has no medusa stage and exists as a solitary polyp. Other hydroids, in the class Hydrozoa with hydra, have both a polyp and medusa stage and so the hydra is unique in not having a medusa stage.

The correct answer is d…
B. Answer b is incorrect because a coral, in the class Anthozoa, has a polyp body form with a plantlike body topped by a tuft of crown of hollow tentacles. Coral secrete a tough outer skeleton or exoskeleton of calcium carbonate that forms a hard protective structure around the coral animals.

The correct answer is d…
C. Answer c is incorrect because anemone, in the class Anthozoa, has a polyp body form with a plantlike body topped by a tuft of crown of hollow tentacles. They are sessile animals with their tentacle projecting up away from the substrate.

The correct answer is d--a jellyfish
D. The jellyfish, in the class Scyphozoa, have both a polyp and medusa stage in their life cycle but the medusa stage is the dominant stage. The polyp stage forms after fertilization and gives rise to the medusa that buds off of the polyp. In some jellyfish that live in the open ocean, the polyp stage is suppressed, and the zygote develops directly into a medusa.

Hint: The species of jellyfish are transparent or translucent marine organisms. These animals spend most of the time floating near the surface of the sea. In all of them, the medusa stage is dominant—much larger and more complex than the polyps. The medusae are bell shaped, with hanging tentacles around their margins. The polyp stage is small, inconspicuous, and simple in structure.

7). Key evolutionary advances of the flatworms are bilateral symmetry and
        a). a coelom.
        b). internal organs.
        c). a one-way digestive tract.
        d). a body cavity.

The correct answer is b…
A. Answer a is incorrect because the flatworms lack a coelom, a body cavity. The only cavity in the solid worms is the digestive tract; the rest of the body is solid.

The correct answer is b--internal organs.
B. Internal organs that perform specific functions are present in the flatworms but were not present in the cnidarians. Organs such as a digestive tract, nerve cords, and reproductive organs are present and serve specific functions in the solid worms.

The correct answer is b…
C. Answer c is incorrect because although the flatworms do possess a digestive tract, the tract has only one opening and so the contents cannot pass one way through the digestive system. Food enters and wastes are released through the same opening.

The correct answer is b...
D. Answer d is incorrect because the flatworms lack a body cavity, also called a coelom. The only cavity in the solid worms is the digestive tract; the rest of the body is solid.

Hint: Flatworms are among the simplest of bilaterally symmetrical animals, but they do have a definite head at the anterior end and they do possess organs. Their bodies are solid; the only internal space consists of the digestive cavity.

8). For excretion, flatworms use
     a). miracidium.
     b). osmosis.
     c). flame cells.
     d). proglottids.

The correct answer is c...
A. Answer a is incorrect because a miracidium is a first-stage larva of the human liver fluke, *Clonorchis sinensis*. The miracidium is the first stage in the somewhat complex life cycle of this fluke.

The correct answer is c...
B. Answer b is incorrect because osmosis is the process whereby water molecules move from a hypotonic solution to a hypertonic solution in order to achieve a state of equilibrium. Excretion, which is the elimination of metabolic waste from the body, involves the elimination of substances other than water.

The correct answer is c--flame cells.
C. Flame cells are specialized cells found in fine tubules that make up the excretory system of flatworms. Flame cells contain tufts of cilia that move water and excretory substances into the tubules and then out through pores. Although flame cells primarily serve a water balance function, they do aid the digestive system in the elimination of metabolic waste.

The correct answer is c...
D. Answer d is incorrect because proglottids are small, repetitive segments that make up the majority of the body of tapeworms (class Cestoda). Proglottids are continually formed in the tapeworm with mature proglottids forming eggs.

Hint: Unlike cnidarians, flatworms have an excretory system, which consists of a network of fine tubules that run throughout the body. Cilia line the hollow centers of bulblike flame cells located on the side branches of the tubules. Cilia in the flame cells move water and excretory substances into the tubules and then to exit pores located between the epidermal cells.

9). The type of body cavity seen in the roundworms is called a(n)
     a). coelom.
     b). acoelom.
     c). pseudocoelom.
     d). gastrovascular cavity.

The correct answer is c...
A. Answer a is incorrect because a coelom is a complete body cavity, forming within the mesoderm layer of tissue. This type of body cavity is found in the coelomates, not in the roundworms.

The correct answer is c...
B. Answer b is incorrect because an acoelom is the body plan present in animals that possess bilateral symmetry and three germ layers but that lack a body cavity except for the cavity present in the digestive cavity.

The correct answer is c--pseudocoelom.
C. Roundworms, called pseudocoelomates, have an internal body cavity that is called a pseudocoel. Unlike a true coelom, which forms within the mesoderm layer, the pseudocoel forms between the endoderm and mesoderm layers.

The correct answer is c...
D. Answer d is incorrect because the gastrovascular cavity is a cavity that is present in animals with radial symmetry, such as cnidarians, and is used in digestion, among other functions.

Hint: All bilaterians except solid worms possess an internal body cavity, the third key transition in the animal body plan. Seven phyla are characterized by their possession of a pseudocoel. Nematodes, eelworms, and other roundworms constitute a large phylum, Nematoda, of pseudocolomates.

10). The type of pseudocoelomates found in soil, freshwater and marine environments, and as parasites are
        a). nematodes.
        b). *Trichinella*.
        c). rotifers.
        d). Cycliophora.

The correct answer is a--nematodes.
A. Nematodes are a group of pseudocoelomate roundworms that are found everywhere: in soil and in freshwater and marine environments. Some are also parasitic, attacking both animals and plants.

The correct answer is a...
B. Answer b is incorrect because *Trichinella* is a genus of nematodes that are parasites found in pork and cause disease in animals that eat encysted meat. Animals in this genus are not present in soil or aquatic environments.

The correct answer is a...
C. Answer c is incorrect because the rotifers are basically aquatic animals although some also live in soil and on plants. However, they are not parasitic animals.

The correct answer is a...
D. Answer d is incorrect because the Cycliophora are aquatic pseudocoelomate animals that live on lobsters, but are not parasitic nor do they live in the soil.

Hint: Nematodes are abundant and diverse in marine and freshwater habitats, and many members of this phylum are parasites of animals and plants. Many nematodes are microscopic and live in soil.

Test Your Visual Understanding

1). What phylum is represented by the two organisms pictured in this figure, and what are some general characteristics of this phylum?
Answer: The phylum Cnidaria, more commonly referred to as the cnidarians, contains animals that have two basic body forms during their life cycles, the polyp stage and the medusa stage. Cnidarians are mostly marine organisms. They have radial symmetry and distinct tissues (epidermis, mesoglea, and gastrodermis). Some organisms alternate between a polyp and medusa stage in their life cycles while some spend most or all of their lives in one stage or the other. They are carnivores, capturing their prey with specialized "weapons" called nematocysts that are held within special cells called cnidocytes. They reproduce both sexually and asexually. A major evolutionary advance seen in the cnidarians, in addition to the presence of distinct tissues, is the internal extracellular digestion of food.

2). What type of organism spends most of its life cycle in the medusa body form? What type of organism spends most of its life cycle in the polyp body form?
Answer: The jellyfish, class Scyphozoa, spend the majority of their lives in the medusa stage. During their life cycle they do form polyps but this is a very short portion of their life cycle. The polyp forms the medusa, which buds off of the polyp to become a free-floating organism. The sea anemones and corals, class Anthozoa, spend most of their life cycles in the polyp stage. Another organism, the genus *Hydra*, spends its life cycle in the polyp stage. This is unique among the organisms in its class Hydrozoa, which usually alternate between a polyp and medusa stage.

Apply Your Knowledge

1). A sponge is a filter feeder, which means it eats by filtering food from the water that passes through its pores and out its osculum. Assume a sponge filters 1.8 milliliters of water per second. How much water is filtered in an hour? In a day?
Answer: If a sponges filters 1.8 ml of water/second and there are 60 seconds in a minute and 60 minutes in an hour, it will filter 6,480 ml of water in 3600 seconds or one hour. If it filters 6480 ml of water in one hour then it will filter 155,520 ml of water in 24 hours or in one day.

2). Coral reefs are often found in nutrient-poor waters. What type of symbiotic relationship helps these coral animals grow actively? What are the advantages for each member in the relationship? What would happen to the coral reefs if the water they are growing in became cloudy with pollution?
Answer: Coral form symbiotic relationships with algae. Algae live among the coral animals producing nutrients through photosynthesis that the coral feed on. The advantage for the coral is the nutrients produced by the algae. Although coral are carnivorous, they obtain important nutrients from the algae. The advantage for the algae is the protection provided by the coral. The coral provide a solid substrate on which the algae can settle and have access to light. If the waters became polluted and cloudy, such that light was blocked from penetrating to the coral, the algae would soon die. Without the algae, the coral would also die.

3). Parasites, especially those that require two or more hosts to complete their life cycles, often produce very large numbers of offspring. What advantage would this present to them?
Answer: Parasites, like many organisms that have very little parental investment in rearing offspring, tend to produce a very large number of offspring. The chances than any one offspring will survive to infect its host are very slim. The risks are even greater when more than one host needs to be infected to complete its life cycle. The organism is merely improving its chances of successful reproduction by producing a very large number of offspring.

Inquiry Questions
None for this chapter.

Self Test

1). Of the mollusks, snails are in the class of
      a). gastropods.
      b). bivalves.
      c). cephalopods.
      d). chitons.

The correct answer is a--gastropods.
A. There are seven classes of mollusks, and snails are members of the class Gastropoda, referred to as the gastropods. These animals are primarily marine but also contain some freshwater and terrestrial species. Gastropods have a definite head region with sensory tentacles, a coelom and many have a shell.

The correct answer is a...
B. Answer b is incorrect because the bivalves, class Bivalvia, contain the clams, scallops, mussels, and oysters. Bivalves have two lateral shells hinged together, which is not a characteristic of snails.

The correct answer is a...
C. Answer c is incorrect because the cephalopods, class Cephalopoda, contain the octopuses, squids, and nautilus. Cephalopods lack an external shell, except for the few species of nautilus, and have tentacles that evolved from the foot. These are not characteristics of snails.

The correct answer is a...
D. Answer d is incorrect because the chitons are in the class Polyplacophora. The chitons have oval bodies with eight overlapping calcareous plates. These are not characteristics of snails.

Hint: The class Gastropoda contains about 40,000 described species of snails, slugs, and similar animals. This class is primarily a marine group, but it also contains many freshwater and terrestrial mollusks. Most gastropods have a shell, but some have lost their shells through the course of evolution.

2). A mantle is
      a). present only in bivalves.
      b). a structure that acts as a lung or contains gills.
      c). a rasping, tonguelike organ in mollusks.
      d). necessary for mollusks to be motile.

The correct answer is b...
A. Answer a is incorrect because although the bivalves have a mantle so do other mollusks.

The correct answer is b--a structure that acts as a lung or contains gills.
B. The mantle is a layer of tissue in a mollusk that is folded and functions in gas exchange either acting as a lung or holding gills that are the site of gas exchange.

The correct answer is b...
C. Answer c is incorrect because a rasping, tonguelike organ in mollusks is the radula, not the mantle.

The correct answer is b...
D. Answer d is incorrect because the primary mechanism of locomotion in mollusks is a muscular foot, not the mantle. The foot has evolved into a series of tentacles in the cephalopods.

Hint: Folds (often two) arise from the dorsal body wall and enclose a cavity between themselves and the visceral mass; these folds constitute the mantle. In some mollusks, the mantle cavity acts as a lung; in others it contains gills. Gills are specialized portions of the mantle that usually consist of a system of filamentous projections rich in blood vessels. These projections greatly increase the surface area available for gas exchange and, therefore, the animal's overall respiratory potential.

3). Segmentation was first apparent in the
          a). flatworms.
          b). annelids.
          c). mollusks.
          d). arthropods.

The correct answer is b…
A. Answer a is incorrect because flatworms were pseudocoelomates with relatively simple body plans and no segmentation.

The correct answer is b--annelids.
B. The annelids, like the mollusks, contained a coelom but also evolved a segmented body plan. An advantage of segmentation the ability to control specific body functions by separating the functions into different segments.

The correct answer is b…
C. Answer c is incorrect because the mollusks were coelomates with more complex body plans and specialized organs, but segmentation did not evolved in this animal group.

The correct answer is b…
D. Answer d is incorrect because although the arthropods do exhibit segmentation in their body plans, they are not the first animal group in which segmentation appeared.

Hint: A key transition in the animal body plan was segmentation, the building of a body from a series of similar segments. The first segmented animals to evolve were most likely the annelid worms, phylum Annelida.

4). Which of the following is not present in polychaetes?
          a). a coelom
          b). parapodia
          c). permanent gonads
          d). setae

The correct answer is c…
A. Answer a is incorrect because polychaetes are coelomates, having a body cavity called a coelom.

The correct answer is c…
B. Answer b is incorrect because polychaetes have parapodia, which are fleshy, paddlelike flaps associated with each segment, and are used in swimming, burrowing, and crawling. In fact, parapodia are a distinctive characteristic of polychaetes, missing in the earthworms and in the leeches.

The correct answer is c--permanent gonads
C. The polychaetes do not have permanent gonads. In fact, their gametes are not produced in a specialized organ, rather they are produced in the lining of the coelom or in their septa.

The correct answer is c...
D. Answer d is incorrect because polychaetes have setae, which are bristles of chitin that help anchor the worms during locomotion. Each segment contains setae or sometimes the setae extend from the parapodia.

Hint: The sexes of polychaetes are usually separate, and fertilization is often external, occurring in the water and away from both parents. Unlike other annelids, polychaetes usually lack permanent gonads. They produce their gametes directly from germ cells in the lining of the coelom or in their septa.

5). The lophophore, the structure characteristic of lophophorates,
        a). functions in gas exchange.
        b). functions in feeding.
        c). can be withdrawn when the animal is disturbed.
        d). All of these are correct.

The correct answer is d...
A. Answer a is incorrect because although the lophophore does function in gas exchange, this is not the only correct answer.

The correct answer is d...
B. Answer b is incorrect because although the lophophore does function in feeding, this is not the only correct answer.

The correct answer is d...
C. Answer c is incorrect because although the lophophore can be withdrawn when the animal is disturbed. It is withdrawn either into the tube-like body of the phoronids and bryozoans or into the protective shells of the brachiopod. However, this is not the only correct answer.

The correct answer is d--All of these are correct.
D. The lophophore is a circular or U-shaped ridge around the mouth of members of the three phyla that make up this group. The lophophore functions as a surface for gas exchange and as a food-collection organ. It can also be withdrawn when the animal is disturbed.

Hint: Three phyla of marine animals—Phoronida, Ectoprocta, and Brachiopoda—are characterized by a lophophore, a circular or U-shaped ridge around the mouth, bearing one or two rows of ciliated, hollow tentacles. The lophophore functions as a surface for gas exchange and as a food-collection organ. The tentacles can be withdrawn into the body of the animal when it is disturbed.

6). The phylum that shows the greatest diversity, or the greatest number of species, is
        a). Arthropoda.
        b). Brachiopoda.
        c). Echinodermata.
        d). Mollusca.

The correct answer is a--Arthropoda.
A. The arthropods, phylum Arthropoda, is the most diverse phylum and Is by far the most successful animal group, especially the largest arthropod class, the insects.

The correct answer is a...
B. Answer b is incorrect because the Brachiopoda, the brachiopods, are a very small phylum with a little more than 300 species. Although the brachiopods do not represent a very large group of species now, more than 30,000 species of this phylum have been identified in the fossil record.

The correct answer is a...
C. Answer c is incorrect because although the echinoderms have successfully invaded marine environments, they are not the most diverse animal group.

The correct answer is a...
D. Answer d is incorrect because although the mollusks have successfully invaded marine, freshwater, and terrestrial environments, they are not the most diverse animal group.

Hint: With the arthropods, two more innovations arose—the development of jointed appendages and an exoskeleton. Jointed appendages and an exoskeleton have allowed arthropods (phylum Arthropoda) to become the most diverse phylum.

7). Air for respiration enters the insect body through the
        a). tracheae.
        b). spiracles.
        c). tracheoles.
        d). Malpighian tubules.

The correct answer is b...
A. Answer a is incorrect because the tracheae are branched air ducts in insects that carry air into and throughout the body. However, air does not enter the body through the tracheae.

The correct answer is b--spiracles.
B. Insects "breathe" through small openings in the exoskeleton called spiracles. Spiracles open to the outside and are regulated by valves. Air that enters the body through the spiracles is transmitted deep inside the body by tracheae and tracheoles.

The correct answer is b...
C. Answer c is incorrect because the tracheoles are a network of small, highly branched air ducts that carry oxygen from the tracheae to the cells throughout the body.

The correct answer is b...
D. Answer d is incorrect because the Malpighian tubules are involved in excretion in insects, not in respiration.

Hint: Air passes into the tracheae by way of specialized openings in the exoskeleton called spiracles, which in most insects, can be opened and closed by valves. The ability to prevent water loss by closing the spiracles was a key adaptation that facilitated the invasion of land by arthropods.

8). Arthropods shed their old exoskeleton as they grow in a process known as
        a). tagmatization.
        b). metamorphosis.
        c). chrysalis.
        d). ecdysis.

The correct answer is d...
A. Answer a is incorrect because tagmatization is the process whereby the segments of the animal body fuse into functional groups, such as the head, thorax, and abdomen. The individual segments can usually be identified during larval development.

The correct answer is d...
B. Answer b is incorrect because metamorphosis is the process whereby insects undergo a change in body structure, from a wormlike larval stage into an adult insect.

The correct answer is d...
C. Answer c is incorrect because chrysalis is not a process but rather a structure that forms during complete metamorphosis. The chrysalis is often referred to as the pupa stage in insect development.

The correct answer is d--ecdysis.
D. As the arthropod body grows, its tough exoskeleton must be shed to allow the body to expand in size. A new exoskeleton forms underneath the old before it is shed. This process is referred to as molting, or ecdysis.

Hint: Arthropods periodically undergo ecdysis, or molting, the shedding of the outer cuticular layer. When they outgrow their exoskeleton, they form a new one underneath. When the new exoskeleton is complete, it becomes separated from the old one by fluid. The fluid increases in volume until, finally, the original exoskeleton cracks open and is shed.

9). Which animal group has radial symmetry, a water-vascular system, moves with tube feet, and has an endoskeleton?
    a). arachnids
    b). crustaceans
    c). echinoderms
    d). cnidarians

The correct answer is c...
A. Answer a is incorrect because arachnids, the animal group that contains spiders, mites, and ticks, do not have these characteristics. They have an exoskeleton and move about with segmented appendages.

The correct answer is c...
B. Answer b is incorrect because crustaceans, the animal group that contains lobsters, crabs, and shrimp, do not have these characteristics. They have an exoskeleton and move about with segmented appendages.

The correct answer is c--echinoderms
C. The echinoderms are radially symmetrical animals in their adult form but begin life as bilaterally symmetrical larvae. Their radial symmetry is referred to as secondary radial symmetry because it is believed to be an adaptation from their larval stage to their aquatic environment. Their water-vascular system moves their tube feet, which allows them to move around. They are the first animal group in which the endoskeleton appears. Their endoskeleton consists of skeletal plates that form under the skin. Sometimes these plates fuse forming an inflexible body.

The correct answer is c...
D. Answer d is incorrect because although the cnidarians are radially symmetrical animals, they don't have water-vascular systems, tube feet, or endoskeletons. In fact, they have no skeletal feature.

Hint: The term echinoderm means "spiny skin" and refers to an endoskeleton composed of hard calcium-rich plates just beneath the skin. Another innovation in echinoderms is the development of a hydraulic system to aid in movement or feeding. Called a water-vascular system, this fluid-filled system is composed of a central ring canal from which five radial canals extend out into the body and arms. All are radially symmetrical as adults.

10). The echinoderms that lack distinct arms are the
    a). brittle stars.
    b). sea urchins.
    c). sea stars.
    d). Asteroidea.

The correct answer is b…
A. Answer a is incorrect because brittle stars, class Ophiuroidea, have slender, branched arms that are very flexible and move the animal with a "rowing" motion.

The correct answer is b--sea urchins.
B. Sea urchins and sand dollars, class Echinoidea, have the five-part body plan that is characteristic of the echinoderms but lack the large extensions referred to as arms.

The correct answer is b…
C. Answer c is incorrect because sea stars, class Asteroidea, are the most familiar echinoderms. They have a central disk that gradually merges with the five arms that extend from the disk.

The correct answer is b…
D. Answer d is incorrect because Asteroidea is the name of the class of echinoderms that contains the sea stars or starfish. The Asteroidea are the most familiar echinoderms. They have a central disk that gradually merges with the five arms that extend from the disk.

Hint: the members of the class Echinoidea, sand dollars and sea urchins, lack distinct arms but have the same five-part body plan as all other echinoderms. Five rows of tube feet protrude through the plates of the calcareous skeleton.

Test Your Visual Understanding

1). The radula shown in the figure above is a feeding structure found in individuals of the phylum Mollusca but is lacking in one group of mollusks. What group of mollusks does not have a radula? How do individuals in this group eat?
Answer: The bivalves, class Bivalvia, do not have radulas. The radula is a rough, tonguelike feeding structure that is scrapped across the substrate or burrowed into prey. The bivalves are filter feeders, meaning that they feed off of small organisms trapped in their mantle cavity as water is passed through.

2). Horticultural oils are sometimes used as insecticides to eliminate insect pests from foliage by coating the insect with oil. Referring to the figure above, can you explain how this method of insecticidal control works?
Answer: The insect "breathes" through small openings in the surface of the body known as spiracles. Air passes into the spiracle and throughout the body by means of a network of tubules (trachea and tracheoles). By coating the insect body with horticultural oil, the spiracles are plugged up and air cannot pass into the body. Without air coming in through the spiracles, the insect suffocates.

Apply Your Knowledge

1). Freshwater bivalves are an important ecological resource because they filter freshwater systems. A population of freshwater bivalves located in a meter-squared area of substratum filters 10 m^3 of water a day. How many liters of water are filtered per day (1 m^3 equals 1000 liters)? How many liters of water are filtered per hour? How many liters of water would be filtered by a population filling a 5 m^2 area of substratum?
Answer: If 1 m^3 equals 1,000 liters, then 10 m^3 would be 10,000 liters and so this population of bivalves would filter 10,000 liters per day. At 10,000 liters per day they would filter 10,000 / 24 hours or 416.7 liters per hour. If a 1 m^3 population filters 10,000 liters of water a day, a population 5 m^3 would filter 50,000 liters of water in a day.

2). Scientists believe the ancestral mollusk had a very limited shell, consisting mainly of calcareous plates. The shell became more developed in some groups but was lost in others. What is the evolutionary advantage of having a shell? Of not having one?

Answer: A mollusk's shell provides the animal with protection. A snail can pull into its shell and a clam can close its shell when threatened. However, a shell also limits mobility. Mollusks such as the cephalopods have essentially lost their shells over time. The cephalopods are predatory animals and as such, mobility is extremely important. The mobility that comes without a shell allows them to catch prey and escape attack if threatened.

3). Although arthropods are very successful in aquatic environments, what are the key adaptations that facilitated the invasion of the land by arthropods?
Answer: The arthropods successfully invaded land with the adaptations of an exoskeleton, jointed appendages, a respiratory system, and specialized structures such as compound eyes and wings. The exoskeleton increased mobility over the hydrostatic skeleton of the worms because it allowed a more solid structure for the anchoring of muscles. This allowed for the movement of individual appendages that increased speed and agility. The jointed appendages also increase agility. The respiratory system in insects (spiracles and tubules) and arachnids (book lungs) increased gas exchange in animals that were encased in a gas-impermeable exoskeleton and reduced water loss. The adaptation of specialized structures such as compound eyes and wings allowed terrestrial arthropods to better perceive and respond to changes in their environment.

4). Why is it believed that echinoderms and chordates, which are so dissimilar, are members of the same evolutionary line?
Answer: Two key evolutionary adaptations link these two animal lines together: deuterostome embryological development and an endoskeleton. No other animal group has these two features. In fact, a main reason why the echinoderms seem so different from the chordates is the radial symmetry that is present in the echinoderms. The larval stage of the echinoderms is bilaterally symmetrical and it is believed that the radial symmetry is a secondary adaptation to an aquatic environment.

Self Test

1). Which of the following is a characteristic of chordates but is *not* found in other animals?
    a). a notochord
    b). jointed appendages
    c). an exoskeleton
    d). all of these

The correct answer is a--a notochord
A. The notochord is a flexible rod that forms on the dorsal side of the early embryo and is present at some developmental stages in all chordates. The notochord may remain in the adult, disappear, or be displaced by bone, such as in the vertebrates.

The correct answer is a...
B. Answer b is incorrect because jointed appendages appear in animal groups other than in chordates, such as in arthropods, and some chordates don't have jointed appendages.

The correct answer is a...
C. Answer c is incorrect because chordates do not have exoskeletons. Most chordates have an internal skeleton to which muscles attach and work to move the body. In the lancelet, the notochord is the internal skeleton that anchors the muscles.

The correct answer is a...
D. Answer d is incorrect because only answer a is the correct answer. Answer b is incorrect because jointed appendages appear in other animals groups, such as the arthropods. Answer c is incorrect because chordates do not have exoskeletons; most chordates have an internal skeleton.

Hint: Four features characterize the chordates and have played an important role in the evolution of the phylum: a nerve cord, a notochord, pharyngeal slits or pouches, and a postanal tail.

2). In which animal(s) does the notochord persist in the adult?
    a). tunicates
    b). lampreys
    c). lancelets
    d). all of these

The correct answer is c...
A. Answer a is incorrect because the notochord is most commonly present only in the larval stage of the tunicate but it is lost in the adult stage.

The correct answer is c...
B. Answer b is incorrect because the lampreys, which are the jawless fishes, are vertebrates and as such, their notochords are replaced by the bony vertebral column in the adult.

The correct answer is c--lancelets
C. The lancelets are fishlike marine animals that spend most of their time partially buried in the sandy or muddy substrate. They are chordates but not vertebrates. The notochord persists in the adult as an anchor to which muscles attach.

The correct answer is c...
D. Answer d is incorrect because the notochord persists only in the adult lancelets, not in adult tunicates or lampreys.

Hint: Lancelets were given their English name because they resemble a lancet—a small, two-edged surgical knife. There are about 23 species of this subphylum. Most of them belong to the genus *Branchiostoma*, formerly called *Amphioxus*, a name still used widely. In lancelets, the notochord runs the entire length of the dorsal nerve cord and persists throughout the animal's life.

3). The very first vertebrates were
        a). cartilaginous fish.
        b). fishes with jaws.
        c). amphibians.
        d). jawless fish.

The correct answer is d...
A. Answer a is incorrect because the cartilaginous fish evolved after the jawless fishes, which were the first vertebrates.

The correct answer is d...
B. Answer b is incorrect because the fish with jaws evolved after the jawless fishes, which were the first vertebrates.

The correct answer is d...
C. Answer c is incorrect because the amphibians were the first vertebrates to invade land but they were not the first vertebrates.

The correct answer is d--jawless fish.
D. The vertebrates, which are characterized by the presence of a vertebral column and a defined head region, evolved in the oceans about 470 million years ago. The first vertebrates were eel-like fishes that lacked jaws and had a single caudal fin. The cartilaginous and bony fish evolved from these fish.

Hint: The first vertebrates evolved in the oceans about 470 million years ago. They were jawless fishes with a single caudal fin. Many of them looked like a flat hot dog, with a hole at one end and a fin at the other. The appearance of a hinged jaw was a major advancement, opening up new food options, and jawed fishes became the dominant creatures in the sea.

4). Which of the following is *not* a characteristic of fishes?
        a). gills
        b). lungs
        c). single-loop blood circulation
        d). nutritional deficiencies

The correct answer is b...
A. Answer a is incorrect because fish do have gills. Most water-dwelling animals must extract oxygen out of the water and use gills for this function. Gills are composed of fine filaments of tissue that are rich in blood vessels. Water passes over the gills and the oxygen diffuses from the water, across the cells that line the gills and into the bloodstream.

The correct answer is b--lungs
B. Lungs are organs that function in gas exchange in terrestrial vertebrates. Fish do not have lungs because they are aquatic animals and gas exchange occurs across the cells lining the gills. The gills are the respiratory structures in fish, not lungs.

The correct answer is b...
C. Answer c is incorrect because fish have single-loop blood circulation. In fish, blood is pumped from the heart to the gills where oxygen enters the blood. The oxygenated blood is then pumped to the rest of the body, returning to the heart. This circulatory system forms a single loop from heart-to-gills-to-body and back to the heart.

The correct answer is b...
D. Answer d is incorrect because fish have nutritional deficiencies in not being able to synthesize aromatic amino acids (amino acids with ringed structures). They must consume foods that contain these amino acids. All their vertebrate descendants have inherited this deficiency.

Hint: Fishes vary considerably in size, shape, color, and appearance. Some live in freezing Arctic seas, others in warm freshwater lakes, and still others spend a lot of time out of water entirely. However varied, all fishes have important characteristics in common: gills, vertebral column, single-loop blood circulation, and nutritional deficiencies.

5). What adaptation of bony fish allows them to detect and orient itself in the upstream direction?
        a). the swim bladder
        b). lobed fins
        c). the operculum
        d). the lateral line system

The correct answer is d...
A. Answer a is incorrect because the swim bladder is an adaptation that improved buoyancy in the heavier bony fish. The swim bladder evolved from an outpocketing of the pharynx.

The correct answer is d...
B. Answer b is incorrect because lobed fins is an adaptation found in lobe-finned fishes. The lobed fins are paired fins that are muscular lobes supported by a bony core and each fin can be moved independently. This adaptation most certainly led to the formation of legs in amphibians but did not assist the bony fish is the detection of water flow.

The correct answer is d...
C. Answer c is incorrect because the operculum is a hard plate that covers the gill in bony fish. While the operculum allowed a more efficient flow of water across the gills, it did not aid the fish in the detection of the flow of water around them.

The correct answer is d--the lateral line system
D. The lateral line system is a series of openings in the sides of the fish that allow water to flow through. Sensory organs that lie within an adjacent canal detect the movement of water around the fish. The lateral line system of trout is able to detect the downstream directional flow of water such that they are able to orient themselves facing upstream.

Hint: The lateral line system consists of a series of sensory organs that project into a canal beneath the surface of the skin. Movement of water past the fish forces water through the canal. Sensory organs located in pits along the canal send nerve impulses that permit the fish to assess its rate of movement through the water. This is how a trout orients itself with its head upstream.

6). In order for amphibians to be successful on land, they had to develop which of the following?
        a). a more efficient swim bladder
        b). cutaneous respiration and lungs
        c). more efficient gills
        d). shelled eggs

The correct answer is b...
A. Answer a is incorrect because amphibians no longer had a need for a swim bladder as they spent less and less time in the water swimming. Their dependence on the water was replaced with the freedom to roam the land.

The correct answer is b--cutaneous respiration and lungs
B. Amphibians could not use gills for breathing on land because gills are composed of delicate tissue that needs to be supported and kept moist by water. Gills are not able to obtain oxygen

from the air. Therefore, amphibians needed a respiratory system that would function on land. The evolution of cutaneous respiration and lungs allowed the amphibians to extract oxygen from air.

The correct answer is b...
C. Answer c is incorrect because gills can not extract oxygen from air. Gills are composed of delicate tissue that needs to be supported by water. Also, gills are actually quite efficient at extracting oxygen from water and so a more efficient gill would not really help amphibians. They needed a different respiratory system.

The correct answer is b...
D. Answer d is incorrect because although shelled eggs would have helped amphibians to be even more successful on land, amphibians do not have shelled eggs. Shelled, watertight eggs did not appear until the evolution of reptiles.

Hint: Frogs, salamanders, and caecilians, the damp-skinned vertebrates, are direct descendants of fishes. They are the sole survivors of a very successful group, the amphibians, and the first vertebrates to walk on land. Amphibians have key characteristics that equipped them for life on land: legs, cutaneous respiration, lungs, pulmonary veins, partially divided heart.

7). Amniotic eggs evolved as a means to
      a). protect the embryo while the parent sits on the egg.
      b). protect the embryo from predators.
      c). allow the parent to gather food, rather than sitting on the nest.
      d). prevent the embryo from drying out.

The correct answer is d...
A. Answer a is incorrect because the advantage offered by the evolution of the amniotic egg was the watertightness. The amniotic egg freed the reptile from a reliance on the water for reproduction, not as protection from crushing when the parent sat on the egg. In fact, reptiles, in which the amniotic egg first evolved, do not usually sit on their eggs.

The correct answer is d...
B. Answer b is incorrect because although the sturdiness of the shell provides protection from predators, the primary advantage of the evolution of the amniotic egg was its watertightness, not its protection from predators.

The correct answer is d...
C. Answer c is incorrect because the freedom to hunt for food is an advantage but that was not the primary advantage of the evolution of the amniotic egg; it was instead its watertightness. In fact, reptiles, in which the amniotic egg first evolved, do not usually tend to a nest and therefore, are not restricted from foraging for food.

The correct answer is d--prevent the embryo from drying out.
D. The watertightness offered by the amniotic egg released the reptile from its reliance on water for reproduction while keeping the embryo moist during its development. Without the evolution of the amniotic egg, the reptiles probably would not have evolved much past the amphibians because they would have still been restricted to live in areas with a reliable source of water.

Hint: All living reptiles share certain fundamental characteristics, features they retain from the time when they replaced amphibians as the dominant terrestrial vertebrates. Among the most important are: the amniotic egg. Amphibians never succeeded in becoming fully terrestrial because amphibian eggs must be laid in water to avoid drying out. Most reptiles lay watertight eggs that contain a food source (the yolk) and a series of four membranes—the yolk sac, the amnion, the allantois, and the chorion.

8). A group of early reptiles that may have been warm-blooded was the
      a). pleycosaurs.
      b). therapsids.
      c). thecodonts.
      d). all of these.

The correct answer is b...
A. Answer a is incorrect because the pleycosaurs were believed to be cold-blooded, meaning that their body temperature was determined by the outside temperature.

The correct answer is b--therapsids.
B. The therapsids are believed to have evolved from the pelycosaurs and eventually replaced them as the dominant large terrestrial animal. They dominated the land animals at a time when the earth had cooled supporting evidence that the therapsids were warm-blooded, fairing much better in colder climates.

The correct answer is b...
C. Answer c is incorrect because the thecodonts replaced the therapsids as the dominant large terrestrial animals at a time in the earth's history when the earth began to warm up. The thecodonts required less food than the therapsids because they were cold-blooded and so could outcompete the therapsid in warmer climates.

The correct answer is b...
D. Answer d is incorrect because there is only one correct answer, answer b. The pelycosaurs and the thecodonts were cold-blooded animals that survived well in warm climates. When the earth's climate turned colder, the warm-blooded therapsids had the advantage.

Hint: During the 250 million years that reptiles were the dominant large terrestrial vertebrates, four major forms of reptiles took turns as the dominant type: pelycosaurs, therapsids, thecodonts, and dinosaurs. Therapsids ate ten times more frequently than their pelycosaur ancestors did. There is evidence that they may have been endotherms, able to regulate their own body temperature (warm-blooded). The extra food consumption would have been necessary to produce body heat.

9). *Archaeopteryx* is believed to be the transition fossil between dinosaurs and birds because, like a bird, *Archaeopteryx* had feathers and
      a). a tail similar to modern birds.
      b). scales.
      c). a toothless, elongated mouth like a beak.
      d). a fused collarbone indicating flying ability.

The correct answer is d...
A. Answer a is incorrect because although *Archaeopteryx* did have a tail, this is not a characteristic of modern birds. They have a vestigial tail but not a tail like the dinosaurs had.

The correct answer is d...
B. Answer b is incorrect because birds and dinosaurs have scales. Dinosaurs may have had scales all over their bodies while birds only have scales on their legs and feet but this isn't a characteristic of *Archaeopteryx* that would indicate that it is a transition fossil.

The correct answer is d...
C. Answer c is incorrect because the mouth of *Archaeopteryx* had teeth; it was not toothless as modern birds are.
The correct answer is d--a fused collarbone indicating flying ability.

D. Modern birds have a fused collarbone, referred to as a "wishbone," that is used as an anchor to which muscles attach. The dinosaurs did not have fused collarbones and so this would be considered a "transitional" characteristic of *Archaeopteryx* that links the birds to the dinosaurs.

Hint: The skeleton of *Archaeopteryx* shares many features with small theropod dinosaurs. Its skull has teeth, and very few of its bones are fused to one another—dinosaurian features, not avian. What makes *Archaeopteryx* distinctly avian is the presence of feathers on its wings and tail. It also has other birdlike features, notably the presence of a wishbone. Dinosaurs lack a wishbone, although thecodonts had them.

10). Mammals that have live births incubate newborns in a pouch through the completion of development are:
- a). monotremes.
- b). marsupials.
- c). duck-billed platypuses.
- d). placental mammals.

The correct answer is b...
A. Answer a is incorrect because the monotremes are the only mammals that lay shelled eggs. The monotremes include the duck-billed platypus and the spiny anteater. Their young hatch from eggs; they are not incubated in a pouch.

The correct answer is b--marsupials.
B. Marsupials are a group of mammals that give birth to live young but birth occurs before embryo development is completed. The young marsupial is tiny and hairless. It crawls into a pouch in the mother where it attaches to a nipple and is nursed by the mother until its development is complete.

The correct answer is b...
C. Answer c is incorrect because the duck-billed platypus is a monotreme and the monotremes are the only mammals that lay shelled eggs. The monotremes include the duck-billed platypus and the spiny anteater. Their young hatch from eggs; they are not incubated in a pouch.

The correct answer is b...
D. Answer d is incorrect because placental mammals produce a true placenta that nourishes the embryo throughout its entire development that is completed before birth.

Hint: The major difference between marsupials and other mammals is their pattern of embryonic development. In marsupials, a fertilized egg is surrounded by chorion and amniotic membranes, but no shell forms around the egg as it does in monotremes. Shortly before birth, a short-lived placenta forms from the chorion membrane. Soon after, the embryonic marsupial is born. It emerges tiny and hairless, and crawls into the marsupial pouch, where it latches onto a nipple and continues its development.

Test Your Visual Understanding

1). Based on this figure, predict the type of consumer is a carnivore, herbivore, or omnivore.
- a). dog
- b). deer
- c). beaver
- d). elephant
- e). human

Answer:
> a). carnivore
> b). herbivore
> c). herbivore
> d). herbivore
> e). omnivore

Apply Your Knowledge

1). Homeothermic animals use 98% of cellular energy in metabolism and "store" 2% for growth. Poikilotherms have lower metabolisms and so are able to store 44% of cellular energy for growth. For homeotherms, 77.5% of chemical energy is converted into cellular energy with an efficiency of 77.5%. By comparison, poikilotherm efficiency is 41.9%. How much food must be consumed by each type of animal to gain one gram of weight?

Answer: For homeotherms the food that needs to be consumed is the unknown—x. This quantity of food must be multiplied by the efficiency (77.5%) and the percent of energy "stored" for growth (2%) to produce one gram of weight such that:

$(0.775)(0.02)x = 1$ gram
$(0.0155)x = 1$ gram
$(0.0155)x \ / (0.0155) = 1 / (0.0155)$
$x = 64.5$ grams

For poikilotherms:
$(0.419)(0.44)x = 1$ gram
$(0.184)x = 1$ gram
$(0.184)x \ / (0.184) = 1 / (0.184)$
$x = 5.43$ grams

2). What characteristics allowed vertebrates to attain great sizes?
Answer: Several of the characteristics that make a vertebrate a vertebrate also contributed to its increased size.

By forming a vertebral column and endoskeleton, the vertebrate was able to grow larger because internal bones could support additional weight and allowed for improved locomotion of a larger animal.

The formation of internal organs allowed compartmentalization of bodily functions (i.e., digestion, respiration, circulation, etc.), which increased efficiency in a larger animal. The localization of neural functions in a "head" centralized the nervous system and allowed it to function more efficiently in a larger animal.

3). What limits the ability of amphibians to occupy the full range of terrestrial habitats and allows other terrestrial vertebrates to occupy them successfully?
Answer: Amphibians are limited from expanding into all terrestrial habitats by their reliance on water, both to keep their bodies moist for cutaneous respiration and to use for reproduction. If water isn't readily available in a habitat, amphibians will not be able to survive. Reptiles and mammals are able to dominate in habitats where amphibians would die due to dehydration but even reptiles are limited to habitats that have moderate temperatures. Reptiles cannot live in habitats that are too cold and need to modify their behavior to survive in extremely hot climates (such as hiding during the day and only coming out at night when it's cooler).

4). List some of the advantages that the early birds, in which flight was not nearly as efficient as it is in most of their modern descendants, might have had as a result of the presence of feathers.
Answer: Feathers would have provided an advantage in insulation. Whether the early birds were endothermic or ectothermic, the ability to trap in heat would have been an advantage in cooler climates. Feathers could have also provided a protection from injury or infection. The feathers could have provided a cushion or layer that predator's teeth or claws would have to penetrate or barrier that pathogens would have to penetrate in order to infect the animal.

Inquiry Questions
None for this chapter.

Self Test

1). Fifteen years ago, your parents hung a swing from the lower branch of a large tree growing in your yard. When you go and sit in it today, you realize it is exactly the same height off the ground as it was when you first sat in it 15 years ago. The reason the swing has not grown taller as the tree has grown is that

      a). the tree trunk is showing secondary growth.
      b). the tree trunk is part of the primary growth system of the plant, but elongation is no longer occurring in that part of the tree.
      c). trees lack apical meristems and so do not get taller.
      d). you are hallucinating, because it is impossible for the swing not to have gotten taller as the tree grew.

The correct answer is a--the tree trunk is showing secondary growth.
A. Answer a is correct because the mature region of the trunk is undergoing secondary growth from lateral meristems. Trees grow taller from their apical meristems.

The correct answer is a...
B. Answer b is incorrect because primary growth occurs at apical meristems. The mature region of a tree shoot (i.e., the trunk) is showing secondary growth from lateral meristems.

The correct answer is a...
C. Answer c is incorrect because trees do grow taller from apical meristems.

The correct answer is a...
D. Answer d is incorrect for obvious reasons.

2). Cloning animals is a relatively new phenomenon, but cloning plants has been done for a long time. Which of the following plant cell types would be the *least* successful to clone a plant from?

      a). a mature xylem vessel element
      b). a mature stomatal guard cell
      c). a quiescent center cell
      d). All of these would work for cloning a plant.
      e). None of these would work for cloning a plant.

The correct answer is a--a mature xylem vessel element
A. Answer a is correct because mature xylem vessel elements are dead, and it is not possible to clone anything from dead cells.

The correct answer is a...
B. Answer b is incorrect because guard cells can be grown in culture and subsequently induced to regenerate an entire plant.

The correct answer is a...
C. Answer c is incorrect because quiescent center cells are an excellent source of tissue for cloning. They are undifferentiated cells that can easily be induced to regenerate an entire plant. Furthermore, because they divide very slowly the likelihood of accumulating new mutations is smaller than normal cells.

The correct answer is a...
D. Answer d is incorrect because only a is true.

The correct answer is a…
E. Answer e is incorrect because both b and c will work for cloning.

3). If you were to relocate the pericycle of a plant root to the epidermal layer, how would it affect root growth?

      a). Secondary growth in the mature region of the root would not occur.

      b). The root apical meristem would produce vascular tissue in place of dermal tissue.

      c). Nothing would change, because the pericycle is normally located near the epidermal layer of the root.

      d). Lateral roots would grow from the outer region of the root and fail to connect with the vascular tissue.

The correct answer is d…
A. Answer a is incorrect because secondary growth occurs from lateral meristems, not the pericycle.

The correct answer is d…
B. Answer b is incorrect because primary vascular tissue arises from the procambium region of the primary meristem, not the pericycle.

The correct answer is d…
C. Answer c in incorrect because the pericycle is normally located inside the endoderm layer, not near the epidermis.

The correct answer is d--Lateral roots would grow from the outer region of the root and fail to connect with the vascular tissue.
D. Answer d is correct because lateral roots form from growth in the pericycle and must be connected with the vascular tissue in the stele of the root. If they grow from the lateral region of the root they would not be connected with the root vascular tissue.

4). In a variation on the old "guess your weight" game, you are playing "guess how big this structure will get" at the yearly carnival. There are a number of bizarre plant structures to choose from, but having read this textbook, you are confident of certain victory. Which of the following plant structures would you choose so that you could accurately predict the final size?

      a). an oak shoot

      b). a lotus flower

      c). a bamboo root

      d). the root of a tomato plant

The correct answer is b…
A. Answer a is incorrect because shoots display indeterminant growth—that is, they will grow with no genetically predetermined limits.

The correct answer is b--a lotus flower
B. Answer b is correct because flowers display determinant growth—that is, they will grow to a genetically predefined size.

The correct answer is b…
C. Answer c is incorrect because roots display indeterminant growth—that is, they will grow with no genetically predetermined limits.

The correct answer is b…
D. Answer d is incorrect because roots display indeterminant growth—that is, they will grow with no genetically predetermined limits.

5). When you peel your Irish potatoes for dinner, you are removing the majority of their
      a). dermal tissue.
      b). vascular tissue.
      c). ground tissue.
      d). Only a and b are removed with the peel.
      e). All of these are removed with the peel.

The correct answer is d…
A. Answer a is incorrect because although dermal tissue covers the outermost surface of plant organs, this is not the only answer.

The correct answer is d…
B. Answer b is incorrect because although potatoes are modified shoots and as such have rings of vascular tissue close to the surface, this is not the only answer.

The correct answer is d…
C. Answer c is incorrect because potatoes are comprised mostly of ground tissue (parenchyma) for storing starch reserves. Removing the outer layers of tissue leaves this ground tissue behind.

The correct answer is d--Only a and b are removed with the peel.
D. Answer d is correct because both dermal and ground tissue are removed when you peel a potato.

6). You can determine the age of an oak tree by counting the annual rings of _____ formed by the _____.
      a). primary xylem/apical meristem
      b). secondary phloem/vascular cambium
      c). dermal tissue/cork cambium
      d). secondary xylem/vascular cambium

The correct answer is d…
A. Answer a is incorrect because primary xylem are functional only in the immature region of a plant shoot. In older trees, secondary growth is taking place in the shoot and the vascular cambium deposits rings of vascular tissue.

The correct answer is d…
B. Answer b is incorrect because the secondary phloem is deposited on the external side of the vascular cambium. The older phloem tissue is crushed against the periderm and eventually is shed.

The correct answer is d…
C. Answer c is incorrect because dermal tissue covers the outermost surface of the tree trunk. As the tree grows in girth, the dermal tissue splits and is repaired by the cork cambium.

The correct answer is d--secondary xylem/vascular cambium
D. Answer d is correct because secondary xylem is deposited on the internal side of the vascular cambium. The production of xylem occurs constantly, but the size of xylem elements changes with the seasons giving the appearance of annual rings.

7). Which of the following does not arise from meristematic activity in a plant?
      a). secondary xylem
      b). boarder cells
      c). tendrils
      d). corms
      e). All of these arise from activity of plant meristems.

The correct answer is e...
A. Answer a is incorrect because although secondary xylem is produced in the vascular cambium—a lateral meristem, this is not the only answer.

The correct answer is e...
B. Answer b is incorrect because although boarder cells are produced by the root apical meristem, this is not the only answer.

The correct answer is e...
C. Answer c is incorrect because although tendrils are either modified shoots or leaves and are the product of apical meristems, this is not the only answer.

The correct answer is e...
D. Answer d is incorrect because although corms are modified shoots and arise from meristematic activity in the shoot, this is not the only answer.

The correct answer is e--All of these arise from activity of plant meristems.
E. Answer e is correct because all plant cell division occurs in meristems. Therefore, all plant tissues arise from meristematic activity.

8). Mosses are thought to resemble the primitive plants that first inhabited the land. Interestingly, these plants lack a vascular system. Therefore they should lack
   a). mesophyll cells.
   b). shoots.
   c). phloem.
   d). collenchyma.

The correct answer is c...
A. Answer a is incorrect because mesophyll cells are a type of ground tissue that is present in the leaves.

The correct answer is c...
B. Answer b is incorrect because the basic structure of all plants includes roots, shoots, and leaves.

The correct answer is c--phloem.
C. Answer c is correct because phloem is one of the types of vascular tissue. Phloem is required for sugar transport in vascular plants.

The correct answer is c...
D. Answer d is incorrect because collenchyma are a type of ground tissue modified for support.

9). Plant organs form by
   a). cell division in gamete tissue.
   b). cell division in meristematic tissue.
   c). cell migration into the appropriate position in the tissue.
   d). rearranging the genetic material in the precursor cells so that the organ-specific genes are activated.

The correct answer is b...
A. Answer a is incorrect because gametes are required for fertilization but not morphogenesis in plants.

The correct answer is b--cell division in meristematic tissue.
B. Answer b is correct because all plant cells arise by cell division in meristems.

The correct answer is b…
C. Answer c is incorrect because plant cells do not move within the organism. Morphogenesis in plants is growth dependant.

The correct answer is b…
D. Answer d is incorrect because activating organ specific gene expression does not involve rearranging the genetic material, but rather requires specific transcription factors in the precursor cells.

Test Your Visual Understanding

1). From this cross section of a plant organ, predict the identity of this tissue.
Answer: This figure shows a dicot root because the xylem elements are organized in a star pattern with phloem between the "arms" of the star.

Apply Your Knowledge

1). Plant organs undergo many modifications to deal with environmental challenges. Define your favorite modified root, shoot, and leaf, and make a case for why it is the best example of a modified plant organ.
Answer: There are many ways to answer this question, as long as you specify which organ is modified, describe the modification, and make your case that the modification provides a solutions to an environmental challenge. To answer this question, start by reviewing examples of modified roots (p. 743), modified stems (p. 747), and modified leaves (p. 751). If you choose pneumatophores, for example, explain that these are modified root outgrowths of submerged roots. These modified roots extend above the surface of the water, allowing the plant to obtain enough oxygen to survive.

2). You design a grand scheme to construct a "super plant" that can increase photosynthetic productivity well above normal levels. To do this, you pack the leaves with palisade parenchyma (mesophyll) cells. Would this increase the photosynthetic productivity of a leaf? Why or why not?
Answer: Increasing the number of mesophyll cells, the site of photosynthesis, could increase photosynthetic productivity. There are, however, many other factors to consider. Photosynthesis requires sufficient gas exchange and water. If you do not increase the stomata on the surface of the leaves the rate of photosynthesis is likely to be limited by the availability of oxygen and the amount of water made available through transpiration. Remember, it is the ratio of oxygen to carbon dioxide that affects the efficiency of RUBISCO, the key enzyme needed to fix carbon dioxide in the Calvin cycle (you can review the biochemistry of photosynthesis in chapter 10 and look ahead to p. 785 for more information on the affect of carbon dioxide on photosynthesis.) In summary, you may increase photosynthesis, but you might not have a "super plant."

3). You have identified a mutant maize plant that cannot differentiate vessel cells. How would this affect the functioning of the plant? Devise an environment that would maximize the growth of this mutant.
Answer: The mutant maize plant would not be able to transport enough water if vessel cells failed to differentiate. As the plant grew, it would wilt, have stunted growth, and perhaps not survive. Remember that there would be some water transport through the tracheids, but this would not be sufficient.

Self Test

1). If you could use a micro-laser to destroy the larger cell in a two-cell plant embryo, how would it likely affect embryonic development?
    a). The embryo would develop normally except it would not become anchored in the seed wall.
    b). The embryo would develop normally except it would have multiple cotyledons.
    c). The embryo would fail to develop, but a fully functional suspensor would form.
    d). The embryo would immediately be aborted, and the seed would not form.

The correct answer is a--The embryo would develop normally except it would not become anchored in the seed wall.
A. Answer a is correct because the larger cell at the two-cell stage gives rise to the suspensor while the smaller cell gives rise to the embryo.

The correct answer is a...
B. Answer b is incorrect because plant embryos have either one (monocot) or two (dicot) cotyledons that form later in embryonic development

The correct answer is a...
C. Answer c is incorrect because the larger cell at the two-cell stage gives rise to the suspensor, not the embryo proper.

The correct answer is a...
D. Answer d is incorrect because while the seed might not form correctly, there would be no immediate termination of development.

2). Loss-of-function mutations in the *suspensor* gene in *Arabidopsis* led to the development of two embryos in a seed. After analyzing the expression of this gene in early embryos, you find high levels of suspensor mRNA in the developing suspensor cells. What is the likely function of the suspensor protein?
    a). Suspensor protein likely stimulates development of the embryonic tissue.
    b). Suspensor protein likely stimulates development of the suspensor tissue.
    c). Suspensor protein likely inhibits embryonic development in the suspensor.
    d). Suspensor protein likely inhibits suspensor development in the embryo.

The correct answer is c...
A. Answer a is incorrect because losing the suspensor protein produces two embryos in a seed, therefore it cannot be responsible for stimulating embryonic development.

The correct answer is c...
B. Answer b in incorrect because if the suspensor protein stimulates development of the suspensor, losing it would eliminate the suspensor and not necessarily lead to embryonic development

The correct answer is c--Suspensor protein likely inhibits embryonic development in the suspensor.
C. Answer c is correct because if you remove the inhibition of embryonic development in suspensor tissue, then the tissue can develop as an embryo.

The correct answer is c...
D. Answer d is incorrect because if you remove the inhibition of suspensor development, you would expect two suspensors to develop.

3). How would plant development change if the functions of *SHOOTMERISTEMLESS (STM)* and *MONOPTEROUS (MP)* were reversed?
        a). The embryo-suspensor axis would be reversed.
        b). The embryo-suspensor axis would be duplicated.
        c). The root-shoot axis would be reversed.
        d). The root-shoot axis would be duplicated.

The correct answer is c…
A. Answer a is incorrect because the embryo-suspensor axis is established at the first cell division, long before STM or MP gene expression.

The correct answer is c…
B. Answer b is incorrect because the embryo-suspensor axis is established at the first cell division, long before STM or MP gene expression.

The correct answer is c--The root-shoot axis would be reversed.
C. Answer c is correct because STM is required for shoot apical meristem development while MP is required for root apical meristem development.

The correct answer is c…
D. Answer d is incorrect because duplication would require that polarity genes be expressed in two separate locations rather than simply exchange functions.

4). The most obvious difference between plant embryonic development and animal embryonic development is that
        a). plants develop from unfertilized eggs, while animals develop from fertilized eggs.
        b). plant morphogenesis is entirely growth dependant, while animal morphogenesis involves movement of cells within the embryo.
        c). plant embryos have an available source of nutrients, while animal embryos must begin feeding to obtain nutrients.

The correct answer is b…
A. Answer a is incorrect because both plants and animals fertilize eggs for sexual reproduction. Note: both plants and animals can also generate embryos without fertilization by apomixis in plants and parthenogenesis in animals.

The correct answer is b…
B. Answer b is correct because plant cells cannot move within the organism like animal cells can. Plant morphogenesis, therefore, depends on the plane of cell division and the degree of cell elongation.

The correct answer is b…
C. Answer c is incorrect because embryos in both plants and animals have a source of nutrients: the endosperm in plants, and the yolk in animals.

5). Which of the following is *not* evident from looking at a plant embryo?
        a). You can tell if the plant is a monocot or dicot.
        b). You can tell where the shoot will form.
        c). You can tell where the root will form.
        d). You can tell when the seed will germinate.

The correct answer is d…
A. Answer a is incorrect because the number of cotyledons on an embryonic plant tells whether it is a monocot (one cotyledon) or a dicot (two cotyledons).

The correct answer is d...
B. Answer b is incorrect because the shoot apical meristem is located at the base of the cotyledons, at the opposite end of the embryo from the suspensor.

The correct answer is d...
C. Answer c is incorrect because the root apical meristem is located in the basal region of the embryo next to the suspensor.

The correct answer is d--You can tell when the seed will germinate.
D. Answer d is correct because there is no way to tell how long a seed will remain dormant simply by looking at the embryo.

6). Both seeds and fruits are well adapted to
        a). provide nutrition to animals.
        b). act as a dispersal mechanism for plants.
        c). allow plant embryos to remain dormant for long periods of time.
        d). all of the above

The correct answer is b...
A. Answer a is incorrect because while some seeds and fruits are attractive to animals, the reason for this is to exploit animals for plant dispersal.

The correct answer is b--act as a dispersal mechanism for plants.
B. Answer b is correct because both seeds and fruits are excellent plant dispersal mechanisms (check where the apple you ate for lunch *really* came from!).

The correct answer is b...
C. Answer c is incorrect because most fruits are not long lived, but the seeds within the fruit are.

The correct answer is b...
D. Answer d is incorrect because only b is correct.

7). The longest period of time that a seed can remain dormant is
        a). days.
        b). weeks.
        c). months.
        d). years.

The correct answer is d...
A. Answer a is incorrect because seeds routinely remain dormant for much longer than days.

The correct answer is d...
B. Answer b is incorrect because seeds routinely remain dormant for much longer than weeks.

The correct answer is d...
C. Answer c is incorrect because while the usual period of dormancy is months, seeds can remain dormant for much longer.

The correct answer is d--years.
D. Answer d is correct. The oldest known seeds remained dormant for 10,000 years while buried in a lemming burrow in the Yukon territories of Canada!

8). Fruits are complex organs that are specialized for dispersal of seeds. Which of the following plant tissues does *not* contribute to mature fruit?

        a). sporophytic tissue from the previous generation
        b). gametophytic tissue from the previous generation
        c). sporophytic tissue from the next generation
        d). gametophytic tissue from the next generation

The correct answer is d…
A. Answer a is incorrect because the fruit develops from the ovary which is derived from the sporophytic tissue of the flower.

The correct answer is d…
B. Answer b is incorrect because the fruit contains tissue derived from the gametophytic portion of the plant within the ovary.

The correct answer is d…
C. Answer c is incorrect because the embryo within the seed is the sporophyte of the next generation (i.e., the result of sexual reproduction in plants).

The correct answer is d--gametophytic tissue from the next generation
D. Answer d is correct because the gametophyte from the next generation will only form on a mature plant, not within the embryo.

9). If you wanted to ensure that a seed failed to germinate, which of the following strategies would be most effective?

        a). prevent imbibition
        b). prevent desiccation
        c). prevent fertilization
        d). prevent dispersal

The correct answer is a--prevent imbibition
A. Answer a is correct because without water the seed tissue cannot resume metabolic activity.

The correct answer is a…
B. Answer b is incorrect because removing water is a major component of establishing dormancy, not metabolic activity.

The correct answer is a…
C. Answer c is incorrect because the seed will not form let alone germinate without fertilization (except in plants that use apomixis to set seeds).

The correct answer is a…
D. Answer d is incorrect because dispersal is independent of germination (except in plants for which there is an obligatory relationship with an animal; e.g., the calvaria tree and the dodo!).

10). How would a loss-of-function mutation in the α-amylase gene affect seed germination?

        a). The seed could not imbibe water.
        b). The embryo would starve.
        c). The seed coat would not rupture.
        d). The seed would germinate prematurely.

The correct answer is b…
A. Answer a is incorrect because breaking down amylase does not increase water uptake.

The correct answer is b--The embryo would starve.
B. Answer b is correct because without the ability to break down amylase (stored carbohydrates) the seedling would not have access to the nutrient reserves in the seed.

The correct answer is b…
C. Answer c is incorrect because breaking down amylase does not rupture the seed coat.

The correct answer is b…
D. Answer d is incorrect because germination does not require amylase breakdown.

Test Your Visual Understanding

1). Label this diagram and predict the future axes of the plant.
Answer: Labels: An arrow to the two dark green cells should say "first cell division." The taupe region above those cells should be labeled "endosperm"
Future axis: Draw a line with arrows at both ends through the cells. The upward arrow should say shoot. The lower arrow should be labeled root. Refer to the second to last image from figure 36.2 on page 756, which shows that the prediction is correct. The shoot is upward and the root apex is downward.

Apply Your Knowledge

1). You are writing a science fiction screenplay in which the best of animal and plant lifestyles and making a "super-species." Discuss the aspects of plant development you would include in this new species.
Answer: You might want to incorporate a truly dormant stage in development so that the embryo could last for hundreds of years or develop immediately in response to environmental signals. Consider how far fruits and seeds travel. It might be fun to have an animal embryo inside a seed in a fruit that suddenly "germinates" on someone's dinner table.
Many plants have axillary buds that replace the shoot if it is removed. Some form of backup "head" for your organism could add a bit of excitement to your screenplay. Remember that some animals also have the ability to regenerate, so this would not be a distinctly plant trait. Finally, plants are far easier to clone than most animals. Including this trait along with animal traits could add intrigue.

2). The oldest known seeds to successfully germinate were found in the Yukon Territory in the Canadian Artic in the 1950s. Radiocarbon dating found these seeds to be approximately 10,000 years old. Discuss the mechanisms that seeds use to remain dormant for long periods of time.
Answer: Seeds can remain dormant for long periods of time because they have extremely low levels of water. This prevents biochemical reactions from occurring. By inhibiting biochemical reactions, not only is germination delayed, enzymes that might breakdown down the seed are also inhibited. The loss of water is triggered by hormonal action.
Another mechanism that ensures long term dormancy is the formation of a hard, often light-proof, seed coat that both protects the embryo and blocks environmental signals, including water, that could trigger germination.
Some seeds require a light signal to germinate. If the seed is deeply buried in the soil, it will not perceive a signal to germinate even if its seed coat is not very thick.

3). How might the reproductive success of angiosperms have changed if seeds had developed without fruit?
Answer: Seed dispersal may be more limited in the absence of fruit. Animals that are attracted to the fruit and carry it and it's encased seed and embryo far distances may not be attracted to just the seed. With more limited seed dispersal, angiosperms may not have colonized so much of the terrestrial environment.

Inquiry Questions
None for this chapter.

Self Test

1). If you could connect and active xylem vessel from a shoot to an active phloem sieve-tube member from a leaf using a "micropipe," which way would the solution flow between the two?
      a). The solution would flow from xylem to phloem.
      b). The solution would flow from phloem to xylem.
      c). The solution would flow back and forth from one to another.
      d). The solution would not flow between the two.

The correct answer is b…
A. Answer a is incorrect because the solution in xylem is under negative pressure (i.e., is being sucked through the xylem) while the solution in the phloem is under positive pressure (i.e., is being blown through the phloem).

The correct answer is b--The solution would flow from phloem to xylem.
B. Answer b is correct because the solution will be blown from the phloem into the xylem.

The correct answer is b…
C. Answer c is incorrect because phloem are under positive pressure and xylem are under negative pressure.

The correct answer is b…
D. Answer d is incorrect because the positive pressure in phloem will move the solution toward the negative pressure in the xylem.

2). If you could override the control mechanisms that open stomata and force them to remain closed, what would you expect to happen to the plant?
      a). Sugar synthesis would likely slow down.
      b). Water transport would likely slow down.
      c). All of these could be the result of keeping stomata closed.
      d). None of these would be the result of keeping stomata closed.

The correct answer is c…
A. Answer a is incorrect because although without functioning stomata the leaf will become depleted in CO_2 and this will slow the synthesis of sugar, this is not the only answer.

The correct answer is c…
B. Answer b is incorrect because although water transport in xylem depends on transpirational loss from stomata, this is not the only answer.

The correct answer is c--All of these could be the result of keeping stomata closed.
C. Answer c is correct. Without functioning stomata, the leaf will become depleted in CO_2 and this will slow the synthesis of sugar and water transport in xylem depends on transpirational loss from stomata.

The correct answer is c…
D. Answer d is incorrect. The correct answer is c, all of these could be the result of keeping stomata closed.

3). If a cell with a solute potential of – 0.2 MPa and a pressure potential of 0.4 MPa is placed in a chamber filled with pure water that is pressurized with 0.5 MPa, what will happen?
    a). Water will flow out of the cell.
    b). Water will flow into the cell.
    c). The cell will be crushed.
    d). The cell will explode.

The correct answer is b...
A. Answer a is incorrect because the water potential in the cell is 0.2 MPa (i.e., – 0.2 + 0.4 = 0.2 MPa), and the water potential in the solution is 0.5 MPa (i.e., 0.0 + 0.5 = 0.5 MPa); water will flow from areas of high water potential to areas of low potential.

The correct answer is b--Water will flow into the cell.
B. Answer b is correct because the water potential in the cell is 0.2 MPa (i.e., – 0.2 + 0.4 = 0.2 MPa), and the water potential in the solution is 0.5 MPa (i.e., 0.0 + 0.5 = 0.5 MPa); water will flow from areas of high water potential to areas of low potential.

The correct answer is b...
C. Answer c is incorrect because the pressure difference is not great enough to crush the cell.

The correct answer is b...
D. Answer d is incorrect because the pressure difference is not great enough to explode the cell.

4). You are a molecule of water traveling through the plant. Which of the following processes would not provide a driving force for you to move at either a cellular level or over longer distances through the plant?
    a). mass flow
    b). osmosis
    c). diffusion
    d). transpiration
    e). All the above are driving forces for water movement.

The correct answer is e...
A. Answer a is incorrect because although mass flow of solution in xylem and phloem carries water throughout the plant, this is not the only answer.

The correct answer is e...
B. Answer b is incorrect because although water moves by osmosis at the cellular level (i.e., it will move towards areas of higher osmolarity (lower water potential)), this is not the only answer.

The correct answer is e...
C. Answer c is incorrect because although osmosis can be thought of as diffusion of water, this is not the only answer.

The correct answer is e...
D. Answer d is incorrect because although transpirational loss of water from the stomata is a major force drawing water up through the xylem, this is not the only answer.

The correct answer is e--All the above are driving forces for water movement.
E. Answer e is correct. Mass flow, osmosis, diffusion, and transpiration are all driving forces for water movement.

5). The movement of water in the xylem relies upon the
      a). ability of water molecules to hydrogen-bond with each other.
      b). active transport.
      c). evaporation of water from the leaf surface.
      d). Both a and b are correct.
      e). Both a and c are correct.

The correct answer is e…
A. Answer a is incorrect because although without the cohesive tension between water molecules the transpirational pull from the aerial parts of a plant would not draw water up through xylem, this is not the only answer.

The correct answer is e…
B. Answer b is incorrect because transpiration of water, which has much cohesive tension between molecules, does not require energy. Water transport is a passive process. Also, active transport refers to movement across a cell membrane. Vessels and tracheids (water transport cells in the xylem) are dead and do not have cell membranes. Neighboring cells do not use active transport to load water into the vessels and tracheids.

The correct answer is e…
C. Answer c is incorrect because although loss of water from the aerial parts of the plant is a major factor in creating the transpirational pull on the water column in the xylem, this is not the only answer.

The correct answer is e…
D. Answer d is incorrect because a and c are correct.

The correct answer is e--Both a and c are correct.
E. Answer e is correct because a and c are correct: without the cohesive tension between water molecules the transpirational pull from the aerial parts of a plant would not draw water up through xylem; loss of water from the aerial parts of the plant is a major factor in creating the transpirational pull on the water column in the xylem.

6). You place a piece of potato weighing 0.3 gram with a water potential of 1 MPa in a beaker of Pepsi. After 10 minutes, you remove the potato piece, and it now weighs 0.25 gram. You conclude that
      a). Pepsi Cola has a water potential greater than 1 MPa.
      b). Pepsi Cola has a water potential of 0 MPa.
      c). Pepsi Cola has a water potential less than 1 MPa.
      d). Pepsi Cola does not have turgor pressure, and so you cannot conclude anything about its water potential.

The correct answer is c…
A. Answer a is incorrect because the potato becomes lighter from the loss of water; therefore the water potential in the solution must be lower than the water potential in the potato tissue (remember water will move from areas of higher water potential towards areas of lower water potential).

The correct answer is c…
B. Answer b is incorrect because Pepsi Cola has a large amount of sugar, therefore will have a low solute potential.

The correct answer is c--Pepsi Cola has a water potential less than 1 MPa.
C. Answer c is correct because the potato becomes lighter from the loss of water; therefore the water potential in the solution must be lower than the water potential in the potato tissue (remember water will move from areas of higher water potential towards areas of lower water potential).

The correct answer is c...
D. Answer d is incorrect because water potential is the sum of pressure potential and solute potential.

7). Sucrose enters a phloem sieve-tube cell because of
      a). osmosis.
      b). water potential.
      c). active transport.
      d). a process regulated by auxin.

The correct answer is c...
A. Answer a is incorrect because osmosis draws water into the phloem after sucrose has been loaded.

The correct answer is c...
B. Answer b is incorrect because water potential is a force moving water, not solutes.

The correct answer is c--active transport.
C. Answer c is correct because cells at the source use energy to move sucrose against a concentration gradient into the phloem sieve-tube cells. The sieve-tube cells can be loaded with very high concentrations of sucrose from neighboring cells because of active transport.

The correct answer is c...
D. Answer d is incorrect because auxin does not influence sucrose loading into phloem.

8). Blowing water up through a drinking straw is most like
      a). guttation.
      b). diffusion.
      c). mass flow in xylem.
      d). mass flow in phloem.

The correct answer is a--guttation.
A. Answer a is correct because guttation is the movement of water up from the roots and is caused when transpirational loss is slower than water uptake in the roots (e.g., during the night when stomata are mostly closed).

The correct answer is a...
B. Answer b is incorrect because diffusion is the passive movement of a substance from areas of high concentration towards areas of lower concentration and only occurs over very short distances (i.e., at the cellular level).

The correct answer is a...
C. Answer c is incorrect because mass flow in xylem is driven by the transpirational water loss from the stomata and works over large distances. Guttation can only move water on the scale of inches.

The correct answer is a...
D. Answer d is incorrect because mass flow in phloem occurs as photosynthate moves from the source to the sink within the plant.

9). If you wanted to force stomata to open, which of the following would work?
   a). Treat the plant with abscisic acid.
   b). Stimulate water movement into the guard cells.
   c). Stimulate water movement out of the guard cells.
   d). Force the dermal cells around the stomata to dehydrate, thereby pulling the guard cells apart.

The correct answer is b…
A. Answer a is incorrect because abscisic acid is a hormone that forces stomata to close during drought stress.

The correct answer is b--Stimulate water movement into the guard cells.
B. Answer b is correct because stomata open by pumping salt into guard cells to draw water inward. Because of the asymmetrically thickened cell wall this causes the cells to bend, opening the stomata.

The correct answer is b…
C. Answer c is incorrect because if water moves out of the guard cells, the stomata close.

The correct answer is b…
D. Answer d is incorrect because dehydration is a severe form of drought stress and would not be an appropriate control mechanism.

10). The Casparian strip is analogous to
   a). caulking to waterproof a seam in the bathtub.
   b). axle grease to lubricate a wheel.
   c). a condom to prevent fertilization.
   d). masking tape to hold things together.

The correct answer is a--caulking to waterproof a seam in the bathtub.
A. Answer a is correct because the Casparian strip is a waterproof layer of cells between the cortex of the root and the stele (i.e., the vascular tissue).

The correct answer is a…
B. Answer b is incorrect because the Casparian strip does not lubricate the plant; this would be analogous to the mucigel lubricant that is secreted from the root cap.

The correct answer is a…
C. Answer c is incorrect because the Casparian strip has nothing to do with fertilization; this would be analogous to self-incompatibility in plants.

The correct answer is a…
D. Answer d is incorrect because the Casparian strip a waterproof barrier but is not designed to hold groups of cells together as a primary function; this would be analogous to pectin that holds cells together in plants (see abscission).

Test Your Visual Understanding

1). Which of the pairs of guard cells in the picture has more water inside?
Answer: The cell on the left actually has more water in its guard cells. When water moves into the guard cells, they expand. The inner wall is more rigid and cannot expand. Thus it gets pulled back leaving an opening in the center. The picture on the right shows guard cells that have lost turgor pressure. The opening in the center is covered as the cells become flaccid.

259

Apply Your Knowledge

1). Design a simple working model of the major transport systems in plants using commonly available equipment (e.g., vacuum cleaners, bicycle pumps, a garden hose). Be sure to discriminate between xylem transport mechanisms and phloem transport mechanisms.
Answer: Xylem transport: Place one end of a garden hose into a garbage can of water and extend the hose upwards. You would need some type of support to keep the hose vertical. Attach a vacuum cleaner (preferably a shop vac that can handle water) to the top of the hose and turn on the vacuum cleaner. The water molecules will be held together by their cohesive properties and the vacuum will provide the transpiration pull that evaporation of water through stomata normally provides in a plant.

Phloem: Seal one end of a garden hose and make tiny holes in the hose at that end. Fill the hose with water, place the sealed end (with its tiny holes) in a garbage can, and raise the other end vertically. You will need some type of support to keep the hose vertical. Take a bicycle pump and raise the handle to fill the pump with air. Now find a way to attach the bicycle pump to the top of the hose so that no water can leak between the pump and that end of the hose. Press the handle of the pump down so that you use the air to force water down in the hose. This should force droplets of water out of the small hole you have made at the other end of the hose into the garbage can. You have created a pressure flow model of phloem transport. In a real plant, sucrose would be actively transported into the phloem near a leaf where photosynthesis occurred. Water would then move by osmosis into the phloem and force the fluid to move away from the leaf, just like the bicycle pump would force water down your garden hose. Note: Since phloem transport is bidirectional, you could turn your model upside down and still have it represent phloem transport.

2). If you could turn a plant upside down without affecting the function of the major organs (roots, shoots, and leaves), would transport of water in xylem move upwards toward the roots, or would it still move toward the leaves? Would transport of photosynthate in phloem change as a result of this inversion?
Answer: Water would still move towards the leaves in the xylem of your inverted plant. Roots don't have stomates for water to move through and there is not a mechanism for water to move from the ground into leaves and then exit through the roots via transpiration. Transpiration would still move water out through the leaves, but this would stop as the roots dried out.

Transport in the phloem would not be altered. Photosynthate would still move from the source to the sink as described by the pressure flow model for phloem transport.

3). Roots are highly specialized to acquire water from the environment, yet plants that grow in wet, boggy environments have roots that are specialized to acquire oxygen! Discuss these structural adaptations and why they are important for survival of the plant.
Answer: Structural adaptations to very wet environments include pneumatophores that are root outgrowths that grow above the surface of the water and allow roots to obtain sufficient oxygen. Other plants have extra lenticels, fairly large openings on stems that enhance the exchange of oxygen. Yet another adaptation occurs in the leaves with extra air space in the mesophyll. This type of tissue is called aerenchyma and it allows the plant to collect an unusually large amount of oxygen that can be transported down to the roots.

Roots need both water and oxygen. For many plants there is not enough dissolved oxygen in very wet environments for the root cells to undergo respiration. Without cellular respiration there is not enough energy for cells to survive.

Inquiry Questions
None for this chapter.

Self Test

1). Phosphate uptake by roots involves
   a). a PO_4 channel in the endoderm of the root.
   b). soil bacteria to make the phosphate bioaccessable.
   c). symbiotic fungal hyphae to increase the effective surface area of the root.
   d). root nodules fixing phosphate from the air.

The correct answer is c…
A. Answer a is incorrect because the endoderm is located in the inner portion of the root and would not be able to acquire PO_4 from the soil.

The correct answer is c…
B. Answer b is incorrect because soil bacterial are involved in nitrogen fixation, not phosphate.

The correct answer is c--symbiotic fungal hyphae to increase the effective surface area of the root.
C. Answer c is correct because most plants associate with mycorrhizal fungi to assist in acquiring phosphate from the soil.

The correct answer is c…
D. Answer d is incorrect because root nodules are involved in converting nitrogen gas to biologically accessible nitrogen.

2). In an attempt to create a nitrogen-fixing bioreactor, you set out to culture *Rhizobium* a). from the root nodules of pea plants. After months of work, you are still having trouble getting the *Rhizobium* to grow, let alone fix nitrogen. What might explain this failure?
   a). *Rhizobium* only grows in association with plant root hairs.
   b). *Rhizobium* from root nodules lacks a cell wall, so it will not grow in culture.
   c). You accidentally put a fungicide in your growth medium that kills all of the *Rhizobium*.
   d). *Rhizobium* from root nodules lacks chromosomal DNA, so it will not grow in culture.

The correct answer is b…
A. Answer a is incorrect because *Rhizobium* forms nodules by entering through the root hair but then growing in the cortex of the root.

The correct answer is b--*Rhizobium* from root nodules lacks a cell wall, so it will not grow in culture.
B. Answer b is correct because *Rhizobium* do lose their cell wall in the later stages of nodule formation and therefore become dependant on the root for protection and osmotic balance.

The correct answer is b…
C. Answer c is incorrect because *Rhizobium* is a bacterium and therefore a fungicide would not affect its growth.

The correct answer is b…
D. Answer d is incorrect because *Rhizobium* maintains its genome to direct synthesis of the nitrogen-fixing enzymes in the root nodules.

3). You are performing an experiment to determine the nutrient requirements for a newly discovered plant and find that for some reason your plants die if you leave boron out of the growth medium but do fine with as low as 5 parts per million in solution. This suggests that boron is

      a). an essential macronutrient.
      b). a nonessential micronutrient.
      c). an essential micronutrient.
      d). a nonessential macronutrient.

The correct answer is c...
A. Answer a is incorrect because while boron is essential, it is only required in small amounts.

The correct answer is c...
B. Answer b is incorrect because boron is required for the plant to live and therefore is an essential nutrient.

The correct answer is c--an essential micronutrient.
C. Answer c is correct because boron is required in small amounts for the plant to live.

The correct answer is c...
D. Answer d is incorrect because boron is required for the plant to live and therefore is an essential nutrient.

4). You are setting up some planters to grow flowers in your apartment and discover that you bought sand rather than potting soil. You decide to go ahead and plant the flowers in the sand to save yourself a trip back to the store. Much to your dismay, all of your plants die! How can you explain this failure?

      a). Sand does not pack tightly enough around the roots to hold the plants upright, so they fall over and die.
      b). Sand does not hold enough water to sustain plant metabolism, so all of the plants die from dessication.
      c). Sand does not contain enough nutrient material to sustain plant growth, so the plants die from starvation.
      d). Sand is too abrasive and damages the roots as they grow through it, so the plants die.

The correct answer is c...
A. Answer a is incorrect because sand can pack very tightly, albeit it is not as good a support medium compared to soil.

The correct answer is c...
B. Answer b is incorrect because sand can become saturated with water in the same way that soil does.

The correct answer is c--Sand does not contain enough nutrient material to sustain plant growth, so the plants die from starvation.
C. Answer c is correct because most of the nutrients in soil are derived from the humus; pure sand would not contain these biological nutrients.

The correct answer is c...
D. Answer d is incorrect because roots are highly specialized to grow through abrasive substrates.

5). If you discover a purely white plant growing on the forest floor, you can safely assume that it is a

a). mutant plant that uses a colorless pigment to carry out photosynthesis.
b). parasitic plant that acquires its macronutrients from other plants.
c). plant that only carries out the dark reactions of photosynthesis and therefore doesn't need green pigments.
d). plant that does not require macronutrients and therefore does not need photopigments.

The correct answer is b...
A. Answer a is incorrect because pigments, by definition, are light-absorbing molecules and as such will have color. Furthermore, the pigments required for photosynthesis give plants their color.

The correct answer is b--parasitic plant that acquires its macronutrients from other plants.
B. Answer b is correct because for a plant to be colorless, it must obtain its carbohydrate requirement from sources other than photosynthesis (i.e., other plants).

The correct answer is b...
C. Answer c is incorrect because the dark reactions of photosynthesis require the productivity of the light reactions so a plant could not only perform half of the photosynthetic complement of reactions.

The correct answer is b...
D. Answer d is incorrect because all plants have macro- and micronutrient requirements.

6). Growing peas that are defective in flavonoid production would

a). prevent bioaccumulation of potassium in the roots.
b). prevent bioaccumulation of nitrogen in the roots.
c). prevent bioaccumulation of phosphorous in the roots.
d). prevent the production of flavor molecules in the seeds so that they would be unpalatable.

The correct answer is b...
A. Answer a is incorrect because flavonoids attract *Rhizobium* bacteria for the production of root nodules that fix N_2 gas.

The correct answer is b--prevent bioaccumulation of nitrogen in the roots.
B. Answer b is correct because flavonoids attract *Rhizobium* bacteria for the production of root nodules that fix N_2 gas.

The correct answer is b...
C. Answer c is incorrect because phosphorous uptake into roots occurs with mycorrhizal fungal symbiotes.

The correct answer is b...
D. Answer d is incorrect because flavonoids do not help the flavor of the plant!

7). Feeding your Venus flytrap a common brand of all-purpose plant fertilizer would likely cause

a). it to die from nitrogen overload.
b). its traps to become large enough to capture small mammals.
c). no change, because these plants can only use nitrogen from insects.
d). its traps to fall off, because it would not need to acquire nitrogen from insects.

The correct answer is d…
A. Answer a is incorrect because nitrogen is usually limiting; in the presence of excess nitrogen, plants will grow more vigorously.

The correct answer is d…
B. Answer b is incorrect because the plant will not need to produce traps for nitrogen acquisition if there is sufficient nitrogen in the soil.

The correct answer is d…
C. Answer c is incorrect because the traps in these plants are an adaptation for acquiring nitrogen from nitrogen poor environments.

The correct answer is d--its traps to fall off, because it would not need to acquire nitrogen from insects.
D. Answer d is correct because it takes a great deal of energy for plants to produce traps. If nitrogen is available from the environment, plants will not expend the energy to produce the specialized traps.

8). If you were asked how to clean up a trichloroethylene (TCE) spill without having to resort to burning or other chemical methods, how would you do it?
    a). Plant poplar trees to phytoremediate the soil.
    b). Plant bean plants to replace the TCE with fixed nitrogen.
    c). Plant *Brassica* plants to phytoaccumulate the TCE.
    d). Plant Indian pipe because it is not adversely affected by TCE in the soil.

The correct answer is a--Plant poplar trees to phytoremediate the soil.
A. Answer a is correct because poplar trees are able to take up TCE and break it down to produce CO_2 and Cl^-.

The correct answer is a…
B. Answer b is incorrect because fixing nitrogen from the atmosphere will not get rid of TCE in the environment.

The correct answer is a…
C. Answer c is incorrect because *Brassica* can phytoaccumulate heavy metals, but not TCE.

The correct answer is a…
D. Answer d is incorrect because while Indian pipe may not be affected by the TCE, they will not remove it from the environment. Furthermore, Indian pipe is a parasitic plant that would require another plant in order to acquire nutrients.

Test Your Visual Understanding

1). If you found a grove of poplar trees like that shown in this image, what might you conclude about the area?
Answer: There are several reasons these poplar trees could be planted in this grove. They may have been planted as a windbreak (notice how they have grown with a bit of a tilt to the one side). However, having just read this chapter, you might hypothesize that they are being used for phytoremediation. Since the area around the trees appears to be barren, there may be toxins in the soil that are affecting the growth of other plants.

Apply Your Knowledge

1). Match each of the following nutrients with its appropriate function in plants, and discuss whether it is a macro- or micronutrient.

a). carbon	____ cell wall formation
b). nitrogen	____ nucleic acid formation
c). phosphorous	____ amino acid production
d). iron	____ nitrogen fixation
e). molybdenum	____ chlorophyll production

Answer:

a). carbon	a	cell wall formation
b). nitrogen	c	nucleic acid formation
c). phosphorous	b	amino acid production
d). iron	e	nitrogen fixation
e). molybdenum	d,e	chlorophyll production

Carbon, nitrogen, and phosphorous are macronutrients that are need in large amounts for the production of carbohydrates, proteins, and nucleic acids. Iron and molybdenum are needed in much smaller amounts and are considered to be micronutrients. Molybdenum is used in nitrogen fixation. Iron is needed for several reasons, including the production of chlorophyll. Plants that are deficient in iron show chlorosis or a bleaching of leaf color.

2). If you were to eat one ton (1000 kg) of potatoes, approximately how much of the following minerals would you eat?
    a). copper between .4 and 3 g
    b). zinc between 1.5 and 10 g
    c). potassium between 0.5 and 6 kg
    d). iron between 2.5 and 30g

Answer: Here is how you solve the problems:
    The macronutrient, potassium is constitutes 0.5 to 6 % of the dry weight. Let's assume that the potato is 90% water. The dry weight would be 10 % of 1000 kg or 100 kg. Next you calculate 0.5% of 100 which is 0.5 kg. You would do the same type of calculation for 6 %.
    The micronutrient problems would also use the estimate of 100 kg dry weight. The conversion you need to use is that 1 ppm is the same as 1 mg per kg. So, 4 ppm of copper is the same as 4 mg/kg. Multiply this by 100 kg of dry weight potato and you have 400 mg of copper. Since there are 1000 mg in a gram, 400 mg X 1g/1000 mg = 0.4 g of copper in a ton of potato. The other micronutrient problems would be calculated in a similar manner.

3). Using what you know about phytoremediation, design a strategy to speculate for gold that would not require any digging or disruption of the soil.

Answer: Gold is a heavy metal. There are some hints that metal transporters exist that load metal in the soil into xylem and that it is later sequestered in vacuoles in leaves. You could start with plants known to hyperaccummulate heavy metals like lead and cadmium and see if they could also accumulate gold. All you would need to do then is to grow your plants, harvest them, dry them down, and isolate the gold. If this didn't work, you could search for plants that did take up gold and use those in your search for gold.

Self Test

1). If you were a plant pathogen, what would be the first obstacle to invading a host plant that you would have to overcome?
        a). chemical toxins on the surface of a plant
        b). physical barriers on the exterior of a plant
        c). animal guardians of the host plant
        d). immune proteins in the plant tissue

The correct answer is b...
A. Answer a is incorrect because while some plants may have toxins on their surface, the majority of plants rely on an impermeable barrier to invasion.

The correct answer is b--physical barriers on the exterior of a plant
B. Answer b is correct because the outside of most plants is covered by an impermeable layer of bark. Further, each plant cell has a rigid cell wall that can prevent pathogen infection.

The correct answer is b...
C. Answer c is incorrect because while some plants do have animal guardians (e.g., ants protecting Acacia plants) this type of coevolution is rare and is unlikely to protect a plant from an invading virus, bacterium or fungus.

The correct answer is b...
D. Answer d is incorrect because while most plants can produce immune proteins, they are not the first line of defense to infection.

2). Some plants are recognized by fungal pathogens on the basis of their stomatal pores. Which of the following would provide these plants immunity from fungal infection?
        a). removing all of the stomata from the plant
        b). changing the spacing of stomatal pores in these plants
        c). reinforcing the cell wall in the guard cells of stomatal pores
        d). increasing the number of trichomes on the surfaces of these plants

The correct answer is b...
A. Answer a is incorrect because removing the stomata from plants would kill the plant regardless of fungal infection.

The correct answer is b--changing the spacing of stomatal pores in these plants
B. Answer b is correct because some fungal pathogens recognize host plants by the spacing of their stomata. Altering this spacing, therefore, would prevent recognition by the fungal pathogen.

The correct answer is b...
C. Answer c is incorrect because reinforcing the guard cell wall would not prevent the stomatal pore from allowing access to fungal pathogens. It may, however, compromise guard cell function because the opening and closing of stomata depends on asymmetric thickening of the guard cell wall.

The correct answer is b...
D. Answer d is incorrect because trichomes play a role in preventing predation by herbivorous animals, but will not prevent fungal infection.

3). Eating unscrubbed cassava root would likely
   a). lead to indigestion because the skin of the cassava plant is very difficult to digest.
   b). make you sick because the soil on the surface may contain harmful microbes.
   c). make you sick because the skin contains cyanogenic glycosides that would produce cyanide in the digestive track.
   d). harm your teeth because of the small stones that would be on the surface of the root.

The correct answer is c...
A. Answer a is incorrect because the skin of the cassava plant is not difficult to digest.

The correct answer is c...
B. Answer b is incorrect because while the soil does contain microbes, in small amounts it is unlikely to make you sick.

The correct answer is c--make you sick because the skin contains cyanogenic glycosides that would produce cyanide in the digestive track.
C. Answer c is correct because the skin of the cassava plant contains high levels of cyanogenic compounds that are converted to cyanide in the digestive track. Cyanide is a poison that blocks electron transport.

The correct answer is c...
D. Answer d is incorrect because it is unlikely that you would hurt your teeth on stones in soil.

4). You decide to plant a garden in which a beautiful black walnut tree is the centerpiece. You are quite disappointed, however, when none of the seeds you plant around the tree grow. What might explain this observation?
   a). the tree filters out too much light, so the seeds fail to germinate
   b). the roots of the tree deplete all of the nutrients from the soil, so the new seedlings starve
   c). the tree produces chemical toxins that prevent seed germination
   d). the roots deplete all of the water from the soil and thereby prevent seed germination

The correct answer is c...
A. Answer a is incorrect because while dense forest canopies can filter enough light to prevent seed germination, one tree would not preclude enough light to have this effect.

The correct answer is c...
B. Answer b is incorrect because there are more than enough nutrient reserves in soil to sustain many plants.

The correct answer is c--the tree produces chemical toxins that prevent seed germination
C. Answer c is correct because black walnut trees produce chemicals that diffuse throughout the soil and prevent seed germination in a process called allelopathy.

The correct answer is c...
D. Answer d is incorrect because there is more than enough water in soil to sustain many plants.

5). Vegetarians whose diet consists largely of soy are less likely to develop prostate cancer because
   a). soy contains the anticancer drug taxol.
   b). eating meat increases the probability of developing prostate cancer, so eliminating it from your diet reduces the chances of developing the disease.
   c). soy protein prevents accumulation of the prostate-specific antigen (PSA) associated with prostate cancer.
   d). soy contains a phytoestrogen that may down-regulate estrogen and androgen receptors in males who consume high soy diets.

The correct answer is d...
A. Answer a is incorrect because the anticancer drug taxol is isolated from Yew trees.

The correct answer is d...
B. Answer b is incorrect because meat does not have a known effect on the incidence of prostate cancer.

The correct answer is d...
C. Answer c is incorrect because PSA is produced in prostate tumor cells and is not down-regulated by soy proteins.

The correct answer is d--soy contains a phytoestrogen that may down-regulate estrogen and androgen receptors in males who consume high soy diets.
D. Answer d is correct because it has been observed that in Asian males where soy is prominent in the diet, the incidence of prostate cancer is reduced.

6). The drink gin and tonic was created by British soldiers in India as a means of
    a). dealing with boredom during the long hours between battles.
    b). increasing revenue by selling the drink in the officer's club.
    c). fighting malaria with the quinine in tonic water.
    d). fighting scurvy with the juniper extract in gin.

The correct answer is c...
A. Answer a is incorrect because drinking gin is not a good way to deal with boredom.

The correct answer is c...
B. Answer b is incorrect because the army would not want to encourage drinking alcohol as a revenue generating endeavor.

The correct answer is c--fighting malaria with the quinine in tonic water.
C. Answer c is correct because tonic water contains quinine which is an antimalarial drug; gin was used to mask the bitter taste of the quinine.

The correct answer is c...
D. Answer d is incorrect because scurvy was caused by a vitamin C deficiency; the British navy used citrus to increase vitamin C in the sailor's diet.

7). Tomato plants are not good to eat because
    a). when their tissue is damaged, it generates a foul odor that makes people sick.
    b). they do not contain any useful nutrients for animals.
    c). they contain chemical toxins that will make animals sick.
    d). when their tissue is damaged, they produce proteinase inhibitors that will prevent digestive enzyme function in animals.

The correct answer is d...
A. Answer a is incorrect because tomato plants do not produce a foul odor.

The correct answer is d...
B. Answer b is incorrect because they do contain macro- and micronutrients that would be useful in animal diets.

The correct answer is d...
C. Answer c is incorrect because tomato plants do not contain toxic chemicals.

The correct answer is d--when their tissue is damaged, they produce proteinase inhibitors that will prevent digestive enzyme function in animals.
D. Answer d is correct because tomato plants do produce proteinase inhibitors in response to tissue damage; these have adverse affects on the digestive tract of animals that eat tomato plants. (The fruit, however, relies on predation by herbivores to disperse seed!).

8). A plant lacking *R* genes would likely
      a). be unable to carry out photosynthesis.
      b). be susceptible to infection by pathogens.
      c). be susceptible to predation by herbivores.
      d). paralyze animals who ingested it.

The correct answer is b…
A. Answer a is incorrect because *R* genes have nothing to do with photosynthesis.

The correct answer is b--be susceptible to infection by pathogens.
B. Answer b is correct because *R* genes confer resistance to pathogen infection; in their absence the plant would be susceptible to infection.

The correct answer is b…
C. Answer c is incorrect because *R* genes do not affect animals, but rather target viral, fungal, or microbial pathogens.

The correct answer is b…
D. Answer d is incorrect because *R* genes do not affect animals.

9). Both plant and animal immune systems can
      a). develop memory of past pathogens to more effectively deal with subsequent infections.
      b). establish physical barriers to infection.
      c). initiate expression of proteins to help fight the infection.
      d). kill their own cells to prevent spread of the infection.
      e). All of these are true.

The correct answer is e…
A. Answer a is incorrect because although both plants and animals have a mechanism to develop memory of past infectious agents, this is not the only answer.

The correct answer is e…
B. Answer b is incorrect because although both plants and animals have physical barriers to infection (i.e., bark in plants, skin in animals), this is not the only answer.

The correct answer is e…
C. Answer c is incorrect because although both plants and animals initiate new gene expression to fight infection, this is not the only answer.

The correct answer is e…
D. Answer d is incorrect because although both plants and animals can kill their own cells to prevent spread of infection (e.g., the hypersensitive response in plants and the cellular immune response in animals), this is not the only answer.

The correct answer is e--All of these are true.
E. Answer e is correct. All of these are true: develop memory of past pathogens to more effectively deal with subsequent infections, establish physical barriers to infection, initiate expression of proteins to help fight the infection, and kill their own cells to prevent spread of the infection.

Test Your Visual Understanding

1). Label structures *a–e* with the plant from which each comes and the effect each has on humans.
Answer:
   a) Morphine – a narcotic pain killer
   b) Quinine – effective in treating malaria
   c) Taxol – effective in treating some forms of cancer
   d) Genistein – can mimic the effects of the human hormone estrogen
   e) Manihotoxin – can be lethal because it releases cyanide when metabolized. Cyanide inhibits cellular respiration.

Apply Your Knowledge

1). Herbal medicine has long relied on plant extracts to cure human disease. Find three examples of herbal remedies that have been exploited by the pharmaceutical industry in modern drug production.
Answer: Quinine has been isolated from the bark of *Cinchona* trees for hundreds of years to treat malaria.
   The pharmaceutical industry found a way to make several synthetic forms of quinine that are effective in treating some forms of malaria.
   Breast cancer can be treated with taxol that is extracted from the Pacific yew. When the Pacific yew population faced possible extinction, the pharmaceutical industry found a way to synthesize taxol.
   Opium poppies have long been used for their narcotic effect, both legally and illegally. The active ingredient is morphine. Understanding the biochemical structure of morphine and its affects on the human nervous system has lead to the synthesis of pain killers for medicinal use.

2). Diagram the events surrounding infection of a plant by a fungal pathogen. Include strategies used both by the pathogen and by the host plant.
Answer: Use figure 39.5 as a sample diagram. Add the following information to these labels which already occur on the diagram:
   Plant epidermal cell – Layers of cutin make it difficult for fungi to get past the plant's surface.
   Fungus entering stoma – Although essential for gas exchange and transpiration, stoma are the weak link in the plant's first line of defense. Fungi locate stoma and enter through that opening.
   Plant cell – Plant cells can sometimes recognize the fungus by proteins it releases. This can trigger a hypersensitive response which kills the fungus and prevents further spread of the infection.

3). If you wanted to find new phytopharmaceuticals that could fight cancer, how would you go about identifying new compounds?
Answer: If you were looking for a new phytopharmaceutical to fight cancer, you could start by studying cultures that have reduced cancer rates. Try to find a correlation between diet or herbal medicines that are used. If you find a very promising species of plant and find out how it is prepared as a food or remedy. Use this information to begin isolating compounds from the plant and testing them in cultured cell lines. This is the approach that an ethnobotanist would use. Ethnobotanists are trained in plant biology, biochemistry, sociology and anthropology.

Self Test

1). Which of the following seeds would likely germinate even if it were located on the floor of a densely leaved forest?
     a). a seed lacking chlorophyll *a*
     b). a seed lacking phytochrome P_r
     c). a seed lacking phytochrome P_{fr}
     d). a seed lacking phototropin

The correct answer is c…
A. Answer a is incorrect because chlorophyll *a* is responsible for light absorption in the leaves and is part of the photosynthetic machinery.

The correct answer is c…
B. Answer b is incorrect because phytochrome P_r absorbs red light and is not biologically active in regulating seed germination.

The correct answer is c--a seed lacking phytochrome P_{fr}
C. Answer c is correct because phytochrome P_{fr} absorbs far red light and inhibits seed germination. If this pigment is lacking, the seed would not know that the red light necessary for photosynthesis is already being absorbed in the forest canopy.

The correct answer is c…
D. Answer d is incorrect because phototropin is a blue light receptor involved in phototropism in plants.

2). Which of the following statements provides a true example of both photomorphogenesis and phototropism?
     a). phototropism is growth toward blue light, and photomorphogenesis is growth toward red light.
     b). phototropism is growth toward blue light, and photomorphogenesis is germination triggered by near-red light.
     c). phototropism is growth toward red light, and photomorphogenesis is germination triggered by blue light.
     d). phototropism is movement toward blue light, that does not involve growth; photomorphogenesis is movement toward red light that does involve growth.

The correct answer is b…
A. Answer a is incorrect because photomorphogenesis is not growth toward red light, but rather is the establishment of form (i.e., germination) triggered by red light.

The correct answer is b--phototropism is growth toward blue light, and photomorphogenesis is germination triggered by near-red light.
B. Answer b is correct because phototropism is growth triggered by blue light receptors and photomorphogenesis is germination triggered by near-red light.

The correct answer is b…
C. Answer c is incorrect because phototropism is growth toward blue light and photomorphogenesis is germination triggered by red light, not blue light.

The correct answer is b…
D. Answer d is incorrect because phototropism is a growth response and photomorphogenesis is a germination response. Photomorphogenesis is not a directional response to light.

3). If you were to plant a de-etiolated (*det2*) mutant *Arabidopsis* seed and keep it in a dark box, what would you expect to happen?

    a). The seed would germinate normally, but the plant would not become tall and spindly while it sought a light source.
    b). The seed would fail to germinate because it would not have light.
    c). The seed would germinate, and the plant would become tall and spindly while it sought a light source.
    d). The seed would germinate, and the plant would immediately die because it could not make sugar in the dark.

The correct answer is a--The seed would germinate normally, but the plant would not become tall and spindly while it sought a light source.
A. Answer a is correct because the *det2* gene encodes an enzyme involved in the etiolation response. Without this gene, plants will not undergo the etiolation response (i.e., they will not grow tall and spindly in a light seeking response).

The correct answer is a…
B. Answer b is incorrect because the *det2* gene does not influence seed germination.

The correct answer is a…
C. Answer c is incorrect because this is the normal etiolation response and requires a wild-type copy of the *det2* gene.

The correct answer is a…
D. Answer d is incorrect because seedlings store some nutrient reserves in the coleoptiles so that they do not have to begin photosynthesis immediately after germination.

4). Growing plants in zero gravity on the space shuttle prevents
    a). phototropism because it is dark in space.
    b). photomorphogenesis because only near-red light filters into space.
    c). gravitropism because there is little gravity in space.
    d). aerotropism because there is no oxygen in space.

The correct answer is c…
A. Answer a is incorrect because there are lights on the space shuttle that could stimulate photosynthesis.

The correct answer is c…
B. Answer b is incorrect because seeds will germinate on the space shuttle under artificial light.

The correct answer is c--gravitropism because there is little gravity in space.
C. Answer c is correct because there is little gravity in space so there will be little or no growth response to gravity.

The correct answer is c…
D. Answer d is incorrect because there is air on the space shuttle.

5). When a Venus flytrap closes, it is an example of
    a). growth.
    b). cell migration.
    c). muscle contraction.
    d). a nervous twitch.

The correct answer is a--growth.
A. Answer a is correct because when Venus flytraps close it involves rapid growth of cell in the hinge region that force the blades of the trap to close.

The correct answer is a...
B. Answer b is incorrect because there is no cell migration in plants.

The correct answer is a...
C. Answer c is incorrect because plants do not have muscles.

The correct answer is a...
D. Answer d is incorrect because plants do not have nerves.

6). We often have the misconception that plants are unable to move in their environment. Many plants, however, display daily movements to maximize their capacity to absorb light energy (e.g., bean leaves). These daily changes in shape are caused by
   a). changes in turgor in specific cells.
   b). growth of specific cells.
   c). muscle contraction in the leaves.
   d). temperature changes in the environment.

The correct answer is a--changes in turgor in specific cells.
A. Answer a is correct because when cells in the pulvini region lose turgor, the leaves will fall and when these cells regain turgor, the leaves will rise in the horizontal plane.

The correct answer is a...
B. Answer b is incorrect because daily shape changes are reversible and growth is defined as an irreversible change in shape.

The correct answer is a...
C. Answer c is incorrect because leaves have no muscles.

The correct answer is a...
D. Answer d is incorrect because while temperature can influence plant growth, it is not responsible for the daily changes in shape that bean plants demonstrate.

7). When Charles and Francis Darwin investigated phototropisms in plants, they discovered that
   a). auxin was responsible for light-dependant growth.
   b). light was detected at the tip of a plant.
   c). light was detected along the shoot of a plant.
   d). only red light stimulated phototropism.

The correct answer is b...
A. Answer a is incorrect because it was Went who discovered that the phototropic response involved a chemical that he named auxin.

The correct answer is b--light was detected at the tip of a plant.
B. Answer b is correct because the Darwin experiments determined that the tip of a plant was responsible for the phototropic response.

The correct answer is b...
C. Answer c is incorrect because when the Darwins blocked light from reaching the stem below the tip of a plant, the phototropic response was normal.

The correct answer is b...
D. Answer d is incorrect because phototropisms are mediated by blue light receptors, phototropin 1.

8). The chemical defoliant Agent Orange was banned because
   a). the synthetic auxin used in the preparation, 2,4,5-trichlorophenoxyacetic acid (2,4,5-T), caused premature growth in humans.
   b). the synthetic auxin used in the preparation, 2,4,5-trichlorophenoxyacetic acid (2,4,5-T), caused plants to grow more vigorously than the environment could sustain.
   c). a contaminant in the preparation of 2,4,5-trichlorophenoxyacetic acid (2,4,5-T) caused disease and birth defects in humans.
   d). a contaminant in the preparation of 2,4,5-trichlorophenoxyacetic acid (2,4,5-T) killed beneficial plants.

The correct answer is c...
A. Answer a is incorrect because auxins do not have any effect on animal growth.

The correct answer is c...
B. Answer b is incorrect because high doses of auxin do not cause growth, but rather lead to defoliation or death in plants.

The correct answer is c--a contaminant in the preparation of 2,4,5-trichlorophenoxyacetic acid (2,4,5-T) caused disease and birth defects in humans.
C. Answer c is correct because the compound dioxin is produced as a byproduct of 2,4,5-T synthesis and causes birth defects and other abnormalities in animals.

The correct answer is c...
D. Answer d is incorrect because it is not the contaminant (dioxin) that kills plants, but the synthetic auxin.

9). You have come up with a brilliant idea to stretch your grocery budget by buying green fruit in bulk and then storing it in a bag that you have blown up like a balloon. As you need fruit, you would take it out of the bag, and it would miraculously ripen. How would this work?
   a). The bag would block light from reaching the fruit, so it would not ripen.
   b). The bag would keep the fruit cool, so it would not ripen.
   c). The high CO_2 levels in the bag would prevent ripening.
   d). The high O_2 levels in the bag would prevent ripening.

The correct answer is c...
A. Answer a is incorrect because fruit will ripen in the absence of light.

The correct answer is c...
B. Answer b is incorrect because the bag is not necessarily cold. Further, cool temperatures may slow the ripening process, but cannot stop it.

The correct answer is c--The high CO_2 levels in the bag would prevent ripening.
C. Answer c is correct because CO_2 is more concentrated in exhaled air and inhibits production of ethylene, which in turn is required for ripening in fruit. If ethylene synthesis is inhibited, ripening will be prevented.

The correct answer is c...
D. Answer d is incorrect because O_2 stimulates production of ethylene, which in turn stimulates fruit ripening. Further, O_2 concentrations are low in exhaled air.

10). If you were to accidentally plant a mutant strain of barley that could not synthesize the plant hormone abscisic acid (ABA), what would you expect to happen?

        a). The shoots would elongate too much and fall over because they could not support themselves.

        b). The shoots would not elongate normally, and you would get short plants.

        c). The seeds would germinate prematurely.

        d). The leaves would fall off the plant.

The correct answer is c…
A. Answer a is incorrect because ABA does not influence cell elongation in plants.

The correct answer is c…
B. Answer b is incorrect because ABA does not influence cell elongation in plants.

The correct answer is c--The seeds would germinate prematurely.
C. Answer c is correct because ABA promotes dormancy in seeds; in the absence of ABA seeds will not remain dormant.

The correct answer is c…
D. Answer d is incorrect because, despite its name, ABA is not involved in abscission.

Test Your Visual Understanding

1). Images *a–c* show tobacco cells cultured under different auxin:cytokinin ratios. Label each image with the appropriate hormone ratio.
Answer:

Auxin:	high	low	intermediate
Cytokinin:	low	high	intermediate

Apply Your Knowledge

1). Discuss the similarities and differences between thigmotropism and turgor movement.
Answer: A thigmotropism is a directional growth movement in response to touch. Cells on one side of a stem may grow faster than cells on the other side, allowing the plant to bend towards or away from the source of the touch. Turgor movements can also occur in response to touch. But unlike thigmotropisms, they are not growth responses. For example, the leaflets on a *Mimosa* plant fold almost instantly when touched. This happens because water leaves cells on one side of the pulvinus (stem-like region at base of the leaflet), but not the other side. Water later returns to the cells that have lost turgor pressure, but no growth has occurred.

2). Compare the mechanisms that animals and plants use to survive harsh environments by thinking of an equivalent animal response for each of the following:

        a). dormancy.

        b). thigmomorphogenesis.

        c). abscission

        d). phototropism

Answer: a). Dormancy in an animal is somewhat like hibernation, but a hibernating animal maintains a higher water content than a dormant seed. Also, hibernation cannot be extended for as long as dormancy is extended in some seeds.

        b). Thigmomorphogenesis is growth in response to touch. Animals respond to touch in a variety of ways, including moving away when they sense danger from touch. A possible example of a thigmomorphogenesis analogy in humans would be wearing a brace for scoliosis (a condition that causes abnormal spine development). The pressure (extended touch) from the brace allows the spine to develop in a more normal pattern. In plants, growth responses can occur in response to a much briefer touch with less pressure.

c). Abscission is analogous to a male deer naturally losing its antlers (its rack). In both cases, cells die at the point of attachment and the body part is discarded.

d). Phototropism is a growth movement towards light. Since most animals move, there is a greater tendency for an animal to **move** towards or away from light rather than **grow** towards or away from light. Tanning would not be a good example of a phototropism equivalent in plants, because it does not involve a directional growth response.

Inquiry Questions
None for this chapter.

Self Test

1). Flowers must
        a). be insect pollinated.
        b). show indeterminate growth.
        c). be part of the angiosperm life cycle.
        d). be self-incompatible.

The correct answer is c…
A. Answer a is incorrect because there are many other modes of pollination including wind, other animals (birds, humans, rodents, etc.), and even water.

The correct answer is c…
B. Answer b is incorrect because most flowers exhibit determinate growth; that is, most flowers grow to a genetically defined size.

The correct answer is c--be part of the angiosperm life cycle.
C. Answer c is correct because angiosperms are the only class of plant with flowers.

The correct answer is c…
D. Answer d is incorrect because there are many flowers that can self-fertilize.

2). In Iowa, a company called Team Corn works to ensure that fields of seed corn outcross so that hybrid vigor can be maintained. They do this by removing the staminate (i.e., pollen-producing) flowers from the corn plants. In an attempt to put Team Corn out of business, you would like to develop genetically engineered corn plants that
        a). contain Z-genes to prevent germination of pollen on the stigmatic surface.
        b). contain S-genes to stop pollen tube growth during self-fertilization.
        c). express B-type homeotic genes throughout developing flowers.

The correct answer is b…
A. Answer a is incorrect because there are no Z-genes in plants.

The correct answer is b--contain S-genes to stop pollen tube growth during self-fertilization.
B. Answer b is correct because S-genes are the genes that allow plants to recognize self-pollen.

The correct answer is b…
C. Answer c is incorrect because expressing the B-type homeotic gene throughout the developing flower would lead to a duplication of petals and stamens, but would not affect self-incompatibility.

3). Monoecious plants such as corn have either staminate or carpelate flowers. Knowing what you do about the molecular mechanisms of floral development, which of the following might explain the development of single-sex flowers?
        a). Expression of B-type genes in presumptive carpels will generate staminate flowers.
        b). Expression of A-type genes in presumptive stamens will generate carpelate flowers.
        c). Restricting B-type gene expression to presumptive petals will generate carpelate flowers.
        d). All of these are correct.

The correct answer is d…
A. Answer a is incorrect because although expressing B-type genes in presumptive carpels will transform them into stamens resulting in a staminate (or pistillate) flower, this is not the only answer.

The correct answer is d…
B. Answer b is incorrect because although expressing A-type genes in presumptive stamens will lead to a duplication of petals and loss of stamens, this is not the only answer. This would result in carpelate flowers.

The correct answer is d…
C. Answer c is incorrect because although restricting B-type gene expression to presumptive petals will lead to a duplication of carpels and a loss of stamens thereby producing a carpelate flower, this is not the only answer.

The correct answer is d--All of these are correct.
D. Answer d is correct because all of these are correct: Expression of B-type genes in presumptive carpels will generate staminate flowers, expression of A-type genes in presumptive stamens will generate carpelate flowers, and restricting B-type gene expression to presumptive petals will generate carpelate flowers.

4). You have been asked to collect plant sperm for a new plant breeding program involving in vitro fertilization. Which of the following tissues would be a good source of sperm?
        a). anthers
        b). ovaries
        c). pollen
        d). spores

The correct answer is a--anthers
A. Answer a is correct if the anthers have produced pollen. Pollen is the male gametophyte that divides and produces sperm cells. You can collect pollen from mature anthers.

The correct answer is a…
B. Answer b is incorrect because eggs form within the ovaries, not sperm.

The correct answer is a…
C. Answer c is incorrect because pollen only contains the generative cell until they germinate during pollination; sperm are not formed until the pollen tube is growing through the style of the carpel.

The correct answer is a…
D. Answer d is incorrect because spores are the haploid cells that will give rise to the gamete producing generation of a plant (gametophyte).

5). Street trees (those lining the roads) are generally male. This reduces the cleanup of the streets because the trees only produce pollen, not fruits. Therefore, the kinds of trees that are normally chosen as street trees are
        a). dioecious.
        b). monoecious.
        c). gymnosperms.
        d). trees producing perfect flowers.
        e). You cannot have a tree that is only male.

The correct answer is a--dioecious.
A. Answer a is correct because dioecious plants are either staminate and contain pollen producing flowers, or carpellate and produce egg producing flowers.

The correct answer is a...
B. Answer b is incorrect because monoecious plants have both male (staminate) and female (carpelate) flowers.

The correct answer is a...
C. Answer c is incorrect because gymnosperms do not contain flowers.

The correct answer is a...
D. Answer d is incorrect because perfect flowers have both stamens and carpels.

The correct answer is a...
E. Answer e is incorrect because there are many dioecious trees that contain single-sex flowers.

6). If you wanted to create a super tobacco plant to increase the number of leaves/acre on a tobacco farm, which of the following strategies would potentially work?
    a). Suppress more root growth in the plants.
    b). Decrease expression of the *LEAFY* gene in the shoot apical meristem.
    c). Harvest lower leaves as the plant is growing so that flowering is delayed.
    d). Remove flowers so that the plant will produce more vegetative internodes than normal.

The correct answer is b...
A. Answer a is incorrect because tobacco roots produce an inhibitor of flowering; this is partly how tobacco regulates the number of internodes required before flowering occurs. Suppressing root growth will accelerate flowering and reduce the amount of vegetative growth.

The correct answer is b--Decrease expression of the *LEAFY* gene in the shoot apical meristem.
B. Answer b is correct because expression of the *LEAFY* gene is required to initiate flowering. By decreasing *LEAFY* gene expression, the vegetative phase of growth will be extended and more leaves will be produced.

The correct answer is b...
C. Answer c is incorrect because the lower leaves may produce a floral inhibitor necessary to delay flowering and extend the production of leaves.

The correct answer is b...
D. Answer d is incorrect because after the tobacco plant has flowered it will stop growing. The shoot tip is consumed in the production of a terminal flower.

7). One of the most notable differences between gamete formation in animals and gamete formation in plants is that
    a). plants produce gametes in somatic tissue, while animals produce gametes in germ tissue.
    b). plants produce gametes by mitosis, while animals produce gametes by meiosis.
    c). plants produce only one of each gamete, while animals produce many gametes.
    d). plants produce gametes that are diploid, while animals produce gametes that are haploid.

The correct answer is b...
A. Answer a is incorrect because plants produce gametes in gametophytic tissue while animals produce gametes in germ tissue.

The correct answer is b--plants produce gametes by mitosis, while animals produce gametes by meiosis.
B. Answer b is correct because plants do produce gametes by mitosis in gametophytic tissue while animals produce gametes by meiosis in the germ line.

The correct answer is b...
C. Answer c is incorrect because plants and animals can produce large numbers of gametes.

The correct answer is b...
D. Answer d is incorrect because both plant and animal gametes are haploid; this is critical for maintaining the ploidy of successive generations.

8). If you were to discover a flower that was small, white, and heavily scented, its most likely pollinator would be
        a). bees.
        b). birds.
        c). humans.
        d). moths.

The correct answer is d...
A. Answer a is incorrect because bees are usually attracted by relatively large flowers and prefer yellow and blue pigmentation.

The correct answer is d...
B. Answer b is incorrect because birds are usually attracted by the color red, not white.

The correct answer is d...
C. Answer c is incorrect because we are usually attracted by large, brightly colored flowers with nice scents.

The correct answer is d--moths.
D. Answer d is correct because moths are usually drawn to small, colorless flowers with strong scents; this helps them find the flowers at night when most moths are active.

9). Under which of the following conditions would pollen from an S_2S_5 plant successfully pollinate an S_1S_5 flower?
        a). If you used pollen from a carpelate flower, to fertilize a staminate flower, it would be successful.
        b). If the plants used gametophytic self-incompatibility, half of the pollen would be successful.
        c). If the plants used sporophytic self-incompatibility, half of the pollen would be successful.
        d). Pollen from an S_2S_5 plant can never pollinate an S_1S_5 flower.

The correct answer is b...
A. Answer a is incorrect because pollen comes from staminate flowers and fertilizes carpelate flowers.

The correct answer is b--If the plants used gametophytic self-incompatibility, half of the pollen would be successful.
B. Answer b is correct because in gametophytic self-incompatibility, the S_2 pollen would successfully pollinate the S_1S_5 flower, but the S_5 pollen would not.

The correct answer is b...
C. Answer c is incorrect because none of the pollen from an S_2S_5 plant would germinate on an S_1S_5 stigma.

The correct answer is b...
D. Answer d is incorrect because S_2S_5 pollen can pollinate S_1S_5 flowers if they use gametophytic self-incompatibility.

10). You have been commissioned by kindergarteners across the country to develop a dandelion-breeding program to improve the quality of dandelion bouquets to give to mom. Initially, you are very excited about this project until you remember that

   a). dandelions reproduce asexually using runners.
   b). dandelion flowers set seed without fertilization.
   c). if dandelion flowers are not yellow, they will fail to attract the correct pollinators.
   d). dandelions are really gymnosperms.

The correct answer is b…
A. Answer a is incorrect because dandelions do produce seeds for reproduction, but use apomixis rather than pollination.

The correct answer is b--dandelion flowers set seed without fertilization.
B. Answer b is correct because apomixis is the process of producing seeds without fertilization and this is how dandelions reproduce.

The correct answer is b…
C. Answer c is incorrect because dandelions do not need to attract pollinators since they set seed without pollination.

The correct answer is b…
D. Answer d is incorrect because only angiosperms produce flowers.

Test Your Visual Knowledge

1). Describe what is taking place in this figure, and predict the genotypes of the staminate and carpelate tissue.
Answer: This must be an example of gametophytic self-incompatibility. Some but not all of the pollen that lands on the stigma fails to develop fully. Since pollen is haploid, you can infer that the staminate tissue had an S1 S2 genotype and produced pollen that was either S1 or S2. The carpelate tissue would have to have one of the alleles, but not the other. Let's say that the carpelate tissue was S1 S3. In this case, the S1 pollen would not fully develop, but the pollen with the S2 allele would be fine.

Apply Your Knowledge

1). We often have the impression that plants lack the ability to move around in the environment. This, however, is far from the truth. Discuss the variety of ways that plants successfully move throughout the environment.
Answer: Plants use animals to move across large distances. The flowering plants are particularly good at dispersing their offspring. Animals carry fruit and seed over long distances. Pollen can be carried to another plant of the same species by wind or an animal pollinator allowing plants to mate even though they are quite far apart. Unlike most animals, however, the plant does not have its own organs for locomotion and must piggyback on an animal to get around in the environment.

FIGURE 42.28
Summation. Muscle twitches summate to produce a sustained, tetanic contraction. This pattern is produced when the muscle is stimulated electrically or naturally by neurons. Tetanus, a smooth, sustained contraction, is the normal type of muscle contraction in the body.
What determines the maximum amplitude of a summated muscle contraction?

Answer: The amplitude of a summated muscle contraction is determined by the number of motor units that are stimulated. Therefore, in order to obtain the maximum amplitude of muscle contraction, all of the motor neurons innervating that muscle must be stimulated.

FIGURE 42.29
Skeletal muscles have different proportions of fast-twitch and slow-twitch fibers. The muscles that move the eye contain mostly fast-twitch fibers, whereas the deep muscle of the leg (the soleus) contains mostly slow-twitch fibers. The calf muscle (gastrocnemius) is intermediate in its composition.
How would you determine if the calf muscle contains a mix of fast-twitch and slow-twitch fibers, or instead is composed of an intermediate form of fiber?

Answer: The graph shows the contraction speed of the entire muscle. In order to determine if the calf muscle contains intermediate muscle fibers or a combination of slow- and fast-twitch muscle fibers, the contraction speed of individual motor units is measured. If some of the individual motor units trigger fast contractions (7.3 msec) and some trigger slower contractions (100 msec) the muscle contains a combination of both fibers. However, if the motor units of the calf muscle trigger contraction speeds that are between 7.3 and 100 msec and are not quick to fatigue, the muscle contains intermediate muscle fibers.

Self Test

1). Given what you know about the hierarchy of chemical organization, answer the following question. If Los Angeles was a molecule, Orange County was a cell, and California was a tissue, what would the United States be?
        a). a sister cell
        b). an organ system
        c). an organ
        d). an organism

The correct answer is c...
A. Answer a is incorrect because the United States would be considered a higher level of organization than a cell.

The correct answer is c...
B. Answer b is incorrect because the next level up from a state is a country, in this case the United States. An organ is the next level up from a tissue.

The correct answer is c--an organ.
C. In this example, the United States would be analogous to an organ, the next level up from a tissue.

The correct answer is c...
D. Answer d is incorrect because an organism would be more analogous to the earth. Rather, United States would be analogous to an organ, the next level up from a tissue.

2). Which organ system is primarily responsible for coordinating, regulating, and integrating the various activities of the body?
- a). nervous
- b). endocrine
- c). muscular
- d). respiratory

The correct answer is b...
A. Answer a is incorrect because while the nervous system is involved in integrating information, the endocrine system plays a wider role in coordinating, regulating, and integrating bodily activities through the release of hormones.

The correct answer is b--endocrine
B. The endocrine system plays a major role in coordinating, regulating, and integrating bodily activities through the release of hormones.

The correct answer is b...
C. Answer c is incorrect because the muscular system is primarily involved in producing body movement.

The correct answer is b...
D. Answer d is incorrect because the respiratory system is primarily involved in gas exchange.

3). Which of the following statements best describes endocrine glands?
- a). Endocrine glands are ductless glands that secrete hormones.
- b). Endocrine glands are ductless glands that secrete sweat, saliva, and digestive enzymes.
- c). Endocrine glands secrete hormones through a duct.
- d). Endocrine glands secrete sweat, saliva, and digestive enzymes through a duct.

The correct answer is a--Endocrine glands are ductless glands that secrete hormones.
A. Endocrine glands secrete hormones directly into the blood stream. Connections between endocrine glands and the epithelium are lost during development.

The correct answer is a...
B. Answer b is incorrect because while endocrine glands are ductless, they do not secrete sweat, saliva, and digestive enzymes.

The correct answer is a...
C. Answer c is incorrect because while endocrine glands do secrete hormones, they are ductless.

The correct answer is a...
D. Answer d is incorrect because endocrine glands are ductless and they do not secrete sweat, saliva, and digestive enzymes. This description applies to exocrine glands.

4). Which of the following is *not* considered a connective tissue?
- a). blood
- b). muscle
- c). adipose tissue
- d). cartilage

The correct answer is b...
A. Answer a is incorrect because blood is classified as a connective tissue due to its abundant extracellular matrix, the fluid plasma.

The correct answer is b--muscle
B. Muscle tissue is not classified as a connective tissue. Vertebrates have three different types of muscle tissue: smooth, skeletal, and cardiac.

The correct answer is b...
C. Answer c is incorrect because adipose tissue is classified as loose connective tissue.

The correct answer is b...
D. Answer d is incorrect because cartilage is classified as a special connective tissue. Cartilage consists of a ground substance called chondroitin along with collagen fibers laid down in long, parallel arrays.

5). Which of the following statements about nerve tissue is false?
        a). Neurons transmit sensory information to the brain.
        b). Both neurons and neuroglia are present in the CNS and PNS.
        c). Neurons conduct electrical impulses.
        d). All types of cells in nerve tissue conduct electrical impulses.

The correct answer is d...
A. Answer a is incorrect because sensory neurons do, in fact, transmit sensory information to the brain.

The correct answer is d...
B. Answer b is incorrect because both neurons and neuroglia are, indeed, present in both the CNS and PNS.

The correct answer is d...
C. Answer c is incorrect because within nerve tissue, neurons are specialized to produce and conduct electrical impulses. By contrast, neuroglia cannot conduct electrical impulses.

The correct answer is d--All types of cells in nerve tissue conduct electrical impulses.
D. Neuroglia, while considered to be nerve tissue, do not conduct electrical impulses.

6). Exoskeletons provide excellent protection to internal organs. However, animals that utilize exoskeletons are usually relatively small. Why?
        a). These animals are only able to produce a limited amount of chitin.
        b). Exoskeletons are not living tissue, and therefore they cannot grow.
        c). A large exoskeleton would be too heavy to move.
        d). During molting, these animals are especially vulnerable to predators and therefore do no usually live long enough to grow bigger.

The correct answer is c...
A. Answer a is incorrect because chitin production is not the limiting factor of animal grow. These animals are capable of producing chitin to form new exoskeletons after every molting period.

The correct answer is c...
B. Answer b is incorrect because while it is true that exoskeletons cannot grow, this fact alone does not limit the size of the animal. As these animals grow, they periodically molt and form a new exoskeleton.

The correct answer is c--A large exoskeleton would be too heavy to move.
C. In order to prevent collapse, the exoskeleton of a large animal would need to become thicker and heavier.

The correct answer is c...
D. Answer d is incorrect because while animals are especially vulnerable to predators during molting, it does influence their size.

7). Which of the following statements best describes the sliding filament mechanism of muscle contraction?
  a). Actin and myosin filaments do not shorten, but rather, slide past each other.
  b). Actin and myosin filaments shorten and slide past each other.
  c). As they slide past each other, actin filaments shorten, while myosin filaments do not shorten.
  d). As they slide past each other, myosin filaments shorten, while actin filaments do not shorten.

The correct answer is a--Actin and myosin filaments do not shorten, but rather, slide past each other.
A. Neither actin nor myosin filaments shorten. Instead, the thin filaments (actin), slide over the thick filaments (myosin), deeper into a band.

The correct answer is a...
B. Answer b is incorrect because neither actin nor myosin filaments shorten during muscle contraction.

The correct answer is a...
C. Answer c is incorrect because neither actin nor myosin filaments shorten during muscle contraction.

The correct answer is a...
D. Answer d is incorrect because neither actin nor myosin filaments shorten during muscle contraction.

8). What is the role of Ca^{++} in muscle contraction?
  a). It binds to tropomyosin, enabling troponin to move and reveal binding sites for cross-bridges.
  b). It binds to troponin, enabling tropomyosin to move and reveal binding sites for cross-bridges.
  c). It binds to tropomyosin, enabling troponin to release ATP.
  d). It binds to troponin, enabling tropomyosin to release ATP.

The correct answer is b...
A. Answer a is incorrect because Ca^{++} does not bind to tropomyosin.

The correct answer is b--It binds to troponin, enabling tropomyosin to move and reveal binding sites for cross-bridges.
B. When Ca^{++} levels are low, tropomyosin blocks the myosin binding site on the actin filament, thereby inhibiting cross-bridge formation.

The correct answer is b...
C. Answer c is incorrect because Ca^{++} does not bind to tropomyosin and troponin does not bind ATP.

The correct answer is b...
D. Answer d is incorrect because Ca^{++} does not bind to troponin and tropomyosin does not bind ATP.

9). Motor neurons stimulate muscle contraction via the release of
        a). Ca^{++}.
        b). ATP.
        c). acetylcholine.
        d). hormones.

The correct answer is c...
A. Answer a is incorrect because the Ca^{++} required for muscle contraction is stored in the sarcoplasmic reticulum.

The correct answer is c...
B. Answer b is incorrect because the ATP required for muscle contraction is obtained through cellular respiration.

The correct answer is c--acetylcholine.
C. Acetylcholine, released by somatic motor neurons, stimulates the muscle fiber to produce its own electrochemical impulse.

The correct answer is c...
D. Answer d is incorrect because while some neurons are known to release hormones, this mechanism is not directly involved in stimulating muscle contraction.

10). Which of the following statements about muscle metabolism is false?
        a). Skeletal muscles at rest obtain most of their energy from muscle glycogen and blood glucose.
        b). ATP can be quickly obtained by combining ADP with phosphate derived from creatine phosphate.
        c). Exercise intensity is related to the maximum rate of oxygen consumption.
        d). ATP is required for the pumping of the Ca^{++} back into the sarcoplasmic reticulum.

The correct answer is a--Skeletal muscles at rest obtain most of their energy from muscle glycogen and blood glucose.
A. Answer a is false because skeletal muscles at rest obtain most of their energy from aerobic respiration of fatty acids.

The correct answer is a...
B. Answer b is incorrect because one way to quickly make ATP is to combine ADP with phosphate derived from creatine phosphate.

The correct answer is a...
C. Answer c is incorrect because exercise intensity is dependent on a person's maximal capacity for aerobic exercise. Exercise intensity is also dependent on the lactate threshold.

The correct answer is a...
D. Answer d is incorrect because the energy obtained from cell respiration is used to make ATP. In turn, ATP is needed for (1) the movement of the cross-bridges in muscle contraction and (2) is required for the pumping of the Ca^{++} back into the sacroplasmic reticulum.

Test Your Visual Understanding

1). Use the following terms to label the structures in the figure.
> sarcomere
> A band
> H band
> I band
> Z line

Answer: The labeling should be like that in figure 42.20a (1 and 2).

Apply Your Knowledge

1). You are planning to travel to a hot and dry desert region where little water is available. If you were able to either (a) increase the amount of keratin in your stratified squamous epithelium, or (b) increase the number of your exocrine sweat glands, which would be a better survival strategy?
Answer: If water was plentiful, it would be best to (b) increase the number of your exocrine sweat glands. In this case, a large number of sweat glands would help your body to remain cool through evaporation of sweat. However, since water is scarce, it would be best to (a) increase the amount of keratin in your stratified squamous epithelium. In this case, the increased keratin would help prevent water loss and dehydration.

2). You have just been hired as a personal trainer. One of your clients asks you if sit-ups are considered isometric or isotonic exercises. What is your response?
Answer: In isometric exercises, a muscle group is contracted without a change in length. By contrast, isotonic exercises contract a muscle through a range of motion. Sit-ups require motion to contract and relax the abdominal muscles, and therefore are considered isotonic exercises.

3). The nerve gas sarin inhibits the enzyme acetylcholinesterase, which is normally present in the neuromuscular junction and required to break down acetylcholine into inactive fragments. Based on this information, what do you think are the likely effects of this nerve gas on muscle function?
Answer: If acetylcholinesterase is inhibited, acetylcholine will continue to stimulate muscles to contract. As a result, muscle twitching, and eventually paralysis, will occur. In March 1995, canisters of sarin were released into a subway system in Tokyo. Twelve people were killed and hundreds injured.

Self Test

1). All of the following have one-way digestive systems except
        a). a nematode.
        b). a planarian.
        c). an earthworm.
        d). a human.

The correct answer is b...
A. Answer a is incorrect because nematodes have a one-way digestive system, although a rather primitive digestive system. There is little specialization in the digestive system of the nematode but it does have separate openings for a mouth and an anus that allows the food to travel one-way through the digestive system.

The correct answer is b--a planarian.
B. The planarian, also known as a flatworm, does not have separate openings for a mouth and an anus, rather one opening serves both functions. Because of the single opening, the pathway of food through the body is not in one direction and so it is said to have a gastrovascular cavity rather than a digestive system.

The correct answer is b...
C. Answer c is incorrect because earthworms have a specialized digestive system with separate openings for a mouth and an anus and so food is able to move in one way through the digestive system.

The correct answer is b...
D. Answer d is incorrect because humans are vertebrates and all vertebrates have one-way digestive systems. They have separate openings for a mouth and an anus and so food is able to move in one way through the digestive system.

Hint: Specialization occurs when the digestive tract, or alimentary canal, have a separate mouth and anus, so that transport of food is one-way. The most primitive digestive tract is seen in nematodes where it is simply a tubular gut lined by an epithelium membrane. Earthworms have a digestive tract specialized in different regions. All higher animal groups, including all vertebrates, show similar specializations.

2). Intestines of herbivores are _____ compared to carnivores.
        a). longer
        b). shorter
        c). about the same size
        d). less convoluted

The correct answer is a--longer
A. Herbivores ingest large amounts of plant material that contain cellulose. Cellulose is hard to digest and so the intestines of herbivores are longer and more convoluted to allow more time for digestion to occur. The food that carnivores eat is easier to digest and so their intestines are usually shorter and less convoluted than an herbivore's.

The correct answer is a...
B. Answer b is incorrect because herbivores require more time to digest their food and so their intestines are generally longer, not shorter, than carnivores' intestines.

The correct answer is a...
C. Answer c is incorrect because herbivores require more time to digest their food and so their intestines are generally longer than carnivores' intestines.

The correct answer is a...
D. Answer d is incorrect because herbivores require more time to digest their food and so their intestines are generally more convoluted than carnivores' intestines. The more convoluted the intestines, the longer the path through the intestines.

Hint: In general, carnivores have shorter intestines for their size than do herbivores. A short intestine is adequate for a carnivore, but herbivores ingest a large amount of plant cellulose, which resists digestion. These animals have long, convoluted small intestines.

3). When a mammal swallows, the food is prevented from going up into the nasal cavity by the
     a). esophagus.
     b). tongue.
     c). soft palate.
     d). epiglottis.

The correct answer is c...
A. Answer a is incorrect because the esophagus is the passageway from the mouth to the stomach; it does not block the passageway to the nasal cavity when swallowing.

The correct answer is c...
B. Answer b is incorrect because the tongue manipulates the food around in the mouth and pushes the food to the back of the mouth for swallowing but it does not block the passageway to the nasal cavity when swallowing.

The correct answer is c--soft palate.
C. The soft palate is the soft tissue on the roof of the mouth back toward the pharynx. When the tongue pushes the food to the back of the mouth, the soft palate pushes up and blocks the passageway between the nasal cavity and the mouth.

The correct answer is c...
D. Answer d is incorrect because the epiglottis is a flap of tissue that covers the opening to the trachea during swallowing. The epiglottis blocks the passage of food down the trachea so that it travels down the esophagus.

Hint: When food is ready to be swallowed, the tongue moves it to the back of the mouth. In mammals, the process of swallowing begins when the soft palate elevates, pushing against the back wall of the pharynx. Elevation of the soft palate seals off the nasal cavity and prevents food from entering it.

4). The first site of protein digestion in the digestive system is
     a). in the mouth.
     b). in the esophagus.
     c). in the stomach.
     d). in the small intestine.

The correct answer is c...
A. Answer a is incorrect because the mouth contains amylase, which is an enzyme that begins the digestion of polysaccharides, but not proteases (protein-digesting enzymes).

The correct answer is c...
B. Answer b is incorrect because no digestion occurs in the esophagus. The esophagus is merely the passageway between the mouth and the stomach.

The correct answer is c--in the stomach.
C. Protein digestion begins in the stomach where the acidic environment denatures proteins and the low pH activates the protease (protein-digesting enzyme) pepsinogen.

The correct answer is c...
D. Answer d is incorrect because although protein digestion finishes in the small intestine where amino acids are absorbed by the body into the blood, it does not begin in the small intestine.

Hint: The low pH in the stomach helps denature food proteins, making them easier to digest, and keeps pepsin (the active form of pepsinogen) maximally active. Active pepsin hydrolyzes food proteins into shorter chains of polypeptides that are not fully digested until the mixture enters the small intestine.

5). How is the digestion of fats different from that of proteins and carbohydrates?
    a). Fat digestion occurs in the small intestine, and the digestion of proteins and carbohydrates occurs in the stomach.
    b). Fats are absorbed into the cells as fatty acids and monoglycerides but are then modified for absorption into the blood; amino acids and glucose are not modified further.
    c). Fats enter the hepatic portal circulation, but digested proteins and carbohydrates enter the lymphatic system.
    d). Digested fats are absorbed in the large intestine, and digested proteins and carbohydrates are absorbed in the small intestine.

The correct answer is b...
A. Answer a is incorrect because the primary digestion of fats, proteins, and carbohydrates all occur in the small intestine, not the stomach. Digestion of carbohydrates begins in the mouth and the digestion of proteins begins in the stomach but the primary digestion occurs in the small intestine.

The correct answer is b--Fats are absorbed into the cells as fatty acids and monoglycerides but are then modified for absorption into the blood; amino acids and glucose are not modified further.
B. In the small intestine, proteins are digested into monomers of amino acids and carbohydrates are digested into monomers of monosaccharides, both of which are absorbed directly into the blood stream. Fats however are first digested into fatty acids and monoglycerides and transported across the plasma membranes into the epithelial cells lining the small intestine. Then they are resynthesized into triglycerides and wrapped in a protein cover. The protein-covered triglycerides, called chylomicrons, are then absorbed into the bloodstream.

The correct answer is b...
C. Answer c is incorrect because digested fats do not enter the hepatic portal circulation, rather they are absorbed into lymphatic capillaries, which empty their contents into the bloodstream via veins in the neck. Digested proteins and carbohydrates are absorbed into the blood and enter the hepatic portal circulation.

The correct answer is b...
D. Answer d is incorrect because the digested products of all three types of molecules are absorbed in the small intestine. Only the absorption of fluids occurs in the large intestine.

Hint: The amino acids and monosaccharides resulting from the digestion of proteins and carbohydrates, respectively, are transported across the epithelial cells that line the small intestine. From there, they are transported into the blood capillaries, which carry these molecules to the hepatic portal circulation. The products of fat digestion are absorbed by a different mechanism. Fats are hydrolyzed into fatty acids and monoglycerides, which are absorbed into the intestinal epithelial cells and reassembled into triglycerides. The triglycerides combine with proteins to form chylomicrons. Instead of entering the hepatic portal circulation, they are absorbed into lymphatic capillaries, which empty their contents into the blood in veins near the neck.

6). The primary function of the large intestine is
      a). the breakdown and absorption of fats.
      b). the absorption of vitamin K.
      c). the absorption of water.
      d). the concentration of solid wastes.

The correct answer is d...
A. Answer a is incorrect because fats are digested and absorbed in the small intestine, not in the large intestine.

The correct answer is d...
B. Answer b is incorrect because although vitamin K is absorbed in the large intestine, that is not its primary function.

The correct answer is d...
C. Answer c is incorrect because although water is absorbed in the large intestine, the absorption of water in the small intestine is many magnitudes greater. The absorption of water is not the primary function of the large intestine.

The correct answer is d--the concentration of solid wastes.
D. By the time food reaches the large intestine, most of the digestible materials have been absorbed by the small intestine, including the majority of fluids that is to be absorbed. What is left to pass through the large intestine is primarily waste product. The primary function of the large intestine is to concentrate the solid waste before it is expelled from the body as feces.

Hint: The large intestine has less than one-thirtieth the absorptive surface area of the small intestine. Although sodium, vitamin K, and some products of bacterial metabolism are absorbed across its wall, the primary function of the large intestine is to concentrate waste material.

7). The _____ secretes digestive enzymes and bicarbonate solution into the small intestine to aid digestion.
      a). pancreas
      b). liver
      c). gallbladder
      d). All of these are correct.

The correct answer is a--pancreas
A. The pancreas is a large gland that performs an exocrine and an endocrine function. As an exocrine gland, it secretes digestive enzymes such as trypsin, chymotrypsin, pancreatic amylase, and lipase. The pancreas also secretes bicarbonate into the duodenum that neutralizes the HCl that flows into the small intestine from the stomach.

The correct answer is a...
B. Answer b is incorrect because although the liver is involved in digestion, it secretes bile salts that play a role in the digestion of fats, not enzymes and bicarbonate.

The correct answer is a...
C. Answer c is incorrect because although the gallbladder is involved in digestion, it stores and concentrates the bile (bile salts and bile pigments) secreted by the liver. The liver secretes bile salts and bile pigment but not directly into the small intestine. Instead it secretes the bile into the gallbladder. The gallbladder stores the bile until fatty foods enter the duodenum, which triggers the gallbladder to contract, and release the bile into the small intestine.

The correct answer is a...
D. Answer d is incorrect because there is only one correct answer, answer a. Although the liver and the gallbladder are involved in digestion, they secrete and store bile. The pancreas secretes digestive enzymes and bicarbonate.

Hint: Pancreatic fluid is secreted into the duodenum through the pancreatic duct; thus, the pancreas functions as an exocrine gland. This fluid contains a host of enzymes, including trypsin and chymotrypsin, which digest proteins; pancreatic amylase, which digests starch; and lipase, which digests fat. Pancreatic fluid also contains bicarbonate, which neutralizes the HCl from the stomach and gives the chyme in the duodenum a slightly alkaline pH.

8). Which of the following represents the action of insulin?
      a). increases blood glucose levels by the hydrolysis of glycogen
      b). increases blood glucose levels by stimulating glucagon production
      c). decreases blood glucose levels by forming glycogen
      d). increases blood glucose levels by promoting cellular uptake of glucose

The correct answer is c...
A. Answer a is incorrect because insulin decreases the blood glucose level by promoting the formation of glycogen. Glucagon, another hormone secreted by the pancreas, functions by increasing the blood glucose level by promoting the hydrolysis of glycogen.

The correct answer is c...
B. Answer b is incorrect because insulin decreases the blood glucose level; it doesn't increase it. Also insulin doesn't stimulate the production of glucagon. Glucagon secretion is stimulated by a drop in blood glucose levels brought on by fasting or exercise.

The correct answer is c--insulin decreases blood glucose levels by forming glycogen
C. Insulin is secreted by the beta cells of the pancreas in response to rising levels of glucose in the blood. This occurs after a person has eaten a carbohydrate-rich meal. Insulin causes a decrease in the amount of glucose in the blood by stimulating the cellular uptake of glucose in liver and muscle cells where it is then converted into glycogen.

The correct answer is c...
D. Answer d is incorrect because although insulin does promote the cellular uptake of glucose, this results in a decrease in blood glucose levels, not an increase.

Hint: After a carbohydrate-rich meal, the liver and skeletal muscles remove excess glucose from the blood and store it as the polysaccharide glycogen. This process is stimulated by the hormone insulin, secreted by the beta cells in the islets of Langerhans of the pancreas.

9). Gastrin functions by
      a). enhancing the secretion of HCl in the stomach.
      b). enhancing the secretion of pepsinogen in the stomach.
      c). a negative feedback loop.
      d). all of these.

The correct answer is d...
A. Answer a is incorrect because although gastrin, which is released in response to protein in the stomach, does enhance the secretion of HCl in the stomach, this is not the only correct answer.

The correct answer is d...
B. Answer b is incorrect because although gastrin, which is released in response to protein in the stomach, does enhance the secretion of pepsinogen in the stomach, this is not the only correct answer.

The correct answer is d...
C. Answer c is incorrect because although gastrin does function by a negative feedback loop, where the secretion of gastrin is inhibited by the acidic pH caused by the gastrin-induced release of HCl, this is not the only correct answer.

The correct answer is d--all of these.
D. Gastrin is a hormone that is released in response to the presence of protein in the stomach. Gastrin stimulates the release of HCl and pepsinogen from the parietal and chief cells respectively in the gastric pits. The release of HCl causes the pH in the stomach to decrease. A lower acidic pH in the stomach inhibits the further release of gastrin. In this way, gastrin secretion is regulated by a negative feedback.

Hint: When food arrives in the stomach, proteins in the food stimulate the secretion of a stomach hormone called gastrin, which in turn stimulates the secretion of pepsinogen and HCl from the gastric glands. The secreted HCl then lowers the pH of the gastric juice, which acts to inhibit further secretions of gastrin. Because inhibition of gastrin secretion will reduce the amount of HCl released into the gastric juice, a negative feedback loop is completed.

10). Essential organic substances that are used in only tiny amounts by the body are called
        a). trace elements.
        b). vitamins.
        c). hormones.
        d). minerals.

The correct answer is b...
A. Answer a is incorrect because trace elements are inorganic, not organic, substances that are required in very small amounts by the body. Trace elements are minerals that are obtained by animals through the consumption of plants or herbivores.

The correct answer is b--vitamins.
B. Vitamins are certain organic substances that are required in only trace amounts in the body. Certain vitamins cannot be manufactured by the body and must be obtained through the diet.

The correct answer is b...
C. Answer c is incorrect because hormones are organic substances but they are secreted in large enough quantities to travel throughout the body as required.

The correct answer is b...
D. Answer d is incorrect because minerals are inorganic, not organic, but they are often only required in very small amounts by the body.

Hint: Substances that an animal cannot manufacture for itself but which are necessary for its health must be obtained in the diet and are referred to as essential nutrients. Included among the essential nutrients are vitamins, certain organic substances required in trace amounts.

1). Match the following descriptions with the appropriate lettered structures:
i). site of sodium and vitamin K absorption
   ii). contracts in response to CCK
   iii). connects the mouth with the stomach
   iv). serves as both an endocrine and an exocrine gland
   v). releases brush border enzymes
   vi). storage area at the end of the large intestine
   vii). site of initial carbohydrate digestion
   viii). secretes bile pigments and bile salts
   ix). site of initial protein digestion
Answer:
   i)--h, colon
   ii)--c, gallbladder
   iii)--a, esophagus
   iv)--f, pancreas
   v)--g, small intestine
   vi)--i, rectum
   vii)--d, pharynx
   viii)--b, liver
   ix)--e, stomach

Apply Your Knowledge

1). The average length of the small intestine, when fully extended after death, is 6 meters, with a diameter of approximately 2.5 centimeters. Because of folds, villi, and microvilli, the surface area is 2,000,000 square centimeters. What percentage of increase is attributed to the folding, villi, and microvilli in the small intestine?
Answer: The small intestine is essentially a long cylinder and to calculate the surface area of a cylinder you multiply the length by the circumference, which in this case is:

$$600 \text{ cm} \times 2.5\pi = 4710 \text{ cm}^2$$

Now, to calculate the percentage of increase attributed to the folding, villi, and microvilli subtract the calculated surface area from the total surface area and divide by the calculated surface area: 2,000,000 − 4710 / 4710 = 424 or 42,400% larger

2). Many birds possess crops, although few mammals do. Suggest a reason for this difference between birds and mammals.
Answer: Birds feed their young with food they acquire from the environment. The adult bird consumes the food but stores it in her crop. When she returns to the nest, she regurgitates the food into the mouths of the fledglings. Mammals on the other hand feed their young with milk that is produced in the mother's mammary glands. Young feed by latching onto the mother's nipples and suck the milk. Mammals have no need for a crop in their digestive system because they don't feed their young in the same way as birds do.

Inquiry Questions

FIGURE 44.20
The relationship between air pressure and altitude above sea level. At the high altitudes characteristic of mountaintops, air pressure is much less than at sea level. At the top of Mount Everest, the world's highest mountain, the air pressure is only one-third that at sea level. **What is the difference in percentage of oxygen between Mount Everest and Mount Whitney?**

Answer: The percentage of oxygen is the same whether on Mt. Everest or Mt. Whitney; a percentage of 20.95. However, there are fewer air molecules present at the altitudes of Mt. Everest and so the partial pressure of oxygen is smaller (260 mmHg x 20.95% = 54 mmHg) compared to the partial pressure of oxygen at Mt. Whitney (500 mmHg x 20.95% = 104 mmHg).

FIGURE 44.32
The oxyhemoglobin dissociation curve. Hemoglobin combines with O_2 in the lungs, and this oxygenated blood is carried by arteries to the body cells. After oxygen is removed from the blood to support cellular respiration, the blood entering the veins contains less oxygen. **How would you determine how much oxygen was unloaded to the tissues?**

Answer: The difference in oxygen content between arteries and veins during rest and exercise shows how much oxygen was unloaded to the tissues.

FIGURE 44.33
The effect of pH and temperature on the oxyhemoglobin dissociation curve. (*a*) Lower blood pH and (*b*) higher blood temperatures shift the oxyhemoglobin dissociation curve to the right, facilitating oxygen unloading. In this example, this can be seen as a lowering of the oxyhemoglobin percent saturation from 60% to 40%, indicating that the difference of 20% more oxygen is unloaded to the tissues. **What effect does high blood pressure have on oxygen unloading to the tissues during exercise?**

Answer: It increases it. At any pH or temperature, the percentage of O_2 saturation falls (e.g. more O_2 is delivered to tissues) as pressure increases.

Self Test

1). Which of the following statements is false?
    a). Only arteries carry oxygenated blood.
    b). Both arteries and veins have a layer of smooth muscle.
    c). Both arteries and veins branch out into capillary beds.
    d). Precapillary sphincters regulate blood flow through capillaries.

The correct answer is a--Only arteries carry oxygenated blood.
A. In addition to arteries, which carry oxygenated blood, the pulmonary vein brings oxygenated blood from the lungs to the heart. Therefore, answer a is false.

The correct answer is a...
B. Answer b is incorrect because both arteries and veins have the same tissue layers. Remember, the question is asking which answer is false.

The correct answer is a...
C. Answer c is incorrect because both arteries and veins branch out into capillary. Remember, the question is asking which answer is false.

The correct answer is a...
D. Answer d is incorrect because precapillary sphincters do open to increase blood flow through capillary beds and close to decrease blood flow through capillary beds. Remember, the question is asking which answer is false.

2). The lymphatic system is like the circulatory system in that they both
        a). have nodes that filter out pathogens.
        b). have a network of arteries.
        c). have capillaries.
        d). are closed systems.

The correct answer is c...
A. Answer a is incorrect because only the lymphatic system has nodes that filter out pathogens.

The correct answer is c...
B. Answer b is incorrect because, while the lymphatic and circulatory systems pump lymph and blood, respectively, the lymphatic system does not have arteries.

The correct answer is c--have capillaries.
C. Answer c is correct because both arteries and veins branch out into capillary beds.

The correct answer is c...
D. Answer d is incorrect because the lymphatic system is an open system.

3). A molecule of CO_2 that is generated in the cardiac muscle of the left ventricle would *not* pass through which of the following structures before leaving the body?
        a). right atrium
        b). left atrium
        c). right ventricle
        d). left ventricle

The correct answer is b...
A. Answer a is incorrect because this molecule of CO_2 would pass through the left ventricle and travel out to the tissues, return to the heart via the superior vena cava, enter the heart through the right atrium, and finally, exit the heart through the pulmonary vein on its way to lungs in order to leave the body.

The correct answer is b--left atrium
B. This molecule of CO_2 would pass through the left ventricle and travel out to the tissues, return to the heart via the superior vena cava, enter the heart through the right atrium, and finally, exit the heart through the pulmonary vein on its way to lungs in order to leave the body.

The correct answer is b...
C. Answer c is incorrect this molecule of CO_2 would pass through the left ventricle and travel out to the tissues, return to the heart via the superior vena cava, enter the heart through the right atrium, and finally, exit the heart through the pulmonary vein on its way to lungs in order to leave the body.

The correct answer is b...
D. Answer d is incorrect because this molecule of CO_2 would pass through the left ventricle and travel out to the tissues, return to the heart via the superior vena cava, enter the heart through the right atrium, and finally, exit the heart through the pulmonary vein on its way to lungs in order to leave the body.

4). In vertebrate hearts, atria contract from the top, while ventricles contract from the bottom. How is this accomplished?

    a). The depolarization from the sinoatrial node proceeds across the atria from the top, while the depolarization from the atrioventricular node is carried to the bottom of the ventricles before it emanates over the ventricular tissue.

    b). The depolarization from the sinoatrial node is initiated from motor neurons coming down from our brain, while the depolarization from the atrioventricular node is initiated from motor neurons coming up from our spinal cord.

    c). Gravity carries the depolarization from the sinoatrial node down from the top of the heart, while contraction of the diaphragm forces the depolarization from the atrioventricular node to move from the bottom up.

    d). This statement is false; both contract from the bottom.

The correct answer is a--The depolarization from the sinoatrial node proceeds across the atria from the top, while the depolarization from the atrioventricular node is carried to the bottom of the ventricles before it emanates over the ventricular tissue.
A. The heart contains specialized self-depolarizing cells that can initiate depolarization without neuronal activation. These cells form the sinoatrial node.

The correct answer is a...
B. Answer b is incorrect because motor neurons do not initiate heart contraction. The heart contains specialized self-depolarizing cells that can initiate depolarization without neuronal activation.

The correct answer is a...
C. Answer c is correct because gravity and the diaphragm are not involved in heart contraction.

The correct answer is a...
D. Answer d is incorrect because atria contract from the top, while ventricles contract from the bottom.

5). Throughout evolution, natural selection has favored changes that optimize respiration mechanisms in animals. According to Fick's Law, which of the following changes would optimize the rate of diffusion, R?

    a). decrease the surface area, A, over which diffusion takes place

    b). increase the distance, d, over which diffusion takes place

    c). increase the concentration difference, Δp, between the interior of the organism and the external environment

    d). increase the diffusion constant, D

The correct answer is c...
A. Answer a is incorrect because a decrease in surface area, A, would reduce the rate of diffusion, R.

The correct answer is c...
B. Answer b is incorrect because an increase in the distance, d, would reduce the rate of diffusion, R.

The correct answer is c--increase the concentration difference, Δp, between the interior of the organism and the external environment
C. An increase in concentration difference would increase the rate of diffusion, R, because gases diffuse down their concentration gradients from an area of high concentration to one of low concentration.

The correct answer is c...
D. Answer d is incorrect because the diffusion constant, D, cannot be changed. The diffusion constant remains the same by mathematical definition.

6). Which type of circulatory system regulation do some vertebrates employ to maintain body temperature in a cold environment?
  a). concurrent exchange
  b). countercurrent exchange
  c). vasodilation
  d). nitric oxide production

The correct answer is b...
A. Answer a is incorrect because concurrent flow does not apply. The blood in arteries and veins flow in opposite directions rather than the same direction. Concurrent flow is used by some animals for gas exchange, however.

The correct answer is b--countercurrent exchange
B. Warm blood is pumped from within the body in arteries, which lose heat to the cooler blood returning from the skin in veins. This method warms the venous blood so that the core body temperature can remain constant in cold water and cools the arterial blood so that less heat is lost when the arterial blood reaches the tip of the extremities.

The correct answer is b...
C. Answer c is incorrect because vasodilation is not an effective means to reduce heat loss. Vasodilation involves an increase in blood vessel diameter and blood flow, and therefore an increase in heat loss.

The correct answer is b...
D. Answer d is incorrect because the production of nitric oxide leads to vasodilation, which involves an increase in blood vessel diameter and blood flow, and therefore an increase in heat loss.

7). What is the stroke volume of a woman with a heart rate of 66 beats/minute and a cardiac output of 4.7 liters/minute?
  a). 310 milliliters/beat
  b). 14 milliliters/beat
  c). 70 milliliters/beat
  d). 71 milliliters/beat

The correct answer is d...
A. Answer a is incorrect because stroke volume is not calculated by multiplying the cardiac output by the heart rate. Rather, stroke volume is calculated by dividing the cardiac output by the heart rate. Remember to convert liters to milliliters. (4,700 milliliters per minute / 66 beats per minute = 71 milliliters/beat).

The correct answer is d...
B. Answer b is incorrect because stroke volume is not calculated by dividing the heart rate by the cardiac output. Rather, stroke volume is calculated by dividing the cardiac output by the heart rate Remember to convert liters to milliliters. (4,700 milliliters per minute / 66 beats per minute = 71 milliliters/beat).

The correct answer is d...
C. Answer c is incorrect because stroke volume is calculated by dividing the cardiac output by the heart rate Remember to convert liters to milliliters. (4,700 milliliters per minute / 66 beats per minute = 71 milliliters/beat).

The correct answer is d--71 milliliters/beat
D. Stroke volume is calculated by dividing the cardiac output by the heart rate. (4,700 milliliters per minute / 66 beats per minute = 71 milliliters/beat).

8). If the total pressure of gas dissolved in blood plasma is 120 mm Hg, what is the partial pressure of nitrogen in the plasma? (Recall that air contains approximately 78% nitrogen.)
       a). 94 mm Hg
       b). 42 mm Hg
       c). 22 mm Hg
       d). 78 mm Hg

The correct answer is a--94 mm Hg
A. Seventy-eight percent of 120 mm Hg equals 94 mm Hg. The relative percentages of nitrogen gas found in the air we breathe and dissolved in blood plasma are the same.

The correct answer is a...
B. Answer b is incorrect because the partial pressure of nitrogen in blood plasma cannot be obtained by subtracting 78% from 120 mm Hg. The correct value can be obtained by multiplying the total pressure of gas dissolved in blood plasma (120 mm Hg) by 78%.

The correct answer is a...
C. Answer c is incorrect because the partial pressure of nitrogen in blood plasma cannot be obtained by subtracting 78% from 100%. The correct value can be obtained by multiplying the total pressure of gas dissolved in blood plasma (120 mm Hg) by 78%.

The correct answer is a...
D. Answer d is incorrect because while the relative percentages of nitrogen gas found in the air we breathe and dissolved in blood plasma are the same (both 78%), this value does not usually equal the partial pressure. Seventy-eight percent of 120 mm Hg equals 94 mm Hg.

9). When you take a deep breath, your stomach moves out because:
       a). swallowing air increases the volume of the thoracic cavity.
       b). your stomach shouldn't move out when you take a deep breath because you want the volume of your chest cavity to increase, not your abdominal cavity.
       c). contracting your abdominal muscles pushes your stomach out, generating negative pressure in your lungs.
       d). when your diaphragm contracts, it moves down, pressing your abdominal cavity out.

The correct answer is d...
A. Answer a is incorrect because swallowing air does not increases the volume of the thoracic cavity. The diaphragm contracts as it moves down, increasing the volume of the thoracic cavity and pressing the abdominal cavity out.

The correct answer is d...
B. Answer b is incorrect because the volume of the abdominal cavity is not increasing. The diaphragm contracts as it moves down, increasing the volume of the thoracic cavity and pressing the abdominal cavity out.

The correct answer is d...
C. Answer c is incorrect because contraction of the diaphragm, not the abdominal muscles, generates negative pressure.

The correct answer is d--when your diaphragm contracts, it moves down, pressing your abdominal cavity out.
D. This action result generates negative pressure, which enables air to be taken up by the lungs.

10). If you holds your breath for a long time, body CO_2 levels are likely to _____, and the pH of body fluids is likely to _____.
        a). increase; increase
        b). decrease; increase
        c). increase; decrease
        d). decrease; decrease

The correct answer is c...
A. Answer a is incorrect because while CO_2 would increase, the pH would decrease. As CO_2 levels rise, production of carbonic acid (H_2CO_3) is increased. Carbonic acid dissociates into HCO_3^- and H^+, increasing blood H^+ concentration and thereby decreasing the pH of body fluids.

The correct answer is c...
B. Answer b is incorrect because holding your breath would result in an accumulation, or increase of CO_2 levels. As CO_2 levels rise, production of carbonic acid (H_2CO_3) is increased. Carbonic acid dissociates to into HCO_3^- and H^+, increasing blood H^+ concentration and thereby decreasing the pH of body fluids.

The correct answer is c--increase; decrease
C. As CO_2 levels rise, production of carbonic acid (H_2CO_3) is increased. Carbonic acid dissociates to into HCO_3^- and H^+, increasing blood H^+ concentration and thereby decreasing the pH of body fluids.

The correct answer is c...
D. Answer d is incorrect because holding your breath would result in an accumulation of CO_2. As CO_2 levels rise, production of carbonic acid (H_2CO_3) is increased. Carbonic acid dissociates to into HCO_3^- and H^+, increasing blood H^+ concentration and thereby decreasing the pH of body fluids.

Test Your Visual Understanding

1). The Bohr effect describes the effect of pH on hemoglobin's affinity for oxygen. This figure shows a standard oxyhemoglobin dissociation curve. Draw a curve that represents the effect of a low pH according to the Bohr effect.
Answer: The drawn line should represent the curve for pH 7.2 found in figure 44.33a.

Apply Your Knowledge

1). Tissue plasminogen is an enzyme that, when activated, breaks down fibrin. How might the drug tissue plasminogen activator, t-PA, help to reduce the damage caused by strokes and heart attacks?
Answer: Heart attacks are very often caused by a blockage that inhibits the passage of blood through the coronary arteries. Similarly, a stroke is caused by an interference with the blood supply from the brain. In both of these cardiovascular diseases, a blood clot may be the involved in the restriction of blood flow. The drug t-PA may help reduce the damage by breaking down fibrin present in blood clots, thereby restoring blood flow.

2). Dr. Hearthealth is so impressed with your knowledge of cardiovascular physiology that he asks you to help with a particularly difficult case. He proceeds to tell you that his patient has a prolonged PQ wave in their electrocardiogram (ECG), which you know means that the delay between the atrial contraction and ventricle contraction is too long. What heart structure is likely causing this problem? Why?
Answer: The atrioventricular node provides the only pathway for the conduction of the depolarization from the atria to the ventricles. If the atrioventricular node is not functioning properly it may lead to an increased delay between the atrial contraction and ventricle contraction.

Self Test

1). _____ nerves carry impulses away from the central nervous system.
    a). Sensory
    b). Motor
    c). Afferent
    d). Association

The correct answer is b...
A. Answer a is incorrect because sensory neurons carry impulses from the sensory receptors to the central nervous system, not away from it.

The correct answer is b--Motor
B. The motor neurons, or efferent neurons, carry signals away from the central nervous system to muscles and glands, collectively known as effectors.

The correct answer is b...
C. Answer c is incorrect because afferent neurons are also known as sensory neurons. Sensory (afferent) neurons carry impulses from the sensory receptors to the central nervous system, not away from it.

The correct answer is b...
D. Answer d is incorrect because association neurons (or interneurons) are neurons located within the central nervous system and conduct nerve impulses between neurons.

Hint: Sensory (or afferent) neurons carry impulses from sensory receptors to the central nervous system (CNS); motor (or efferent) neurons carry impulses from the CNS to effectors—muscles and glands.

2). Which of the following best describes the electrical state of a neuron at rest?
    a). The inside of a neuron is more negatively charged than the outside.
    b). The outside of a neuron is more negatively charged than the inside.
    c). The inside and the outside of a neuron have the same electrical charge.
    d). K^+ ions leak into a neuron at rest.

The correct answer is a--The inside of a neuron is more negatively charged than the outside.
A. The inside of the neuron, and in fact any cell in the body, is more negatively charged than the outside of the cell because of three factors: 1). The interior contains large negatively charged molecules that can't diffuse out of the cell; 2). the sodium-potassium pump brings in only 2 K^+ for every 3 Na^+ that it pumps out; 3). ion channels allow more K^+ to leak out of the cell than allow Na^+ to leak in.

The correct answer is a...
B. Answer b is incorrect because the outside of neuron is more positively charged compared to the inside. More negatively charged molecules are trapped inside the cell and more positively charged ions are pumped out of the cell, creating a resting membrane potential that is negative.

The correct answer is a...
C. Answer b is incorrect because the neuron must maintain an electrical potential across the membrane in order for the neuron to function properly. A charge difference across the membrane is needed in order that the neuron is able to conduct a nerve impulse down the length of the axon.

The correct answer is a...

D. Answer d is incorrect because K^+ leaks out of neuron at rest, across the membrane down its concentration gradient. The interior of the cell contains more K^+ compared to the outside of the cell, therefore if a potassium channel is leaky, the ions will travel down their concentration gradient to where there are fewer K^+ ions.

Hint: In a battery, electrical charges are separated to the two poles. There is said to be a potential difference, or voltage, between the poles, with one pole being positive and the other negative. Similarly, a potential difference exists across every cell's plasma membrane. The side of the membrane exposed to the cytoplasm is the negative pole, and the side exposed to the extracellular fluid is the positive pole. This potential difference is called the membrane potential.

3). A nerve impulse is initiated when
      a). physical disruption of the cell membrane causes some of its contents, including ions, to leak out.
      b). the Schwann cells move to into their new positions.
      c). voltage-gated channels close.
      d). a reversal in the polarized state of the cell causes it to reach threshold.

The correct answer is d...
A. Answer a is incorrect because while a physical stimulus could initiate a nerve impulse, this occurs by the opening of sodium ion channels that begin the depolarization of the membrane, not a physical disruption of the membrane that causes ions to leak out.

The correct answer is d....
B. Answer b is incorrect because Schwann cells do not move or change position along the cell. Schwann cells remain in place creating openings along the axon called the nodes of Ranvier.

The correct answer is d...
C. Answer c is incorrect because a nerve impulse is initiated with the opening of voltage-gated channels, not the closing of them.

The correct answer is d--a reversal in the polarized state of the cell causes it to reach threshold.
D. The polarized state of the membrane when at rest, the resting potential, is – 70mV. When a neuron is stimulated, Na^+ ion channels open and Na^+ begins rushing into the cell that causes a reversal in the polarized state toward a more positive membrane potential, a depolarization. If this depolarization continues until the neuron reaches the threshold potential, a nerve impulse also called an action potential will be initiated.

Hint: If the plasma membrane is depolarized slightly, an oscilloscope will show a small upward deflection. These small changes in membrane potential are called graded potentials because their amplitudes depend on the strength of the stimulus. Once a particular level of depolarization is reached (about – 55mV in mammalian axons), a nerve impulse, or action potential, is produced. The level of depolarization needed to produce an action potential is called the threshold.

4). An action potential travels from one neuron to the next across the synapse using
      a). calcium ions.
      b). Schwann cells.
      c). neurotransmitters.
      d). All of these are involved.

The correct answer is c...
A. Answer a is incorrect because although an influx of calcium ions triggers the fusion of presynaptic vesicles with the membrane which then empty their contents of neurotransmitters into

303

the synaptic cleft; calcium ions are not responsible for carrying the nerve impulse across the synaptic cleft.

The correct answer is c...
B. Answer b is incorrect because Schwann cells are involved in the propagation of the action potential down the axon but they are not involved in the transmission of the action potential to another cell.

The correct answer is c--neurotransmitters.
C. Neurotransmitters are molecules that are released from a presynaptic cell into a synaptic cleft where they travel to the postsynaptic cell to stimulate the postsynaptic cell. Neurotransmitters are stored in vesicles in the presynaptic cell and following an influx of Ca^{++} the vesicles fuse with the presynaptic cell membrane and release the neurotransmitters into the synaptic cleft. They diffuse across the cleft where they bind to postsynaptic receptors and trigger a response in the postsynaptic cell.

The correct answer is c...
D. Answer d is incorrect because although all three answer options are in some way involved in the transmission of an action potential from one cell to the next, only neurotransmitters actually "carry" the signal across the synaptic cleft between the two cells.

Hint: The end of the presynaptic axon is swollen and contains numerous synaptic vesicles, which are packed with chemicals called neurotransmitters. When action potentials arrive at the end of the axon, they stimulate the opening of voltage-gated Ca^{++} channels, causing a rapid inward diffusion of Ca^{++}. This serves as the stimulus for the fusion of synaptic vesicle membranes with the plasma membrane of the axon, so that the contents of the vesicles can be released by exocytosis. The neurotransmitters diffuse rapidly to the other side of the cleft and bind to receptor proteins in the membrane of the postsynaptic cell.

5). Synapses are excitatory or inhibitory based on
        a). integration.
        b). summation.
        c). autonomic control.
        d). saltatory conduction.

The correct answer is a--integration.
A. A postsynaptic cell receives many inputs an any given time. Some neurotransmitters cause a depolarization and some cause hyperpolarization. All of these signals are combined by the postsynaptic cell and their summed influence determines if the postsynaptic cell is depolarized enough to produce an action potential.

The correct answer is a...
B. Answer b is incorrect because while summation is contributes to integration they are not the same. Summation is the ability of graded potentials to combine. Integration is the process of summation that occurs in a postsynaptic cell to produce an excitatory or an inhibitory synapse.

The correct answer is a...
C. Answer c is incorrect because autonomic control is the unconscious control of body processes. While integration certain plays a part in the control of body processes, they are not the same.

The correct answer is a...
D. Answer d is incorrect because saltatory conduction is the process whereby an action potential is propagated down a myelinated axon. Saltatory condition is not involved in the transmission of the action potential across the synapse.

Hint: The activity of a postsynaptic neuron in the brain and spinal cord of vertebrates is influenced by different types of inputs from a number of presynaptic neurons. Each postsynaptic neuron may receive both excitatory and inhibitory synapses. The EPSPs and IPSPs from these synapses interact with each other when they reach the cell body of the neuron. Small EPSPs add together to bring the membrane potential closer to the threshold, while IPSPs subtract from the depolarizing effect, keeping the membrane below the threshold. This process is called synaptic integration.

6). Modern-day fish are like early vertebrates in that the dominate part of their brains is the
   a). forebrain.
   b). midbrain.
   c). hindbrain.
   d). optic lobes.

The correct answer is c...
A. Answer a is incorrect because the forebrain, which includes the thalamus, hypothalamus, cerebrum, and olfactory tract, is not well developed in fish and nor was it well developed in early vertebrates. The evolutionary trend of a more dominant forebrain began with the amphibians and continued through to the mammals.

The correct answer is c...
B. Answer b is incorrect because the midbrain, which primarily includes the optic lobes for the processing of visual sensory information, is significant in fish but it is not the dominant part of their brains.

The correct answer is c--hindbrain.
C. The hindbrain, which includes the cerebellum, pons, and medulla oblongata, is primarily involved in the processing and coordinating motor reflexes. The cerebellum plays an especially important role in the coordination of movements. This is the area of the brain that is most developed in fish and in early vertebrates. The cerebellum plays an even more important role as body movements become more complex in higher vertebrates.

The correct answer is c...
D. Answer d is incorrect because while the optic lobes, part of the midbrain, form a significant part of the fish brain, it is not the dominant structure in the brains of fish or early vertebrates.

Hint: The hindbrain was the major component of these early brains, as it still is in fishes today. Composed of the cerebellum, pons, and medulla oblongata, the hindbrain may be considered an extension of the spinal cord devoted primarily to coordinating motor reflexes. Much of this coordination is carried on within a small extension of the hindbrain called the cerebellum.

7). Much of the sensory, motor, and associative neural activity of the cerebrum occurs on the surface, a layer called the
   a). corpus callosum.
   b). cerebral cortex.
   c). limbic system.
   d). basal ganglia.

The correct answer is b...
A. Answer a is incorrect because the corpus callosum is the structure that connects the left and right hemispheres of the cerebrum. It is located within the cerebrum, not on the surface. It is a passageway through which nerve tracts cross over from one side of the body to the opposite side of the brain.

The correct answer is b--cerebral cortex.
B. A layer of gray matter lies on the surface of the cerebrum and is called the cerebral cortex. The cerebral cortex is gray because it contains the cell bodies of the neurons that are nonmyelinated. Myelinated portions of the neurons appear white. These cells are involved in much of the sensory, motor, and associative neural activity in the cerebrum.

The correct answer is b...
C. Answer c is incorrect because the limbic system, although not an actual structure found in the brain but rather the interaction of several structures, is involved in emotions and memory. The hypothalamus along with the hippocampus and the amygdala make up the limbic system. All of these structures are found deep within the cerebrum and not on its surface.

The correct answer is b...
D. Answer d is incorrect because the basal ganglia are collections of cell bodies that appear embedded within the white matter deep in the cerebrum. These aggregates of neuron cell bodies receive sensory information from the body and send out motor commands, however there is little associative activity where cognitive thought is involved. Damage to these areas is associated with the tremors seen with Parkinson's disease.

Hint: Much of the neural activity of the cerebrum occurs within a layer of gray matter only a few millimeters thick on the outer surface of the cerebrum. This layer, called the cerebral cortex, is densely packed with nerve cells. The activities of the cerebral cortex fall into one of three general categories: motor, sensory, and associative.

8). Which is not involved in the knee-jerk reflex?
        a). stretching of the muscle
        b). motor neuron
        c). muscle spindle
        d). an interneuron

The correct answer is d...
A. Answer a is incorrect because the stretching of the muscle is the stimulus that triggers the knee-jerk reflex. When the patellar ligament is tapped it stretches the muscle attached to the ligament and that stretching of the muscle triggers the reflex action.

The correct answer is d...
B. Answer b is incorrect because a motor neuron is involved in the knee-jerk reflex. When the patellar ligament is tapped it stretches the muscle attached to the ligament and that stretching of the muscle stimulates an action potential in the sensory neuron embedded within the muscle. The sensory neuron synapses with a motor neuron in the spinal cord. The motor neuron stimulates a muscle contraction that causes the leg to kick.

The correct answer is d...
C. Answer c is incorrect because the muscle spindle is the sensory stretch receptor embedded within the muscle that is stretched by the tapping of the patellar ligament. The muscle spindle is the sensory neuron that carries the action potential to the spinal cord where it synapses with a motor neuron.

The correct answer is d--an interneuron
D. The knee-jerk reflex is a monosynaptic reflex meaning the sensory neuron that is stimulated by the stretching of the patellar ligament synapses directly with the motor neuron that causes the leg muscle to contract. There is no interneuron involved in this reflex.

Hint: Many reflexes never reach the brain. The nerve impulse travels only as far as the spinal cord and then comes right back as a motor response. A few reflexes, like the knee-jerk reflex, are monosynaptic reflex arcs. When the muscle is briefly stretched by tapping the patellar ligament with a rubber mallet, the muscle spindle apparatus is also stretched. The spindle apparatus is embedded within the muscle and is stretched along with the muscle. This activates the sensory neurons that synapse directly with somatic motor neurons within the spinal cord.

9). The _____ cannot be controlled by conscious thought.
        a). motor neurons
        b). somatic nervous system
        c). autonomic nervous system
        d). skeletal muscles

The correct answer is c...
A. Answer a is incorrect because motor neurons can be controlled by conscious thought. Sometimes motor neurons are stimulated automatically through reflex arcs but these motor neurons are also connected to neurons in the brain that have conscious control of the actions of the muscles.

The correct answer is c...
B. Answer b is incorrect because the somatic nervous system is the part of the nervous system that controls the contraction of skeletal muscles through the stimulation of somatic motor neurons. Sometimes somatic motor neurons are stimulated automatically through reflex arcs but these motor neurons are also connected to neurons in the brain that have conscious control of the actions of the muscles.

The correct answer is c--autonomic nervous system
C. The autonomic nervous system is composed of sensory and motor neurons of the sympathetic and parasympathetic division and the medulla oblongata located in the hindbrain. Although the medulla oblongata is involved in the autonomic nervous system, there is no conscious control over the actions of the sensory and motor neurons. The sympathetic and parasympathetic control smooth muscles and glands and work in an antagonistic manner.

The correct answer is c...
D. Answer d is incorrect because although some skeletal muscles contract without conscious control, such as those involved in reflex arcs, all skeletal muscles are also under control of conscious thought and the contraction of skeletal muscles can be controlled.

Hint: Somatic motor neurons stimulate skeletal muscles to contract, and autonomic motor neurons innervate involuntary effectors—smooth muscles, cardiac muscle, and glands. Somatic motor neurons stimulate the skeletal muscles of the body to contract in response to conscious commands and as part of reflexes that do not require conscious control.

10). A fight-or-flight response in the body is controlled by the
        a). sympathetic division of the nervous system.
        b). parasympathetic division of the nervous system.
        c). release of ACh from postganglionic neurons.
        d). somatic nervous system.

The correct answer is a--sympathetic division of the nervous system.
A. The sympathetic division is a component of the autonomic nervous system and controls the contractions of smooth and cardiac muscles and the actions of glands. When a body is frightened or angered, the sympathetic division of the autonomic nervous system is activated and the body prepares to fight or flight. Norepinephrine is released from postsynaptic neurons and epinephrine is released from the adrenal glands. Both act to stimulate cardiac muscles and inhibit smooth muscle contraction.

The correct answer is a...
B. Answer b is incorrect because the parasymphathetic division of the autonomic nervous system acts in an antagonistic manner to the sympathetic division. The sympathetic division stimulates the body to fight or flight while the parasympathetic division relaxes the body to rest.

The correct answer is a...
C. Answer c is incorrect because the release of ACh from postganglionic neurons occurs in the parasympathetic division of the autonomic nervous system and affects the body by slowing the heart rate and increasing activities of the digestive organs. These are response are not fight-or-flight reactions but rather rest reactions.

The correct answer is a...
D. Answer d is incorrect because the somatic nervous system controls the skeletal muscles in the body and while the contraction of skeletal muscles will no doubt be involved in a fight-or-flight response, the somatic NS does not control the overall fight or flight response.

Hint: When the sympathetic division becomes activated, epinephrine is released into the blood as a hormonal secretion, and norepinephrine is released at the synapses of the postganglionic neurons. Epinephrine and norepinephrine act to prepare the body for fight or flight. The heart beats faster and stronger, blood glucose concentration increases, blood flow is diverted to the muscles and heart, and the bronchioles dilate.

Test Your Visual Understanding

1). Match the following descriptions with the appropriate numbered steps on the figure.
   a). Na^+ channels open, and Na^+ flows into the cell, causing rapid depolarization.
   b). K^+ channels open, and K^+ flows out of the cell, causing rapid repolarization.
   c). Na^+ channels are closed, and some K^+ leaks out to maintain a resting potential.
   d). K^+ continues to flow out of cell, producing a hyperpolarization of the membrane.
   e). Na^+ channels close, and K^+ channels begin to open.
   f). A stimulus causes a depolarization of the membrane.

Answer:
   Step 1—c
   Step 2—f
   Step 3—a
   Step 4—e
   Step 5—b
   Step 6—d

Apply Your Knowledge

1). The equilibrium potentials for particular ions are determined by their concentrations inside and outside of the cell and are calculated using the Nernst equation: $V = 58 \text{ mV} \times \log_{10} C_o/C_i$ where C_o is the concentration of the ion outside the cell and C_i is the concentration of the ion inside the cell. Using this equation, calculate the equilibrium potential across the plasma membrane assuming that it is due solely to (a) K^+ and (b) Na^+. The concentrations for K^+ are 150 mM inside and 5 mM outside. The concentrations for Na^+ are 15 mM inside and 150 mM outside. *Answer:* a). The equilibrium potential for K^+ is $V = 58 \text{ mV} \times \log_{10} 5 \text{ mM}/150 \text{ mM}$ or $58 \times (-1.477) = -85.67 \text{ mV}$.
b). The equilibrium potential for Na^+ is $V = 58 \text{ mV} \times \log_{10} 150 \text{ mM}/15 \text{ mM}$ or 58×1 or 58 mV.

2). Tetraethylammonium (TEA) is a drug that blocks voltage-gated K^+ channels. What effect would TEA have on the action potentials produced by a neuron? If TEA could be applied selectively to a presynaptic neuron that releases an excitatory neurotransmitter, how would it alter the synaptic effect of that neurotransmitter on the postsynaptic cell?

Answer: TEA blocks K^+ channels so that they will not permit the passage of K^+ out of the cell, thereby not allowing the cell to return to the resting potential. Voltage-gated Na^+ channels would still be functional and Na^+ would still flow into the cell but there would be no repolarization. Na^+ would continue to flow into the cell until an electrochemical equilibrium was reached for Na^+, which is + 60 mV. After the membrane potential reached + 60 mV, there would be no net movement of sodium but the membrane would also not be able to repolarize back to the resting membrane potential. The neuron would no longer be able to function.

The effects on the postsynaptic cell would be somewhat similar if TEA were applied to the presynaptic cell. The presynaptic cell would depolarize and would continue to release neurotransmitter until it had exhausted its store of synaptic vesicles. As a result, the postsynaptic cell would be bombarded with neurotransmitters and would be stimulated continuously until the stores of presynaptic neurotransmitter were depleted. The postsynaptic cell however would recover, being able to repolarize it membrane and return to the resting membrane potential.

Self Test

1). All sensory receptors are able to initiate nerve impulses by opening or closing
    a). voltage-gated ion channels.
    b). exteroceptors.
    c). interoceptors.
    d). stimulus-gated ion channels.

The correct answer is d...
A. Answer a is incorrect because voltage-gated ion channels are not the first channels to open in response to a stimulus. Once a stimulus has triggered a receptor potential, like an EPSP, of a significant amplitude to reach threshold, then voltage-gated ion channels open in the axon, but not until the initial receptor potentials have reached threshold.

The correct answer is d...
B. Answer b is incorrect because exteroceptors are a class of sensory receptors that respond to external stimuli. Exteroceptors themselves do not open or close in response to stimuli.

The correct answer is d...
C. Answer c is incorrect because interoceptors are a class of sensory receptors that respond to internal stimuli. Interoceptors themselves do not open or close in response to stimuli.

The correct answer is d--stimulus-gated ion channels.
D. Stimulus-gated ion channels are found in the membranes of the dendrites of sensory receptors. A stimulus specific to that receptor will cause these channels to open (or sometimes close) causing a change in membrane potential called a receptor potential. Receptor potentials are similar to excitatory postsynaptic potentials (EPSPs) in that they are graded and undergo summation. The larger the sensory stimulus the greater the degree of depolarization until threshold is achieved and an action potential is produced.

Hint: Sensory cells respond to stimuli because they possess stimulus-gated ion channels in their membranes. The sensory stimulus cause these ion channels to open or close, depending on the sensory system involved. In doing so, a sensory stimulus produces a change in membrane potential of the receptor cell called a receptor potential.

2). What type of stimulus triggers a response in nociceptors?
    a). pressure
    b). pain
    c). heat
    d). touch

The correct answer is b...
A. Answer a is incorrect because pressure is detected by mechanoreceptors called Pacinian corpuscles. These receptors are found deep below the surface of the skin. Pacinian corpuscles are stimulated by the initial application of pressure and then the release of the pressure.

The correct answer is b--pain
B. Sensory receptors that detect pain are called nociceptors. There are different types of nociceptors that respond to different types of pain stimuli. Most are free nerve endings scattered throughout the body, usually near the surface. They detect pain caused by extreme temperatures, very intense mechanical stimuli, and specific extracellular chemicals.

The correct answer is b...
C. Answer c is incorrect because thermoreceptors detect heat stimuli. Warm receptors are located somewhat below the surface of the skin and are also located in the hypothalamus, along with cold receptors, to sense the internal temperature of the body. Warm receptors are stimulated by a rise in temperature and inhibited by a drop in temperature. Some nociceptors detect extreme temperature but those are considered pain receptors because the extreme temperature is painful.

The correct answer is b...
D. Answer d is incorrect because several different types of receptors detect touch but they don't include nociceptors unless the touch is damaging to the body; then it is considered pain not touch. Touch receptors include hair follicle receptors, Meissner's corpuscles, Ruffini endings, and Merkel cells.

Hint: A stimulus that causes or is about to cause tissue damage is perceived as pain. The receptors that transmit impulses that are perceived by the brain as pain are called nociceptors. They consist of free nerve endings located throughout the body, especially near surfaces where damage is most likely to occur. Different nociceptors may respond to extremes in temperature, very intense mechanical stimulation, or specific chemicals in the extracellular fluid.

3). What is the function of baroreceptors?
        a). They detect changes in blood pressure.
        b). They detect muscle contractions and the movement of limbs.
        c). They are exteroceptors.
        d). They detect changes in blood chemistry.

The correct answer is a--They detect changes in blood pressure.
A. Baroreceptors are a specific type of mechanoreceptor that is found in the walls of certain arteries in the body. They detect tension in the walls of the arteries and so monitor drops in blood pressure. If blood pressure drops, the frequency of impulses from the baroreceptors decreases and the CNS responds by stimulating the sympathetic division of the autonomic nervous system.

The correct answer is a...
B. Answer b is incorrect because proprioceptors, which include muscle spindles and Golgi tendon organs, detect movements of the animal's limbs, not baroreceptors.

The correct answer is a...
C. Answer c is incorrect because baroreceptors detect changes inside the body, not outside, which means they are interoceptors.

The correct answer is a...
D. Answer d is incorrect because chemoreceptors, such as peripheral chemoreceptors, detect changes in blood chemistry. Baroreceptors are mechanoreceptors, which are sensitive to mechanical forces.

Hint: Blood pressure is monitored at two main sites in the body. One is the carotid sinus, which supplies blood to the brain. The other is the aortic arch, the portion of he aorta very close to its emergence from the heart. The walls of the blood vessels at both sites contain a highly branched network of afferent neurons called baroreceptors, which detect tension in the walls.

4). Cilia from sensory cells that detect a body in motion are located within the
        a). lateral line system.
        b). cochlea.
        c). semicircular canals.
        d). pit organ.

The correct answer is c...
A. Answer a is incorrect because the cilia in the sensory cells in the lateral line system detect the movement of the water around the fish. Fish are able to find prey or follow in a school of fish by sensing the movement of the water around them using the sensory receptors in the lateral line system.

The correct answer is c...
B. Answer b is incorrect because the cilia in the sensory cells in the cochlea detect sound. The cilia extend from hair cells that are embedded in a basilar membrane and touch up against a gelatinous membrane called the tectorial membrane. Sound waves cause the basilar membrane to move in relation to the stationary tectorial membrane, which stimulates receptor potentials in the sensory hair cells.

The correct answer is c--semicircular canals.
C. Sensory cells in the semicircular canals detect a body in motion in relation to gravity. There are actually two separate groups of sensory cells that are located in the vestibular apparatus that includes the semicircular canals. Statocysts are located at the base of the semicircular canals, in the utricle and the saccule, and detect the directional pull of gravity, detecting linear acceleration. Each semicircular canal contains an ampulla embedded in a cupula. These sensory receptors detect angular acceleration.

The correct answer is c...
D. Answer d is incorrect because pit organs are specialized sensory structures found in one type of snake, the pit viper. The pit organ detects infrared radiation, heat from its prey or a predator, but accomplishes this using thermosensors, not cilia.

Hint: The receptors for gravity in vertebrates consist of two chambers of the membranous labyrinth called the utricle and saccule. The membranous labyrinth of the utricle and saccule is continuous with three semicircular canals, oriented in different planes so that angular acceleration in any direction can be detected. The saccule, utricle, and semicircular canals are collectively referred to as the vestibular apparatus. While the saccule and utricle provide a sense of linear acceleration, the semicircular canals provide a sense of angular acceleration.

5). Two senses that detect changes in chemical concentrations are
        a). touch and pressure.
        b). sight and smell.
        c). hearing and balance.
        d). taste and smell.

The correct answer is d...
A. Answer a is incorrect because the senses of touch and pressure are detected by mechanoreceptors that are stimulated by physical contact, not chemical concentrations.

The correct answer is d...
B. Answer b is incorrect because while the sense of smell detects changes in chemical concentrations the sense of sight is detected by photoreceptors that are sensitive to wavelengths of light.

The correct answer is d...
C. Answer c is incorrect because the senses of hearing and balance are detected by mechanoreceptors that are stimulated by the movement of the body in relation to the pull of gravity.

The correct answer is d...
D. The senses of taste and small are detected by chemoreceptors that are stimulated by the presence of chemicals in the environment. Certain chemicals and in higher concentrations of chemicals will stimulate a larger response in the chemoreceptors.

Hint: Some sensory cells, called chemoreceptors, contain membrane proteins that can bind to particular chemicals in the extracellular fluid. In response to this chemical interaction, the membrane of the sensory neuron becomes depolarized, leading to the production of action potentials. Chemoreceptors are used in the senses of taste and smell and are also important in monitoring the chemical composition of the blood and cerebrospinal fluid.

6). A person with defective otolith sensory receptors
      a). is deaf.
      b). has a difficult time maintaining balance.
      c). cannot detect external temperature changes.
      d). has a faulty sense of smell.

The correct answer is b...
A. Answer a is incorrect because deafness results from damage or a defects in hair cells present in the organ of Corti found in the cochlea of the inner ear, not with defects in the otolith sensory receptors.

The correct answer is b--has a difficult time maintaining balance.
B. The ability to maintain balance is controlled by structures found in the saccule and utricle. These areas contain receptors for detecting horizontal and vertical acceleration, important in maintaining balance. These sensations are detected by otolith sensory receptors (hair cells) that are embedded in otolith membranes. As the membrane moves with changes in horizontal and vertical movements the receptors are stimulated.

The correct answer is b...
C. Answer c is incorrect because the detection of changes in external temperature occurs through the stimulation of thermoreceptors, not through otolith sensory receptors.

The correct answer is b...
D. Answer d is incorrect because the detection of odors, as in the sensation of smell, occurs through the stimulation of chemoreceptors, not through otolith sensory receptors.

Hint: The receptors for gravity in vertebrates consist of two chambers of the membranous labyrinth called the utricle and saccule. Hairlike processes that project from hair cells are embedded within a gelatinous membrane contain calcium carbonate crystals; this is known as an otolith membrane. Because the otolith organ is oriented differently in the utricle and saccule, the utricle is more sensitive to horizontal acceleration (as in a moving car) and the saccule to vertical acceleration (as in an elevator).

7). The ear detects sound by the movement of
      a). the basilar membrane.
      b). the tectorial membrane.
      c). the cupula that surrounds the hair cells.
      d). fluid in the semicircular canals.

The correct answer is a--basilar membrane.
A. The organ of Corti, which is the structure that detects sound waves through the air, is located in the cochlea of the inner ear. Sound waves cause bones in the middle ear to move that force pressure on an area called the oval window. Movement of the oval window causes the cochlear duct within the cochlea to move. The sensory receptors, hair cells, are mounted on a flexible

basilar membrane. As the cochlear duct vibrates, the basilar membrane vibrates causing the hair cells to be stimulated, producing the perception of sound in the brain.

The correct answer is a...
B. Answer b is incorrect because the tectorial membrane found in the cochlea of the inner ear is a stationary membrane. The hairs cells, which are the sensory receptors in the ear, are mounted on a flexible basilar membrane and project into the tectorial membrane. As the basilar membrane moves in response to sound waves, the hair cells bend against the stationary tectorial membrane and are stimulated.

The correct answer is a...
C. Answer c is incorrect because cupula is a structure found in the lateral line system in fish and in the semicircular canals but not in the sensory system involved with the detection of sound waves through the air.

The correct answer is a...
D. Answer d is incorrect because the semicircular canals are involved in the detection of angular movement of the body, not in the detection of sound waves.

Hint: As the pressure waves produced by the vibrations of the oval window are transmitted through the cochlea to the round window, they cause the cochlear duct to vibrate. The bottom of the cochlear duct, called the basilar membrane, is quite flexible and vibrates in response to these pressure waves. The surface of the basilar membrane contains sensory hair cells. As the basilar membrane vibrates, the cilia of the hair cells bend in response to the movement of the basilar membrane relative to the tectorial membrane. The bending of the cilia depolarizes the hair cells, which stimulates the production of action potentials in sensory neurons.

8). Which of the following statements is incorrect?
      a). Vertebrates focus the eye by changing the shape of the lens.
      b). All vertebrate and invertebrate eyes use the same light-capturing molecule.
      c). The vertebrate eye adjusts the amount of light entering the eye by contracting the ciliary muscles.
      d). Fish focus the eye by moving the lens closer to or farther from the retina.

The correct answer is c...
A. Answer a is incorrect because this statement is correct. Changing the shape of the lens focuses the vertebrate eye. To focus on images up close, the lens becomes rounder and thicker, bending the light more. To focus on images farther away, the lens becomes flatter and thinner, bending the light less.

The correct answer is c...
B. Answer b is incorrect because this statement is correct. Even though eyes differ in shape and function in vertebrates and invertebrates, they all utilize the same light-capturing molecule, *cis*-retinal. This suggests that there may not be many molecules that are able to serve this function.

The correct answer is c--The vertebrate eye adjusts the amount of light entering the eye by contracting the ciliary muscles.
C. This statement is incorrect because the amount of light that is able to enter the cell is controlled by the contracting of the iris muscles, the colored part of the eye, that changes the size of the pupil. The contraction of ciliary muscles adjusts the shape of the lens, not the size of the pupil.

The correct answer is c...
D. Answer d is incorrect because this statement is correct. Mammalian eyes focus light on the retina by changing the shape of the lens but the eyes of fish and amphibians work more like a

camera. They focus light on the retina by moving the lens closer to or farther away from the retina.

Hint: Light enters the eye through a transparent cornea, which begins to focus the light. This occurs because light is refracted (bent) when it travels into a medium of different density. The colored portion of the eye is the iris; contraction of the iris muscles in bright light decreases the size of its opening, the pupil. Light passes through the pupil to the lens, a transparent structure that completes the focusing of the light onto the retina at the back of the eye.

9). Most sensory receptors function by producing depolarizing potentials. Which of the following function by hyperpolarization rather depolarization?
        a). proprioceptors
        b). nociceptors
        c). olfactory receptors
        d). rods and cones

The correct answer is d...
A. Answer a is incorrect because proprioceptors, found in the muscles, tendons, and ligaments of the body, detect the relative position and movements in the limbs of the body. The movements of these structures are detected by proprioceptors and send depolarizing receptor potentials to the CNS.

The correct answer is d...
B. Answer b is incorrect because nociceptors, found throughout the body, detect pain. These are primarily free nerve endings that detect damage, or potential damage, to the body and respond by producing depolarizing potentials that are sent to the CNS.

The correct answer is d...
C. Answer c is incorrect because olfactory receptors are found in the mucous membranes of the nasal cavity. The olfactory nerve extends dendrites into the olfactory mucosa that are excited by different chemicals in the air inhaled.

The correct answer is d--rods and cones
D. The eye contains several layers of cells that trigger the response to light. The photoreceptor cells found in the eye, rods and cones, release an inhibitory neurotransmitter when not stimulated by light, thereby inhibiting bipolar neurons from releasing their excitatory neuron transmitter onto the ganglion cells. The ganglion cells are the cells that send the nerve impulses to the CNS. Light causes a hyperpolarization of the photoreceptor cells that inhibits their release of neurotransmitter, thereby causing an excitation in the bipolar cells.

Hint: The transduction of light energy into nerve impulses follows a sequence that is the inverse of the usual way that sensory stimuli are detected. This is because, in the dark, the photoreceptors release an inhibitory neurotransmitter that hyperpolarizes the bipolar neurons. Thus inhibited, the bipolar neurons do not release excitatory neurotransmitter to the ganglion cells. Light inhibits the photoreceptors, by hyperpolarizing the cells, such that they are not able to release their inhibitory neurotransmitter.

10). Which of the following stimuli is not detected by fish?
        a). infrared radiation
        b). sound
        c). electricity
        d). magnetism

The correct answer is a--infrared radiation
A. Infrared radiation, also called radiant heat, is radiation with wavelengths longer than those of visual light. While terrestrial animals can sense heat, it is a poor environmental stimulus in water

because water has a high heat capacity—it absorbs heat very well. For this reason, fish do not readily detect infrared radiation. However, only one terrestrial vertebrate actually has the ability to sense infrared radiation and not just temperature differences, the pit vipers.

The correct answer is a...
B. Answer b is incorrect because fish are able to detect sound. The lateral line system in fish detects vibrations of pressure waves in the water from objects that are relatively close. Their hearing system detects vibrations in water waves that originate from greater distances. The fish hearing system utilizes otolith organs in the utricle and saccule that terrestrial vertebrates use for sensing vertical and horizontal acceleration of the body.

The correct answer is a...
C. Answer c is incorrect because fish are able to detect electricity. Water is a good conductor of electricity and some types of fish use this property of water to interpret their surroundings. Some fish, such as the sharks, rays, and skates, can detect the electrical currents generated when fish swim and use this to detect prey. Sensory organs called the ampullae of Lorenzini serve this function in these fish.

The correct answer is a...
D. Answer d is incorrect because fish are able to detect magnetic fields. The sensory systems that detect magnetism are the least understood of all the sensory systems, but many animals including eels, sharks, bees, and birds are able to detect magnetic fields.

Hint: Electromagnetic radiation with wavelengths longer than those of visible light is too low in energy to be detected by photoreceptors. Radiation from this infrared portion of the spectrum is what we normally think of as radiant heat. Heat is an extremely poor environmental stimulus in water because water has a high thermal capacity and readily absorbs heat. Air, in contrast, has a low thermal capacity, so heat is a potentially useful stimulus. However, the only vertebrates known to have the ability to sense infrared radiation are the snakes known as pit vipers.

Test Your Visual Understanding

1). Corrective lenses are used to refocus the image correctly on the retina of the eye. Explain how each corrective lens in the figure modifies the refraction of the light from the image and why each is able to correct their respective eye problem.
Answer: In the top panel, nearsightedness is the condition where the eye can focus correctly on objects close up but the eye cannot focus correctly on objects far away. To correct this, a concave lens is used to spread the light from the image out more before entering the cornea. By doing this, the concave lens is able to make the light travel farther through the eye, allowing the focus point to fall on the retina, forming a clearer image.

In the lower panel, farsightedness is the condition where the eye can focus correctly on objects far away but the eye cannot focus correct on objects close up. To correct this, a convex lens is used to bend the light coming from the object inward before entering the cornea. By doing this, the convex lens is able to shorten the path of the light through the eye, allowing the focus point to fall on the retina, forming a clearer image.

Apply Your Knowledge

1). The human tongue contains about 10,000 taste buds, with each taste bud housing about 50 taste cells. Each taste cell has a life span of about 10 days. How many taste cells are replaced while you sleep (assume 7 hours of sleep)?

Answer: There are 10,000 taste buds with 50 taste cells in each for a total of 500,000 taste cells. If each taste cell is replaced every 10 days then:

500,000 cells / 10 days = 50,000 cells replaced per day (24 hours)
50,000 cells / 24 hours = 2,083.3 cells replaced per hour
2,083.3 cells x 7 hours = 14,583.1 taste cells replaced while you sleep.

2). How would the otolith organs of an astronaut in zero gravity behave? Would the astronaut still have a subjective impression of motion? Would the semicircular canals detect angular acceleration equally well at zero gravity?

Answer: Without gravity to force the otoliths down toward the hair cells, the otolith organ will not function properly. The otolith membrane would not rest upon the hair cells and would not move in response to movement of the body parallel or perpendicular to the pull of gravity. Consequently, the hair cell would not bend and so would not produce receptor potentials. Because the astronaut can see, they would have an impression of motion—they can see themselves move in relation to objects around them—but with their eye closed, they would not know if they were moving in relation to their surroundings. Because their proprioceptor would still function, they would be able to sense when they moved their arm or leg, but they would not have the sensation of their enter body moving through space.

The semicircular canals would not function equally well in zero gravity conditions. While the fluid in the semicircular canals is still able to move around, some sensation of angular movement would most likely occur, but the full function of the semicircular canals requires the force of gravity to aid in the directional movement of the fluid in the canals.

Self Test

1). Which of the following best describes hormones?
  a). Hormones are relatively unstable and work only in the area adjacent to the gland that produced them.
  b). Hormones are stable, long-lasting chemicals released from glands.
  c). All hormones are lipid-soluble.
  d). Hormones are chemical messengers that are released into the environment.

The correct answer is b...
A. Answer a is incorrect because hormones are very stable molecules, having to travel throughout the body to reach their target cells.

The correct answer is b--Hormones are stable, long-lasting chemicals released from glands.
B. Hormones are stable chemicals that are released into the bloodstream from glands or other organs. Unlike neurotransmitters, which are also chemical messengers, hormones are long lasting to remain active while they travel throughout the body.

The correct answer is b…
C. Answer c is incorrect because not all hormones are lipid-soluble. One class of hormones, the steroids, is lipid-soluble and can pass into the cell unaided, but all other hormones are water-soluble and require a membrane receptor protein to trigger its cellular response.

The correct answer is b...
D. Answer d is incorrect because hormones are active in the body only and are not released into the environment. Pheromones are chemical messengers that are released into the environment.

Hint: A hormone is a regulatory chemical that is secreted into the blood by an endocrine gland or an organ of the body exhibiting an endocrine function. The blood carries the hormone to every cell in the body, but only the target cells for a given hormone can respond to it. Thus, the difference between a neurotransmitter and a hormone is not in the chemical nature of the regulatory molecule, but rather in the way it is transported to its target cells, and its distance from these target cells.

2). The receptor for steroid hormones lies
  a). in the cytoplasm.
  b). within the plasma membrane.
  c). within the nuclear envelope.
  d). in the blood plasma.

The correct answer is a--in the cytoplasm.
A. Steroid hormones are lipophilic which means that they are able to cross the plasma membrane. Once the steroid hormone enters the cell, it binds to its specific receptor in the cytoplasm or nucleus and elicits its actions on transcription.

The correct answer is a...
B. Answer b is incorrect because the receptor for steroid hormones is not within the plasma membrane. Steroid hormones are lipophilic which means that they do not require a membrane protein to transport it across the plasma membrane. The hormone passes through the membrane to trigger its response.

The correct answer is a...
C. Answer c is incorrect because the steroid hormone is able to pass into the nucleus without the aid of a receptor bound to the nuclear envelope.

The correct answer is a...
D. Answer d is incorrect because the steroid hormones travel through the blood stream attached to protein carriers, but these are not receptors; these are merely carrier proteins that release the hormone once it reaches its target cell.

Hint: The lipophilic hormones—all of the steroid hormones and thyroxine—as well as other lipophilic regulatory molecules can easily enter cells. Because these hormones are not water-soluble, they don't dissolve in plasma but rather travel in the blood attached to protein carriers. When they arrive at their target cell, they dissociate from their carriers and pass through the plasma membrane. Some steroid hormones then bind to very specific receptor proteins in the cytoplasm. Other steroids travel directly into the nucleus before encountering their receptor proteins.

3). Second messengers are activated in response to
      a). steroid hormones.
      b). thyroxine.
      c). peptide hormones
      d). all of these.

The correct answer is c...
A. Answer a is incorrect because steroid hormones are able to cross the plasma membrane and trigger their response in the cell directly. A second messenger is not needed.

The correct answer is c...
B. Answer b is incorrect because thyroxine is able to cross the plasma membrane and trigger their response in the cell directly. A second messenger is not needed.

The correct answer is c--peptide hormones.
C. Peptide hormones are polar molecules that are not able to cross the plasma membrane. In order to carry out their response in the cell, they need to either be transported across the membrane or somehow trigger their response from outside the cell. They perform their function by binding to a receptor on the outside of the membrane, which activates a second messenger inside the cell that carries out the response.

The correct answer is c...
D. Answer d is incorrect because answer c is the only correct answer. Both steroid hormones and thyroxine are nonpolar molecules and are able to cross the plasma membrane and carry out their respective responses directly from inside the cell. A second messenger is not needed.

Hint: Hormones that are too large or too polar to cross the plasma membranes of their target cells include all of the peptide and glycoprotein hormones, as well as the catecholamine hormones epinephrine and norepinephrine. These hormones bind to receptor proteins located on the outer surface of the plasma membrane but do not enter the cell. A second messenger is needed within the target cell to produce the effects of the hormone.

4). _____ regulates the kidney's retention of water. Its secretion is suppressed by alcohol.
      a). Prolactin
      b). Oxytocin
      c). Thyroxine
      d). Vasopressin (ADH)

The correct answer is d...
A. Answer a is incorrect because prolactin, which is released from the anterior pituitary, stimulates milk production in the mammary glands of mammals and is not involved in water retention in the body.

The correct answer is d...
B. Answer b is incorrect because oxytocin, which is released from the posterior pituitary, stimulates smooth muscle contraction in the milk ducts to eject milk from mammary glands. It also stimulates muscle contractions during childbirth. Oxytocin is not involved in water retention.

The correct answer is d...
C. Answer c is incorrect because thyroxine, which is released from the thyroid gland, stimulates metabolism and is not involved in controlling water retention.

The correct answer is d--Vasopressin (ADH)
D. Antidiuretic hormone (ADH), also called vasopressin, is released from the posterior pituitary and stimulates water retention by the kidneys. Dehydration triggers the release of ADH from the posterior pituitary and the kidneys, in response, retain water from the blood that filters through the kidneys. Without ADH, or when it is suppressed by alcohol, the kidneys do not retain water from the blood and most of the water leaves the body in the urine.

Hint: In the 1950s, antidiuretic hormone was isolated from the posterior pituitary and found to stimulate water retention by the kidneys. When ADH is missing, the kidneys do not retain water and excessive quantities of urine are produced.

5). Which of the following hormones is not released by the anterior pituitary?
    a). melanocyte-stimulating hormone
    b). gonadotropin-releasing hormone
    c). thyroid-stimulating hormone
    d). growth hormone

The correct answer is b...
A. Answer a is incorrect because melanocyte-stimulating hormone is released by the anterior pituitary gland and functions in stimulating color changes in reptiles and amphibians, but its function is unknown in mammals.

The correct answer is b--gonadotropin-releasing hormone
B. The gonadotropin hormones, luteinizing hormone (LH) and follicle-stimulating hormone (FSH), are released from the anterior pituitary but gonadotropin-releasing hormone (GnRH), which triggers the release of these two hormones from the pituitary, is secreted from the hypothalamus.

The correct answer is b...
C. Answer c is incorrect because thyroid-stimulating hormone is released from the anterior pituitary and functions in stimulating the thyroid to release thyroxine.

The correct answer is b...
D. Answer d is incorrect because growth hormone is released from the anterior pituitary gland and functions in stimulating protein synthesis and growth of muscles and connective tissues and indirectly stimulates the elongation of bones.

Hint: The hypothalamus controls production and secretion of the anterior pituitary hormones. Neurons in the hypothalamus secrete releasing hormones and inhibiting hormones into blood capillaries at the base of the hypothalamus. Each releasing hormone delivered by the hypothalamohypophyseal system regulates the secretion of a specific anterior pituitary hormone. For example, thyrotropin-releasing hormone stimulates the release of TSH and gonadotropin-releasing hormone (GnRH) stimulates the release of FSH and LH.

6). _____ hormone stimulates the adrenal cortex to produce several of its hormones.

        a). Follicle-stimulating
        b). Luteinizing
        c). Adrenocorticotropic
        d). Growth

The correct answer is c...
A. Answer a is incorrect because follicle-stimulating hormone functions in the development of ovarian follicles in females and in the development of sperm in males. It does not act on the adrenal gland.

The correct answer is c...
B. Answer b is incorrect because luteinizing hormone functions in triggering ovulation in the female and stimulating the secretion of testosterone in the male. It does not act on the adrenal gland.

The correct answer is c--Adrenocorticotropic
C. The anterior pituitary releases adrenocorticotropic hormone (ACTH) in response to the secretion of corticotropin-releasing hormone (CRH) from the hypothalamus. ACTH released from the anterior pituitary stimulates the adrenal cortex to secrete corticosteroid hormones.

The correct answer is c...
D. Answer d is incorrect because growth hormone functions in stimulating the growth of muscles, bone (indirectly), and other tissues and is essential for proper metabolic regulation.

Hint: Adrenocorticotropic hormone (ACTH) stimulates the adrenal cortex to produce corticosteroid hormones, including cortisol in humans and corticosterone in other vertebrates, which regulate glucose homeostasis.

7). Parathyroid hormone acts to ensure that
        a). calcium levels in the blood never drop too low.
        b). sodium levels in urine are constant.
        c). potassium levels in the blood don't escalate.
        d). the concentration of water in the blood is sufficient.

The correct answer is a--calcium levels in the blood never drop too low.
A. Parathyroid hormone (PTH) released from the parathyroid glands is one of only two hormones that are absolutely essential for survival. PTH controls the levels of calcium in the blood by stimulating the release of calcium from bone and by increasing calcium absorption and reabsorption. Too much calcium levels however in the blood can cause problems, so PTH must be released in the proper amounts.

The correct answer is a...
B. Answer b is incorrect because parathyroid hormone (PTH) controls calcium levels in the blood, not the reabsorption of sodium.

The correct answer is a...
C. Answer c is incorrect because parathyroid hormone (PTH) controls calcium levels in the blood, not potassium levels in the blood.

The correct answer is a...
D. Answer d is incorrect because parathyroid hormone (PTH) controls calcium levels in the blood, not the maintenance of water levels in the blood.

Hint: PTH is synthesized and released in response to falling levels of Ca^{++} in the blood. This cannot be allowed to continue uncorrected, because a significant fall in the blood Ca^{++} level can cause severe muscle spasms. A normal blood Ca^{++} is important for the functioning of muscles, including the heart, and for the proper functioning of the nervous and endocrine systems.

8). The adrenal cortex releases _____, which stimulates Na^+ reabsorption by the kidneys.
      a). epinephrine
      b). aldosterone
      c). glucose
      d). cortisol

The correct answer is b...
A. Answer a is incorrect because epinephrine is released from the adrenal medulla, not the cortex, and it triggers the "alarm" response in the body in conjunction with the sympathetic division of the autonomic nervous system.

The correct answer is b--aldosterone
B. Aldosterone is one of only two hormones that are absolutely necessary for survival (the other is parathyroid hormone). Aldosterone stimulates Na^+ reabsorption by the kidneys. Without aldosterone, the kidneys would lose excessive amounts of Na^+ followed by Cl^- and water. This results in decreases in blood volume leading to a drop in blood pressure.

The correct answer is b...
C. Answer c is incorrect because the adrenal cortex releases hormone and glucose is not a hormone. A group of hormones that it releases, the glucocorticoids, regulate the levels of glucose in the blood but the gland does not release glucose.

The correct answer is b...
D. Answer d is incorrect because although cortisol is released from the adrenal cortex, it functions to maintain glucose homeostasis in the body, not in Na^+ reabsorption.

Hint: The hormones from the adrenal cortex are all steroids and are referred to collectively as corticosteroids. Aldosterone, a major corticosteroid, is classified as a mineralocorticoid because it helps regulate mineral balance through two functions. One of the functions of aldosterone is to stimulate the kidneys to reabsorb Na^+ from the urine. By stimulating the kidneys to reabsorb salt and water, aldosterone maintains the normal blood volume and pressure essential to life.

9). Individuals with type I diabetes
      a). lack ß cells in the islets of Langerhans.
      b). produce enough insulin but lack functional receptors on their cells.
      c). can control their diabetes with diet and exercise.
      d). All of these are correct.

The correct answer is a--lack ß cells in the islets of Langerhans.
A. Individuals with type I diabetes do not produce enough insulin and therefore require injections of insulin. The cells in the pancreas that produce insulin, called ß cells of the islets of Langerhans, are not functional in patients with type I diabetes.

The correct answer is a...
B. Answer b is incorrect because individuals with type I diabetes do not produce enough insulin but they do have functional receptors on their cells. When given injections of insulin, the cells of these individuals are able to respond to the insulin and take up glucose.

The correct answer is a...
C. Answer c is incorrect because individuals with type I diabetes cannot control their diabetes with diet and exercise. While they can better maintain their blood glucose levels with diet and exercise, they require insulin injections to treat their diabetes. Type II diabetes can often be controlled with diet and exercise.

The correct answer is a...
D. Answer d is incorrect because there is only one correct answer, answer a. Individuals with type I diabetes do not produce enough insulin and they cannot control their diabetes with just diet and exercise; they need insulin injections.

Hint: Two forms of diabetes are now recognized. People with type I, or insulin-dependent diabetes mellitus, lack the insulin-secreting ß cells. Treatment for these patients therefore consists of insulin injections.

10). The hormone melatonin, which is involved in skin blanching in lower vertebrates, is released from the
        a). anterior pituitary gland.
        b). melanocytes.
        c). pineal gland.
        d). suprachiasmatic nucleus of the hypothalamus.

The correct answer is c...
A. Answer a is incorrect because the anterior pituitary gland does not release melatonin. A secretion from the anterior pituitary gland is involved in skin coloration in some vertebrates but that hormone is MSH, or melanocyte stimulating hormone, which stimulates the production of the pigment melanin in melanocytes.

The correct answer is c...
B. Answer b is incorrect because melanocytes are pigment-producing cells and not endocrine glands. The melanocytes produce the pigment melanin in response to the secretions of MSH from the anterior pituitary gland, but melanin is not the same as the hormone melatonin.

The correct answer is c--pineal gland.
C. The pineal gland evolved from pineal eye (a "third eye") found in primitive vertebrates. The pineal gland is found deep in the brain of vertebrates and secretes the hormone melatonin. Melatonin functions in blanching the skin in lower vertebrates by reducing the dispersal of melanin granules. Melatonin may also be involved in the establishment of circadian rhythms.

The correct answer is c...
D. Answer d is incorrect because the suprachiasmatic nucleus (SCN) of the hypothalamus stimulates the secretion of melatonin, but it is not the endocrine gland that produces and releases melatonin. The SCN, in conjunction with melatonin secretions coordinates the circadian rhythms that function in vertebrates.

Hint: Another major endocrine gland is the pineal gland, located in the roof of the third ventricle of the brain in most vertebrates. The pineal gland evolved from a median light-sensitive eye (sometimes called a "third eye") at the top of the skull in primitive vertebrates. In other vertebrates, however, the pineal gland is buried deep in the brain and functions as an endocrine gland by secreting the hormone melatonin. One of the actions of melatonin is to cause blanching of the skin of lower vertebrates.

1). A goiter results when the thyroid gland becomes enlarged. The figure above shows the regulation of thyroxine secretion, with the different steps in the process numbered. Indicate which numbered step or steps are disrupted in the process that leads to the formation of a goiter, and explain why this happens and what results.

Answer: The appearance of a goiter is the result of overstimulation of the thyroid gland, which causes it to continually grow. There are two different steps in the regulation pathway that can lead to overstimulation: the inhibition of steps 6 or 7. Under normal conditions, the production of thyroxine has a negative effect on further stimulation of the thyroid gland. This is called negative feedback inhibition. When the production of thyroxine is interrupted, the hypothalamus will stimulate the anterior pituitary gland, which in turn stimulates the thyroid gland to produce more thyroxine. When enough thyroxine is produced, the negative feedback inhibition steps are followed. If thyroxine is not produced, there is no negative feedback, no shutting down of the pathway. Therefore, the hypothalamus and the anterior pituitary continue to stimulate the thyroid. Eventually, the thyroid becomes enlarged, resulting in a goiter.

Applying Your Knowledge

1). The adrenal medulla secretes epinephrine in response to stimulation from the sympathetic division of the autonomic nervous system. Epinephrine triggers the fight or flight response in the body, which causes an increase in the heart rate. In a person at rest, the heart beats about 72 beats per minute and moves about 70 ml of blood per beat. Epinephrine causes the heart rate to double and the volume per beat to triple.

a). How much blood is moved per minute in a resting heart and in a hormone-stimulated heart?

b). As a percentage, how much more blood is moved by a hormone-stimulated heart compared to a resting heart?

Answer:

1a). In a resting heart: 72 beats/min x 70 ml/beat = 5,040 ml/min or 5.04 liters/min
In a stimulated heart: 144 beats/min x 210 ml/beat = 30,240 ml/min or 30.24 liters/min

1b). As a percentage the stimulated heart pumps 500% more blood:
(30.24 - 5.04) / 5.04 = 5.0 or 500%

2). Suppose that two different organs, such as the liver and heart, are sensitive to a particular hormone (such as epinephrine). The cells in both organs have identical receptors for the hormone, and hormone-receptor binding produces the same intracellular second messenger in both organs. However, the hormone produces different effects in the two organs. Explain how this can happen.

Answer: The same hormone can affect two different organs in different ways because the second messengers triggered by the hormone, have different targets inside the cell because the cells have different functions. Epinephrine affects the cells of the heart by increasing metabolism so that their contractions are faster and stronger. However, liver cells do not contract and so the second messenger in liver cells triggers the conversion of glycogen into glucose. That is why hormones are so valuable but also economical to the body. One hormone can be produced, one receptor can be made, and one second messenger system can be used, but there can be two different targets inside the cell.

3). Many physiological parameters, such as blood Ca^{++} concentration and blood glucose levels, are controlled by two hormones that have opposite effects. What is the advantage of achieving regulation in this manner instead of by using a single hormone that changes the parameters in one direction only?

Answer: Hormones such as thyroxine, whose effects are slower and have a broader range of activity, a negative feedback system using one hormone adequately controls the system. However, for certain parameters that have a very narrow range and change constantly within that

324

range, a regulatory system that uses "up" and "down" regulation is desirable. Too much or too little Ca^{++} or glucose in the blood can have devastating effects on the body and so those levels must be controlled within a very narrow range. To rely on negative feedback loops would restrict the quick "on" and "off" responses needed to keep the parameters in a very narrow range.

Inquiry Questions

FIGURE 48.11

IgM and IgG antibodies. The first antibodies produced in the humoral immune response are IgM antibodies, which are very effective at activating the complement system. This initial wave of antibody production peaks after about one week and is followed by a far more extended production of IgG antibodies.
Why does the production of IgM antibodies cease after one week?

Answer: IgM is the body's defensive response to a primary infection and if this defense is going to be effective, it will be so within a week. There is no point in continuing production, because within a week after an infection begins, the secondary response of IgG plasma cells kick in.

FIGURE 48.15

The development of active immunity. Immunity to smallpox in Jenner's patients occurred because their inoculation with cowpox stimulated the development of lymphocyte clones with receptors that could bind not only to cowpox but also smallpox antigens. A second exposure stimulates the immune system to produce large amounts of the antibody more rapidly than before.
Would a secondary exposure to cowpox rather than smallpox have produced as strong an antibody response?

Answer: Yes, the secondary response would be just as strong. The lymphocytes that were cloned following the first exposure have receptors that bind to the cowpox virus. It just so happens that the antigens on the smallpox virus are so similar to the antigens on the cowpox virus that they are recognized by these same lymphocytes.

FIGURE 48.24

Survival of T cells in culture after exposure to HIV. The virus has little effect on the number of $CD8^+$ cells, but it causes the number of $CD4^+$ T cells to decline dramatically.
Are the surviving $CD4^+$ T cells any different than those destroyed? How could you be sure?

Answer: If surviving $CD4^+$ T cells are somehow more resistant to HIV, then the cell culture prepared from these survivors should not show dramatic declines in cell numbers after HIV infection.

Self Test

1). The epidermis fights microbial infections by
    a). making the surface of the skin acidic.
    b). excreting lysozyme to attack bacteria.
    c). producing mucus to trap microorganisms.
    d). all of these.

The correct answer is d…
A. Answer a is incorrect because although the oil and sweat glands produce substances on the surface that make the surface acidic enough to inhibit the growth of microorganisms, this is not the only correct answer.

The correct answer is d…
B. Answer b is incorrect because although the sweat that is secreted on the surface of the skin contains lysozyme that digests bacterial cell walls, this is not the only correct answer.

The correct answer is d...
C. Answer c is incorrect because although the epidermal cells that line the respiratory tract secrete a sticky mucus that traps microorganisms before they enter the lungs, this is not the only correct answer.

The correct answer is d--all of these.
D. The skin is the first line of defense against the invasion of microorganisms into the body. The skin provides a nearly impenetrable barrier, but also secretes chemicals that kill microorganisms or traps them so that they can't enter the body.

Hint: The skin not only defends the body by providing a nearly impenetrable barrier, but also reinforces this defense with chemical weapons on the surface. Oil and sweat glands give the skin's surface a pH of 3 to 5, acidic enough to inhibit the growth of microorganisms. Sweat also contains the enzyme lysozyme, which digests bacterial cell walls. The cells lining the smaller bronchi and bronchioles secrete a layer of sticky mucus that traps most microorganisms before they can reach the lungs.

2). Cells that target and kill body cells infected by viruses is are
      a). macrophages.
      b). natural killer cells.
      c). monocytes.
      d). neutrophils.

The correct answer is b...
A. Answer a is incorrect because macrophages engulf the microorganism such as a virus directly; they do not kill body cells infected by the virus.

The correct answer is b--natural killer cells.
B. A natural killer cell is a type of leukocyte involved in the nonspecific immune response. The natural killer cell identifies a body cell that has been infected by a virus and punctures a hole in the cell with proteins called perforins. The invading virus dies with the cell.

The correct answer is b...
C. Answer c is incorrect because monocytes are the precursors of macrophage cells. Monocytes circulate throughout the body and in response to an infection they travel to the site of an infection and transform into a macrophage.

The correct answer is b...
D. Answer d is incorrect because neutrophils are cells that, like microphages, engulf invading microorganisms through phagocytosis. But, unlike macrophages, neutrophils release chemicals that kill microorganisms in the immediate vicinity of the attacked cell but also end up killing themselves.

Hint: Natural killer cells do not attack invading microbes directly. Instead, they kill cells of the body that have been infected with viruses. They kill not by phagocytosis, but rather by creating a hole in the plasma membrane of the target cell. Proteins, called perforins, are released from the natural killer cells and inserted into the plasma membrane of the target cell, forming a pore. This pore allows water to rush into the cell, causing the cell to swell and burst.

3). A molecule present on the plasma membrane that induces an immune response is called
      a). an antigen.
      b). an interleukin.
      c). an antibody.
      d). a lymphocyte.

The correct answer is a--an antigen.
A. Cells contain proteins and other molecules on their surface, which are identified by the cells of the immune system. If the cells are recognized as being body cells, they are left alone. If the surface molecules are determined to be foreign, they trigger an immune response. Molecules that trigger an immune response are called antigens.

The correct answer is a…
B. Answer b is incorrect because an interleukin belongs to a class of proteins that are released from cells of the immune system to trigger steps in the immune response. They are not surface molecules and they do not induce an immune response; they are part of the immune response.

The correct answer is a…
C. Answer c is incorrect because an antibody is a molecule that is released from plasma cells as part of the humoral immune response. Antibodies are not surface molecules and they do not induce an immune response; they are part of the immune response.

The correct answer is a…
D. Answer d is incorrect because a lymphocyte is a white blood cell, specifically a T cell or B cell. These cells carry out the specific immune response and are not surface molecules.

Hint: An antigen is a molecule that provokes a specific immune response. Antigens are large, complex molecules such as proteins; they are generally foreign to the body, usually present on the surface of pathogens.

4). Which one of the following acts as the "alarm signal" to activate the body's immune system by stimulating helper T cells?
     a). B cells
     b). interleukin-1
     c). interleukin-2
     d). histamines

The correct answer is b…
A. Answer a is incorrect because B cells are part of the body's immune system that provide humoral immunity, which is activated by the "alarm signal," and so it can not be the alarm signal.

The correct answer is b--interleukin-1
B. Interleukin-1 is released by macrophages after they've encountered an antigen. The release of interleukin-1 stimulates the proliferation of helper T cells. The helper T cells then release other chemicals that stimulate macrophage activity and cytotoxic T cells.

The correct answer is b…
C. Answer c is incorrect because interleukin-2 is released from helper T cells after they've been stimulated to divide by interleukin-1.

The correct answer is b…
D. Answer d is incorrect because histamines are released by mast cells. While histamines are important in triggering the inflammatory response, it is not the "alarm signal" that begins the stimulation of T cell and B cell proliferation, which is the third line of defense.

Hint: Macrophages that encounter antigens or antigen-presenting cells release a protein called interleukin-1 that acts as a chemical alarm signal. Helper T cells respond to interleukin-1 by simultaneously initiating two parallel lines of immune system defense: the cell-mediated response carried out by T cells and the humoral response carried out by B cells.

5). Cytotoxic T cells are called into action by the
      a). presence of histamine.
      b). presence of interleukin-1.
      c). presence of interleukin-2.
      d). B cell stimulating factor.

The correct answer is c...
A. Answer a is incorrect because histamine stimulates are released by mast cells and stimulate the inflammatory response by causing vasodilation and increased permeability of capillaries to lymphocytes. However, it does not stimulate cytotoxic T cells.

The correct answer is c...
B. Answer b is incorrect because while interleukin-1 stimulates the proliferation of helper T cells, it does not trigger the proliferation of cytotoxic T cells.

The correct answer is c--presence of interleukin-2.
C. Interleukin-1 is released from macrophages that have encountered an antigen. Interleukin-1 then stimulates the proliferation of helper T cells. The helper T cells then in turn release interleukin-2, which stimulates the proliferation of cytotoxic T cells that can attack cells that carry the antigen.

The correct answer is c...
D. Answer d is incorrect because although B cell stimulating factor is an interleukin, it functions in stimulating B cell proliferation, not T cell proliferation.

Hint: Once the helper T cells have been activated by the antigens presented to them by the macrophages, they secrete the cytokines known as macrophage colony-stimulating factor and gamma interferon, which promote the activity of macrophages. In addition, the helper T cells secrete interleukin-2, which stimulates the proliferation of cytotoxic T cells that are specific for the antigen.

6). The immunoglobin _____ is involved in the primary response to an invading microorganism, and _____ is involved in the secondary response.
      a). IgG / IgM
      b). IgM / IgE
      c). IgE / histamines
      d). IgM / IgG

The correct answer is d...
A. Answer a is incorrect because IgG is the immunoglobin primarily involved in the secondary response and IgM is primarily involved in a quicker, primary response.

The correct answer is d...
B. Answer b is incorrect because while it is true that IgM is involved in the primary response, IgE is not involved in the secondary response. IgE is involved in the inflammatory response, promoting the release of histamines.

The correct answer is d...
C. Answer c is incorrect because IgE and histamines are involved in the inflammatory response, not in the general humoral immune response.

The correct answer is d--IgM / IgG
D. The first antibodies produced in the humoral immune response are the IgM antibodies, which are very effective at activating the complement system. This initial wave of antibody production peaks after about one week; this is called the primary response. The primary response is followed by a far more extended production of IgG antibodies, which is the secondary response.

Hint: Unlike the receptors on T cells, which bind only to antigens presented by certain cells, B receptors can bind to free antigens. This provokes a primary response in which antibodies of the IgM class are secreted, and also stimulates cell division and clonal expansion. Upon subsequent exposure, the plasma cells secrete large amounts of antibodies that are generally of the IgG class.

7). How does your body detect millions of different antigens?
      a). The few hundred immunoglobulin genes can be rearranged or can undergo mutations to form millions of antibody molecules.
      b). There are millions of different antibody genes.
      c). The few hundred immunoglobulin genes undergo antigen shifting.
      d). Each B cell has a different set of immunoglobulin genes, and so the activation of different B cells produces different antibodies.

The correct answer is a--The few hundred immunoglobulin genes can be rearranged or can undergo mutations to form millions of antibody molecules.
A. There are only a few hundred genes encoding for immunoglobulins but those genes can be rearranged, a process called somatic rearrangement, or can undergo mutations, a process called somatic mutation, to produce millions of gene combinations. Each gene combination produces a different immunoglobulin molecule.

The correct answer is a…
B. Answer b is incorrect because the human genome only has some 30,000 genes, therefore it could not contain a separate gene for every immunoglobulin molecules that is produced in the body.

The correct answer is a…
C. Answer c is incorrect because antigen shifting is the process whereby a pathogen is able to "get around" the immune system, by the mutation of genes that encode for surface proteins (antigens) so that the antibodies that were produced to fight the pathogen are no longer effective.

The correct answer is a…
D. Answer d is incorrect because there is only one set of genes per organism and each and every cell in the body contains the same genes (although gametes only contain one copy of each gene). Different cells cannot have a different set of genes.

Hint: The millions of immunoglobulin receptor genes in the B cell are not inherited at conception because they do not exist as single sequences of nucleotides. Rather, they are assembled by stitching together three of four DNA segments that code for different parts of the receptor molecule. This process is called somatic rearrangement. Also, random mistakes occur during successive DNA replications as the lymphocytes divide during clonal expansion. This produces changes in amino acid sequences, a phenomenon known as somatic mutations.

8). The blood from a person with an AB blood type
      a). would agglutinate with anti-A antibodies only.
      b). would agglutinate with anti-B antibodies only.
      c). would agglutinate with both anti-A and anti-B antibodies.
      d). would not agglutinate with either anti-A or anti-B antibodies.

The correct answer is c…
A. Answer a is incorrect because AB blood contains red blood cells that carry both A and B antigens on their cell surfaces and so their blood would reaction with anti-B antibodies, and not just with anti-A antibodies.

The correct answer is c...
B. Answer b is incorrect because AB blood contains red blood cells that carry both A and B antigens on their cell surfaces and so their blood would reaction with anti-A antibodies, and not just with anti-B antibodies.

The correct answer is c--would agglutinate with both anti-A and anti-B antibodies.
C. AB blood contains red blood cells that carry both A and B antigens on their cell surfaces and so their bodies do not produce antibodies against either of these two proteins because they are not seen as foreign. If either anti-A or anti-B antibodies are mixed with these red blood cells, the blood would agglutinate.

The correct answer is c...
D. Answer d is incorrect because AB blood contains red blood cells that carry both A and B antigens on their cell surfaces and so their blood would reaction with either anti-A antibodies or anti-B antibodies. The addition of either antibody would result in agglutination.

Hint: The immune system is tolerant to its own red blood cell antigens. A person who is type A, for example, does not produce anti-A antibodies. Surprisingly, however, people with type A blood do make antibodies against the B antigen and conversely, people with blood type B make antibodies against the A antigen. People who are type AB develop tolerance to both antigens and thus do not produce either anti-A or anti-B antibodies.

9). The HIV virus is particularly dangerous because it attacks
    a). cells with the CD4$^+$ coreceptor.
    b). helper T cells.
    c). 60 to 80% of circulating T cells in the body.
    d). all of these.

The correct answer is d...
A. Answer a is incorrect because while it is true that HIV attacks all cells with the CD4+ coreceptor, which are T cells, and eventually kills the cells it attacks essentially wiping out the immune system, this is not the only correct answer.

The correct answer is d...
B. Answer b is incorrect because while it is true that the HIV virus attacks and kills helper T cells in the body, which are key to mounting a specific immune response, this is not the only correct answer.

The correct answer is d...
C. Answer c is incorrect because while it is true that the HIV virus attacks helper T cells, which make up 60 to 80% of circulating T cells in the body, this is not the only correct answer.

The correct answer is d--all of these.
D. The HIV virus is so destructive to the body because it recognizes, attacks, and eventually kills cells that carry the CD4$^+$ coreceptor, which is present on the surfaces of the helper T cells. Helper T cells make up 60 to 80% of the circulating T cells in the body and are necessary for the stimulation of cytotoxic T cells and B cell proliferation. Without helper T cells, the immune system essentially shuts down.

Hint: One mechanism for defeating the vertebrate immune system is to attack the immune mechanism itself. Helper T cells and inducer T cells are CD4$^+$ T cells. Therefore any pathogen that inactivates CD4$^+$ T cells leaves the immune system unable to mount a response to any foreign antigen. HIV attacks cells with the CD4$^+$ coreceptor and essentially eliminates 60 to 80% of the circulating T cells in the body.

10). Diseases in which the person's immune system no longer recognizes its own MHC proteins are called
  a). allergies.
  b). autoimmune diseases.
  c). immediate hypersensitivity.
  d). delayed hypersensitivity.

The correct answer is b…
A. Answer a is incorrect because allergies are caused by an overactive immune system, not a failure of the immune system to recognize "self" proteins. Allergies, also called hypersensitivity, is when the immune system over reacts to harmless antigens, called allergens, and triggers a full blown immune response when it is not needed.

The correct answer is b--autoimmune diseases.
B. Autoimmune diseases occur when the body's immune system doesn't recognize the "self" MHC proteins on one's own cells and mounts an immunological attack of "self" antigens. This results in inflammation and organ damage against the tissues of the body.

The correct answer is b…
C. Answer c is incorrect because immediate hypersensitivity is a form of allergic reaction that involves an abnormal B cell response to an allergen, producing symptoms in seconds or minutes of exposure. This is not the body attacking its own tissues, but rather the body acting in a hypersensitive way to a harmless allergen.

The correct answer is b…
D. Answer d is incorrect because delayed hypersensitivity is a form of allergic reaction that involves an abnormal T cell response to an allergen, producing symptoms within 48 hours of exposure. This is not the body attacking its own tissues, but rather the body acting in a hypersensitive way to a harmless allergen.

Hint: Autoimmune diseases are produced by failure of the immune system to recognize and tolerate self antigens. This failure results in the activation of autoreactive T cells and the production of autoantibodies by B cells, causing inflammation and organ damage. There are over 40 known or suspected autoimmune diseases that affect 5 to 7% of the population.

Test Your Visual Understanding

1). When a children have chicken pox, they run a fever and develop a rash that leaves them contagious for 5 to 7 days. In that time, the immune system mounts an attack resulting in the production of antibodies that help the cells of the immune system fight the infection. If these children are exposed to the chicken pox virus again, they do not develop the disease. Using the figure above, explain why a person doesn't develop chicken pox a second time.
Answer: When the child is first exposed to the chicken pox virus, the immune system is "starting from scratch" to mount its attack. Macrophages, neutrophils, and natural killer cells begin the attack. Macrophages then stimulate the proliferation of helper T cells. Helper T cells, through the release of interleukin-2, activate B cells. The B lymphocytes, shown in the figure, transform into plasma cells that begin producing the specific antibodies that will help the immune system fight off the chicken pox infection. This whole process can take several days, which is why the child exhibits the symptoms and is contagious for 5 to 7 days. However, at the same time the B cells are transforming into plasma cells, they are also transforming into memory cells, which produces a clone of memory cells. This battery of memory cells is all prepared to begin producing the antibodies specific to the chicken pox virus. Later in life, if the chicken pox virus enters the body, the memory cells quickly transform into plasma cells and begin producing antibodies. This occurs in a matter of hours, not days as with the first infection. Therefore, the new virus doesn't have a chance to establish an infection the second time around.

Apply Your Knowledge

1). Sometimes a doctor may order a differential blood count to determine whether a person has an infection. The differential blood count detects the levels of white blood cells (WBCs) in the body. Elevated white blood counts indicate an infection. The normal ranges of WBCs in the body are approximately:

    neutrophils—60%
    lymphocytes—25%
    monocytes—8%
    eosinophils—4%
    basophils—3%

A man has a total WBC of 6000/ml, and the differential blood count values are: neutrophils, 3720/ml; lymphocytes, 1500/ml; monocytes, 480/ml; eosinophils, 180/ml; basophils, 120/ml. Is his WBC within normal range?

Answer: In order for the patient to have a normal WCB count, the values of his differential count should be close to the indicated percentages. The total WBC count is 6000/ml, therefore:

The % of neutrophils is 3720/6000 = 0.62 or 62%

The % of lymphocytes is 1500/6000 = 0.25 or 25%

The % of monocytes is 480/6000 = 0.08 or 8%

The % of eosinophils is 180/6000 = 0.03 or 3%

The % of basophils is 120/6000 = 0.02 or 2%

The patient's differential blood count is essentially normal. He has no clear infection.

FIGURE 49.4
Thermoregulation in insects. Some insects, such as the sphinx moth, contract their thoracic muscles to warm up for flight.
Why does muscle temperature stop warming after two minutes?

Answer: After two minutes of shivering, the thoracic muscles have warmed up enough to engage in full contractions. The muscle contractions that allow the full range of motion of the wings utilizes kinetic energy in the movement of the wings, rather than releasing the energy as heat, which occurred in the shivering response.

Self Test

1). Which of the following is *not* a method used in maintaining homeostasis in the body?
        a). behavioral changes
        b). negative feedback loops
        c). hormonal actions
        d). positive feedback loops

The correct answer is d…
A. Answer a is incorrect because behavioral changes are used to maintain homeostasis in the body. Ectothermic animals cannot control their body temperature internally, but rather depend upon the environmental conditions. For example, a lizard may bask in the sun to heat up their bodies.

The correct answer is d…
B. Answer b is incorrect because negative feedback loops are the internal mechanisms used in vertebrates to maintain constancy. The body establishes set points, and sensors monitor the body's internal conditions compared to those set points. Deviations from the set points are detected and modifications in the body are made to bring the conditions back to set point. This is called a negative feedback loop.

The correct answer is d…
C. Answer c is incorrect because hormonal actions are used by effectors in the body to bring internal conditions back to the set point established by the body. For example, the hormone insulin is used to bring the level of blood glucose back to set points by stimulating the uptake of glucose by cells in the body.

The correct answer is d--positive feedback loops
D. The body uses negative feedback loops, not positive feedback loops to maintain homeostasis. Negative feedback loops work to bring conditions in the body back to set point, while positive feedback loops work to augment a deviation in a condition from the set point. Only a few, specialized processes in the body work through positive feedback and the goal in these instances is not to maintain homeostasis.

Hint: Homeostasis may be defined as the dynamic constancy of the internal environment. A state of homeostasis can be maintained by negative feedback loops that correct for deviations from a set point. Ectothermic vertebrates attempt to maintain some degree of temperature homeostasis through behavioral means, contracting muscles or basking in the sun can raise body temperature. Hormones can also help to maintain homeostasis by regulating body functions.

2). Which of the following describes an osmoconformer?
    a). mammals
    b). hagfish
    c). an animal that maintains a relatively constant blood osmolarity independent of its surroundings
    d). all of these

The correct answer is b...
A. Answer a is incorrect because mammals are osmoregulators. Osmoconformers have blood osmolarity levels equal to their environment, namely seawater. Mammals, on the other hand, regulate their blood osmolarities independent of the osmolarity of their surroundings.

The correct answer is b--hagfish
B. The primitive animal is the only vertebrate that is truly an osmoconformer, which is an animal whose blood osmolarity is the same as seawater. Because the osmolarity levels are the same in the animal and in the environment, there is no net movement of water into or out of the body. Sharks' blood osmolarities are equal with seawater, but they maintain these levels storing urea in their blood.

The correct answer is b...
C. Answer c is incorrect because an animal that maintains a relatively constant blood osmolarity independent of its surroundings is an osmoregulator, not an osmoconformer.

The correct answer is b...
D. Answer d is incorrect because there is only one correct answer, answer b. Mammals are osmoregulators, which are animals that maintain relatively constant blood osmolarities independent of their surroundings.

Hint: Most marine invertebrates are osmoconformers; the osmolarity of their body fluids is the same as that of seawater. Because the extracellular fluids are isotonic to seawater, there is no osmotic gradient and no tendency for water to leave or enter the body. Among the vertebrates, only the primitive hagfish are strict osmoconformers.

3). Which of the following animals uses Malpighian tubules for excretion?
    a). ants
    b). birds
    c). mammals
    d). earthworms

The correct answer is a--ants
A. Ants are insects and the excretory organs used by insects are a group of tubules, called Malpighian tubules that extend from the hindgut. Waste molecules and potassium ions are pumped into the tubules through active transport and water follows in through osmosis. The K^+ ions and water are reabsorbed in the hindgut, leaving the waste molecules to be excreted with the feces.

The correct answer is a...
B. Answer b is incorrect because birds utilize nephrons as excretory organs. The nephrons in birds are highly efficient as they are able to produce urine with a higher osmotic concentration than their body fluids, which helps the body retain water.

The correct answer is a...
C. Answer c is incorrect because mammals utilize nephrons as excretory organs. The nephrons in mammals are highly efficient as they are able to produce urine with a higher osmotic concentration then their body fluids, which helps the body retain water.

The correct answer is a...
D. Answer d is incorrect because earthworms utilize nephridia as excretory organs. The nephridia obtain fluid from the body cavity through filtration, but as the fluid passes through the tubules of the nephridia, NaCl is reabsorbed by the body through active transport. Because salt is reabsorbed from the filtrate, the urine excreted is more dilute than the body fluids (is hypotonic).

Hint: The Malpighian tubules of insects are extensions of the digestive tract that collect water and wastes from the body.

4). A shark's blood is isotonic to the surrounding seawater because of the reabsorption of
_____ in its blood.
        a). ammonia
        b). uric acid
        c). urea
        d). NaCl

The correct answer is c...
A. Answer a is incorrect because ammonia is toxic to cells and is only safe in very dilute concentrations. The reabsorption of ammonia in the blood of sharks would kill them.

The correct answer is c...
B. Answer b is incorrect because uric acid is a waste product produced by birds, reptiles, and insects. Uric acid is only slightly soluble in water and would precipitate in the blood of sharks, killing them.

The correct answer is c--urea
C. Sharks produce urea as a metabolic waste product, which is water-soluble and far less toxic than ammonia or uric acid. By reabsorbing urea in their blood, the sharks and other elasmobranchs are able to maintain blood osmolarity that is isosmotic with the surrounding seawater. This isosmotic condition reduces water loss.

The correct answer is c...
D. Answer d is incorrect because although the body reabsorbs NaCl, this molecule does not maintain the isosmotic condition of a shark's blood.

Hint: Elasmobranchs have solved the osmotic problem posed by their seawater environment by having body fluids that are isotonic to the surrounding seawater. Elasmobranchs reabsorb urea from the nephron tubules and maintain a blood urea concentration that is 100 times higher than that of mammals.

5). Which of the following animals has the least concentrated urine relative to its blood plasma?
        a). bird
        b). freshwater fish
        c). human
        d). camel

The correct answer is b...
A. Answer a is incorrect because birds produce a urine that contains very little water. Birds excrete metabolic waste in the form of uric acid, which when it enters the cloaca becomes concentrated by the reabsorption of even more water to form a white pasty material called guano. Guano is highly concentrated relative to the bird's blood plasma.

The correct answer is b--freshwater fish
B. Fish found in freshwater have higher osmotic concentrations in their body fluids than that of the surrounding water environments. This results in the loss of solutes (ions and molecules) to

the environment and the absorption of water into the body from the environment by osmosis. To offset these problems, freshwater fishes do not drink in water and they produce a very diluted urine that his hypoosmotic relative to their body fluids.

The correct answer is b…
C. Answer c is incorrect because humans are mammals and mammals produce urine that is hyperosmotic relative to their body fluids. By doing so, mammals are able to retain water in the body.

The correct answer is b…
D. Answer d is incorrect because camels are mammals and mammals produce urine that is hyperosmotic relative to their body fluids. By doing so, mammals are able to retain water in the body. However, camels are extremely efficient at conserving water, producing a urine that is 8 times more concentrated than their blood plasma.

Hint: Because the body fluids of a freshwater fish have a greater osmotic concentration then the surrounding water, these animals face two serious problems: (1) water tends to enter the body from the environment, and (2) solutes tend to leave the body and enter the environment. Freshwater fishes address the first problem by not drinking water and by excreting a large volume of dilute urine, which is hypotonic to the body fluids.

6). Which of the following is a function of the kidneys?
     a). The kidneys remove harmful substances from the body.
     b). The kidneys recapture water for use by the body.
     c). The kidneys regulate the levels of salt in the blood.
     d). All of these are functions of the kidneys.

The correct answer is d…
A. Answer a is incorrect because although the kidneys do function in the elimination of harmful substances from the body, that may be ingested by the body or as byproducts of metabolism, this is not the only correct answer.

The correct answer is d…
B. Answer b is incorrect because although the kidneys do function in the recapturing of water for use in bodily functions and to maintain blood volumes, this is not the only correct answer.

The correct answer is d…
C. Answer c is incorrect because although the kidneys do junction in the regulation of salt levels in the blood, thereby controlling blood volumes through altering osmotic pressure in the blood, this is not the only correct answer.

The correct answer is d--All of these are functions of the kidneys.
D. The purpose of the kidneys is in maintaining homeostasis in the body. By eliminating harmful substances and waste products, the body can function normally. By regulating the salt levels in the blood, which in turn regulates the water levels in the blood, the kidneys control blood volume and blood pressure in the body.

Hint: A major function of the kidney is the elimination of a variety of potentially harmful substances from the body. Moreover, the excretion of water in urine contributes to the maintenance of blood volume and pressure; the larger the volume of urine excreted, the lower the blood volume.

7). The longer loops of Henle and the collecting ducts are located in the
     a). renal cortex.
     b). renal medulla.
     c). renal pelvis.
     d). ureter.

The correct answer is b…
A. Answer a is incorrect because the renal cortex contains the upper portions of the nephron which include the glomerulus, the Bowman's capsule, and the proximal and distal tubules. In birds and mammals, the loop of Henle projects down away from the cortex.

The correct answer is b--renal medulla.
B. The nephrons found in birds and mammals contain a loop of the tubules, called the loop of Henle that projects down into the kidney away from the cortex; this deep lying area of the kidney is called the renal medulla. The collecting ducts also project down into the renal medulla.

The correct answer is b…
C. Answer c is incorrect because the renal pelvis is the area between the nephrons in the kidneys—the pelvis is not part of the nephron system.

The correct answer is b…
D. Answer d is incorrect because the ureter is the structure that carries the urine from the kidneys to the urinary bladder.

Hint: After the filtrate enters Bowman's capsule it goes into a portion of the nephron called the proximal convoluted tubule, located in the cortex. The fluid then moves down into the medulla and back up again into the cortex in a loop of Henle. Only the kidneys of mammals and birds have loops of Henle, and this is why only birds and mammals have the ability to concentrate their urine. The collecting duct also descends into the medulla.

8). Selective reabsorption of components of the glomerular filtrate occurs where?
     a). Bowman's capsule
     b). glomerulus
     c). loop of Henle
     d). collecting duct

The correct answer is c…
A. Answer a is incorrect because the Bowman's capsule is the site of the initial filtration process, where all ions and small molecules including water are filtered out of the blood. Selective reabsorption occurs at a later point in the passing of the filtrate through the nephron.

The correct answer is c…
B. Answer b is incorrect because the glomerulus is the blood capillary network from which the components are filtered. The components can't be filtered and reabsorbed at the same time.

The correct answer is c--loop of Henle
C. After the filtrate passes out of the Bowman's capsule of the proximal tubule, it enters the loop of Henle. The descending limb of the loop of Henle is permeable to water and so water passes out of the loop. The ascending limb of the loop is selectively permeable to Na^+ and Cl^- but it is not permeable to water, therefore NaCl leaves the ascending loop and becomes concentrated in the tissue.

The correct answer is c…
D. Answer d is incorrect because the collecting duct is the site of water reabsorption through osmosis but no other ions or molecules are reabsorbed here. The reabsorption of water is not selective reabsorption.

Hint: The ascending limb of the loop of Henle actively extrudes Na^+ and Cl^- follows. The mechanism that extrudes NaCl from the ascending limb of the loop differs from that which extrudes NaCl from the proximal tubule, but the most important difference is that the ascending limb is not permeable to water.

9). Humans excrete their excess nitrogenous wastes as
      a). uric acid crystals.
      b). compounds containing protein.
      c). very toxic ammonia.
      d). relatively nontoxic urea.

The correct answer is d…
A. Answer a is incorrect because uric acid crystals are excreted by birds and reptiles, not by mammals, which include humans.

The correct answer is d…
B. Answer b is incorrect because compounds containing protein are the source of the excess nitrogen wastes. The body doesn't want to rid itself of proteins because it needs proteins. However, during the metabolism of proteins, nitrogenous wastes are produced and must be excreted from the body.

The correct answer is d…
C. Answer c is incorrect because ammonia, which is very toxic, can be excreted only in very dilute urine. Bony fish and tadpoles are able to convert the nitrogenous waste to ammonia because they are able to eliminate it through diffusion from the gills, but they also produce a dilute urine. Humans produce a very concentrated urine and so can't excrete nitrogenous wastes in the form of ammonia.

The correct answer is d--relatively nontoxic urea.
D. In humans and other mammals, as well as cartilaginous fish and adult amphibians, the nitrogenous waste is converted into urea, which is relatively nontoxic and can be carried in the bloodstream and excreted in the urine.

Hint: In elasmobranchs, adult amphibians, and mammals, the nitrogenous wastes are eliminated in the far less toxic form of urea. Urea is water-soluble and so can be excreted in large amounts in the urine.

10). Which of the following statements is *not* true?
      a). ADH makes the collecting duct more permeable to water.
      b). Guano contains high concentrations of uric acid.
      c). Aldosterone is produced by the hypothalamus in response to high levels of sodium ions in the blood.
      d). Uric acid is the least soluble of the nitrogenous waste products.

The correct answer is c…
A. Answer a is incorrect because this statement is true. ADH, antidiuretic hormone, is produced by the hypothalamus and is secreted by the posterior pituitary gland. ADH is released in response to conditions of dehydration in the body. ADH causes the collecting ducts of the kidneys to become more permeable to water, allowing more water to be reabsorbed into the blood.

The correct answer is c…
B. Answer b is incorrect because this statement is true. Guano is the white pasty material excreted by birds and contains nitrogenous waste in the form of uric acid.

The correct answer is c--Aldosterone is produced by the hypothalamus in response to high levels of sodium ions in the blood.
C. The hormone aldosterone is released from the adrenal cortex in response to a drop in blood sodium ion concentrations. Aldosterone stimulates more Na^+ to be reabsorbed from the distal convoluted tubules. This results in increase blood Na^+ concentrations, which also results in increases in blood volumes by the movement of more water into the blood through osmosis.

The correct answer is c...
D. Answer d is incorrect because this statement is true. Uric acid, excreted by birds, reptiles, and insects is only slightly soluble in water. As a result of its low solubility, uric acid precipitates and thus can be excreted using very little water.

Hint: A drop in the blood Na^+ concentration is normally compensated by the kidneys under the influence of the hormone aldosterone, which is secreted by the adrenal cortex. Aldosterone stimulates the distal convoluted tubules to reabsorb Na+, decreasing the excretion of Na^+ in the urine.

Test Your Visual Understanding

1). Indicate the areas of the nephron that the following hormones target, and describe when and how the hormones elicit their actions.
    a). antidiuretic hormone
    b). aldosterone
    c). atrial natriuretic hormone
Answer:
    1a). Antidiuretic hormone (ADH) is produced in the hypothalamus and is secreted by the posterior pituitary. ADH targets the collecting duct of the nephron and stimulates the reabsorption of water from the urine by increasing the permeability of water in the walls of the duct. The primary stimulus for ADH secretion is an increase in the osmolarity of blood plasma, which occurs when a person is dehydrated or when a person eats salty foods. Osmoreceptors in the hypothalamus detect the increased osmolarity and stimulate the release of ADH.
    1b). Aldosterone is produced and secreted by the adrenal cortex in response to a drop in blood Na^+ concentration. Aldosterone stimulates the distal convoluted tubules to reabsorb Na^+, decreasing the excretion of Na^+ in the urine. The reabsorption of Na^+ is followed by Cl^- and water, and so aldosterone has the net effect of retaining both salt and water. Aldosterone secretion however, is not stimulated by a decrease in blood osmolarity, but rather by a decrease in blood volume. A group of cells located at the base of the glomerulus, called the juxtaglomerular apparatus, detect drops in blood volume that then stimulates the renin-angiostensin-aldosterone system.
    1c). Atrial natriuretic hormone (ANH) is produced and secreted by the right atrium of the heart, in response to an increase in blood volume. The secretion of ANH results in the reduction of aldosterone secretion. With the secretion of ANH, the distal convoluted tubules reduce the amount of Na^+ that is reabsorbed, and likewise reduces the amount of Cl^- and water that is reabsorbed. The final result is the reduction in blood volume.

Apply Your Knowledge

1). John's doctor is concerned that John's kidneys may not be functioning properly due to a circulatory condition. The doctor wants to determine if the blood volume that is flowing through the kidneys (called renal blood flow rate) is within normal range. Calculate what would be a "normal" renal blood flow rate based on the following information:
    John weighs 90 kg. Assume a normal total blood volume is 80 ml/kg body weight, and a normal heart pumps the total blood volume through the heart once per minute (cardiac output). Also assume that the normal renal blood flow rate is 21% of cardiac output.

Answer: Under normal conditions, John's total blood volume would be 80 ml/kg body weight or 90 x 80 = 7,200 ml or 7.2 liters

His cardiac output would be 7.2 l/min

His normal renal blood flow rate would be 21% of cardiac output or 7.2 l/min x 0.21 = 1.5 l/min

If John's kidneys are not affected by his circulatory condition, his renal blood flow rate should be about 1.5 l/min.

2). The glomeruli filter out a tremendous amount of water and molecules needed by the body, which must later be reclaimed by the energy-requiring process of reabsorption. The Malpighian tubules of the insects might seem to function more logically, secreting molecules and ions that need to be excreted. What advantages might a filtration-reabsorption process provide over a strictly secretion process of elimination?

Answer: The Malpighian tubules work very well for insects that may not require the "fine-tuning" of electrolyte balance that is required in mammals and other animals that utilize a filtration-reabsorption process for excretion. The advantages of a filtration-reabsorption system allows for the maintenance of electrolyte balance within a very narrow range, which affects blood volume, blood pressure, and many other vital body functions. Without the regulation of Na^+ reabsorption (increasing when necessary and decreasing when necessary), which affects water reabsorption, the body could not function properly. This is evident by the absolute necessity of aldosterone in the body. Without aldosterone, a person would die.

Inquiry Questions
None for this chapter.

Self Test

1). Sexual reproduction
      a). requires internal fertilization.
      b). does not require meiosis.
      c). increases the genetic diversity within a population.
      d). often occurs between individuals of different species.

The correct answer is c...
A. Answer a is incorrect because sexual reproduction can involve internal or external fertilization.

The correct answer is c...
B. Answer b is incorrect because sexual reproduction involves the production of haploid gametes, which are formed from meiosis.

The correct answer is c--increases the genetic diversity within a population.
C. Gametes from two genetically different individuals both contribute haploid chromosomes, increasing genetic diversity.

The correct answer is c...
D. Answer d is incorrect because while, there are rare examples of cross-breeding between different species, most sexual reproduction occurs between individuals of the same species.

2). An animal that is oviparous reproduces by
      a). giving birth to free-living young.
      b). producing internally fertilized eggs that develop externally.
      c). producing eggs that are fertilized externally.
      d). incubating eggs internally while the fetus develops.

The correct answer is b...
A. Answer a is incorrect because only animals that are ovoviviparous and viviparous give birth to free-living young.

The correct answer is b--producing eggs internally fertilized eggs that develop externally.
B. An oviparous animal reproduces by fertilizing eggs internally. The eggs are then deposited externally where they complete their development.

The correct answer is b...
C. Answer c is incorrect because animals that are oviparous produce eggs that are fertilized internally.

The correct answer is b...
D. Answer d is incorrect because only animals that are ovoviviparous and viviparous incubate eggs internally while the fetus develops.

3). The testicles of male mammals are suspended in the scrotum because
      a). the optimum temperature for sperm production is less than the normal core body temperature of the organism.
      b). the optimum temperature for sperm production is higher than the normal core body temperature of the organism.
      c). there is not enough room in the pelvic area for the testicles to be housed internally.
      d). it is easier for the body to expel sperm during ejaculation.

The correct answer is a--the optimum temperature for sperm production is less than the normal body temperature of the organism.
A. The optimum temperature for sperm production is 34°C, while the core body temperature is 37°C.

The correct answer is a...
B. Answer b is incorrect because the optimum temperature for sperm production (34°C) is less than the normal core body temperature (37°C) of the organism.

The correct answer is a...
C. Answer c is incorrect because this physical adaptation is not related to insufficient space in the pelvic region. Rather, the testicles are suspended outside the body because the optimum temperature for sperm production is 34°C, while the core body temperature is 37°C.

The correct answer is a...
D. Answer d is incorrect because this physical adaptation is not related to ejaculation. Rather, the testicles are suspended outside the body because the optimum temperature for sperm production is 34°C, while the core body temperature is 37°C.

4). Spermatogenesis is *not* directly affected by which hormones?
      a). GnRH
      b). inhibin
      c). FSH
      d). LH

The correct answer is d...
A. Answer a is incorrect because GnRH is released by the hypothalamus, which signals to the anterior pituitary gland to release FSH, which stimulates the Sertoli cells to facilitate sperm development.

The correct answer is d...
B. Answer b is incorrect because Sertolic cells secrete inhibin, which inhibits FSH secretion. FSH stimulates the Sertoli cells to facilitate sperm development.

The correct answer is d...
C. Answer c is incorrect because FSH stimulates the Sertoli cells to facilitate sperm development.

The correct answer is d--LH
D. Spermatogenesis is not directly affected by release LH. This hormone stimulates the Leydig cells to secrete testosterone, but is not directly involved in spermatogenesis.

5). Eggs and sperm are genetically very similar, but structurally very different. Why is this so?
      a). Both contain a haploid chromosome number, but eggs must provide nutrients for early development, while sperm must be able to move efficiently.
      b). Both contain a diploid chromosome number, but eggs must provide nutrients for early development, while sperm must be able to move efficiently.
      c). Both contain maternal chromosomes, but only sperm can control which chromosomes are passed on.
      d). Both contain a haploid chromosome number, but only eggs can control which chromosomes are passed on.

The correct answer is a--Both contain a haploid chromosome number, but eggs must provide nutrients for early development, while sperm must be able to move efficiently.
A. Both eggs and sperm contain a haploid chromosome number, however, eggs are larger than sperm and contain yolk and other nutrients vital for early embryonic development. By comparison,

sperm are relatively simple cells, with very little cytoplasm and a propulsion mechanism to help them swim and fertilize the egg.

The correct answer is a...
B. Answer b is incorrect because eggs must provide nutrients for early development while sperm must be able to move efficiently; both cells contain a haploid, not a diploid chromosome.

The correct answer is a...
C. Answer c is incorrect because eggs contain maternal chromosomes while sperm contain paternal chromosomes. Both gametes pass chromosomes on to the embryo.

The correct answer is a...
D. Answer d is incorrect because while both cells contain a haploid chromosome number, both gametes pass chromosomes on to the embryo.

6). How would mammalian reproduction be affected if the meiotic strategy of spermatogenesis and oogenesis were reversed?
   a). Not enough eggs would be made each month to ensure reproductive success.
   b). Sperm production would decrease to one-fourth.
   c). Eggs would be diploid while sperm would be haploid.
   d). Sperm would be diploid while eggs would be haploid.

The correct answer is b...
A. Answer a is incorrect because if meiotic strategy of spermatogenesis and oogenesis were reversed, four eggs would be produced each month, while sperm production would decrease to one-fourth of the original level.

The correct answer is b--Sperm production would decrease to one-fourth.
B. If meiotic strategy of spermatogenesis and oogenesis were reversed, four eggs would be produced each month, while sperm production would decrease to one-fourth of the original level.

The correct answer is b...
C. Answer c is incorrect because if meiotic strategy of spermatogenesis and oogenesis were reversed, both eggs and sperm would still contain a haploid chromosome number. However, four eggs would be produced each month, while sperm production would decrease to one-fourth of the original level.

The correct answer is b...
D. Answer d is incorrect because if meiotic strategy of spermatogenesis and oogenesis were reversed, both eggs and sperm would still contain a haploid chromosome number. However, four eggs would be produced each month, while sperm production would decrease to one-fourth of the original level.

7). Early in the ovarian cycle, estrogen, produced in the follicle, _____ gonadotropin release, while later in the cycle, estrogen _____ gonadotropin release because
   a). inhibits; stimulates; feedback mechanisms are not involved early in the ovarian cycle.
   b). stimulates; inhibits; feedback mechanisms are not involved early in the ovarian cycle.
   c). inhibits; stimulates; the feedback mechanisms are dependent on the concentration of estrogen.
   d). stimulates; inhibits; the feedback mechanisms are dependent on the concentration of estrogen.

The correct answer is c...
A. Answer a is incorrect because while low levels of estrogen early in the ovarian cycle inhibit gonadotropin release, and high levels in mid-cycle stimulate gonadotropin release, the feedback mechanisms are dependent on the concentration of estrogen.

The correct answer is c...
B. Answer b is incorrect because low levels of estrogen early in the ovarian cycle inhibit gonadotropin release, and high levels in mid-cycle stimulate gonadotropin release. Further, the feedback mechanisms are dependent on the concentration of estrogen.

The correct answer is c--inhibits; stimulates; the feedback mechanisms are dependant on the concentration of estrogen.
C. Low levels of estrogen early in the ovarian cycle inhibit gonadotropin release, while high levels in mid-cycle stimulate gonadotropin release. These feedback mechanisms are dependent on the concentration of estrogen.

The correct answer is c...
D. Answer d is incorrect because low levels of estrogen early in the ovarian cycle inhibit gonadotropin release, and high levels in mid-cycle stimulate gonadotropin release.

8). At what stage of the ovarian cycle are mammalian eggs most likely to become fertilized?
     a). at the beginning of the proliferative phase
     b). immediately after ovulation
     c). during the middle of the secretory phase
     d). during the menstrual phase

The correct answer is b...
A. Answer a is incorrect because ovulation, the time at which a viable egg is released for fertilization, marks the end of the proliferative phase.

The correct answer is b--immediately after ovulation
B. Ovulation results in release of an egg, which remains viable and capable of being fertilized for approximately 24 hours.

The correct answer is b...
C. Answer c is incorrect because while ovulation, the time at which a viable egg is released for fertilization, marks the beginning of the secretory phase, the egg is only viable and capable of being fertilized for approximately 24 hours.

The correct answer is b...
D. Answer d is incorrect because ovulation, the time at which a viable egg is released for fertilization, does not usually occur during the menstrual phase.

9). If we could monitor the amount of total gonadotropin activity in pregnant women, we would expect
     a). high levels of FSH and LH in the uterus to stimulate endometrial thickening.
     b). high levels of circulating FSH and LH to stimulate implantation of the embryo.
     c). high levels of hCG in the uterus to stimulate endometrial thickening.
     d). high levels of circulating hCG to stimulate estrogen and progesterone synthesis.

The correct answer is d...
A. Answer a is incorrect because FSH and LH do not stimulate endometrial thickening. Estrogen and progesterone stimulate endometrial thickening.

The correct answer is d...
B. Answer b is incorrect because FSH and LH do not stimulate implantation of the embryo. This process is not directly related to FSH and LH.

The correct answer is d...
C. Answer c is incorrect because high levels of hCG circulate in the blood and are not concentrated in the uterus. Further, hCG does not directly stimulate the endometrial thickening. Rather, hCG helps to maintain the corpus luteum, which produces estrogen and progesterone.

The correct answer is d--high levels of circulating hCG to stimulate estrogen and progesterone synthesis.
D. High levels of circulating hCG help to maintain the corpus luteum, which produces estrogen and progesterone. These hormones are essential for pregnancy.

10). Which contraceptive method is effective at preventing fertilization *and* protecting against transmission of sexually transmitted disease?
    a). oral contraceptives
    b). diaphragm
    c). condom
    d). intrauterine device (IUD)

The correct answer is c...
A. Answer a is incorrect because while oral contraceptives prevent fertilization, they cannot protect against transmission of sexually transmitted disease.

The correct answer is c...
B. Answer b is incorrect because while diaphragms prevent fertilization, they cannot protect against transmission of sexually transmitted disease.

The correct answer is c--condom
C. Condoms can prevent fertilization and protect against transmission of sexually transmitted disease.

The correct answer is c...
D. Answer d is incorrect because while an intrauterine device can prevent fertilization, it cannot protect against transmission of sexually transmitted disease.

Test Your Visual Understanding

1). The process of oogenesis involves a number of developmental stages and structures. Label this diagram by writing the name of the correct structure next to the appropriate letter:
    a).
    b).
    c).
    d).
    e).
    f).

Answer:
    a). Primary follicles
    b). Developing follicle
    c). Mature follicle with secondary oocyte
    d). Ruptured follicle
    e). Secondary oocyte
    f). Corpus luteum

Apply Your Knowledge

1). Sex determination in mammals is influenced by the *SRY* region of the Y chromosome. If during meiosis, this region of the Y chromosome was accidentally translocated to an X chromosome and this gamete went on to fertilize an egg, what would be the gender of this offspring?
Answer: This individual would be genetically female, but develop as a male due to the presence of the *SRY* region.

FIGURE 51.23
Hormonal secretion by the placenta. The placenta secretes human chorionic gonadotropin (hCG), which peaks in the second month and then declines. After five weeks, it secretes increasing amounts of estradiol and progesterone.
The high levels of estradiol and progesterone secreted by the placenta prevent ovulation and thus formation of any additional embryos during pregnancy. What would be the expected effect of these high hormone levels in the absence of pregnancy?

Answer: High levels of estradiol and progesterone in the absence of pregnancy would still affect the body in the same way. High levels of both hormones would inhibit the release of FSH and LH, thereby preventing ovulation. This is how birth control pills work. The pills contain synthetic forms of either both estradiol and progesterone or just progesterone. The high levels of these hormones in the pill trick the body into thinking that it is pregnant and so the body does not ovulate.

Self Test

1). An egg surrounded by a granulosa layer is most likely from a
      a). sea urchin.
      b). human.
      c). frog.
      d). fruit fly.

The correct answer is b...
A. Answer a is incorrect because sea urchin eggs do not have a granulosa layer.

The correct answer is b--human.
B. Humans are mammals, and mammalian reproductive cells contain a layer of granulosa cells, or granulosa.

The correct answer is b...
C. Answer c is incorrect because, although frogs are vertebrates, their eggs do not have a granulosa layer.

The correct answer is b...
D. Answer d is incorrect because fruit fly eggs do not have a granulosa layer.

2). The first thing a sea urchin sperm encounters when it makes contact with the egg is the
      a). plasma membrane.
      b). vitelline membrane.
      c). jelly coat.
      d). zona pellucida.

The correct answer is c...
A. Answer a is incorrect because the sperm must first penetrate the jelly coat and vitelline membrane before reaching the plasma membrane.

The correct answer is c...
B. Answer b is incorrect because the sperm must first penetrate the jelly coat before reaching the vitelline membrane.

The correct answer is c--jelly coat.
C. Sea urchin eggs are surrounded by a protective jelly coat. The sperm must first penetrate this layer before reaching the vitelline membrane.

The correct answer is c...
D. Answer d is incorrect because sea urchin eggs do not have a zona pellucida.

3). Holoblastic cleavage results in
      a). formation of a symmetrical blastula composed of cells of approximately equal size.
      b). formation of an asymmetrical blastula composed of cells of approximately unequal size.
      c). cell division of only the cells near the animal pole.
      d). cell division of only the cells near the vegetal pole.

The correct answer is a--formation of a symmetrical blastula composed of cells of approximately equal size.
A. Holoblastic cleavage occurs when eggs have little or no yolk.

The correct answer is a...
B. Answer b is incorrect because the formation of an asymmetrical blastula occurs when eggs are yolk-rich. The cells near the animal pole divide faster than those near the vegetal pole. By comparison, holoblastic cleavage occurs when eggs have little or no yolk.

The correct answer is a...
C. Answer c is incorrect because asymmetric cell division occurs only in yolk-rich eggs. By comparison, holoblastic cleavage occurs when eggs have little or no yolk.

The correct answer is a...
D. Answer d is incorrect because asymmetric cell division occurs only in yolk-rich eggs. By comparison, holoblastic cleavage occurs when eggs have little or no yolk.

4). If the trophoblast layer failed to form in a mammalian embryo, which of the following structures would not develop?
      a). the blastopore
      b). the inner cell mass
      c). the archenteron
      d). the fetal placenta

The correct answer is d...
A. Answer a is incorrect because mammals never form a blastopore.

The correct answer is d...
B. Answer b is incorrect because the inner cell mass does not develop from the trophoblast. Rather, both structures are present in early embryogenesis.

The correct answer is d...
C. Answer c is incorrect because mammals never form an archenteron.

The correct answer is d--the fetal placenta
D. The outer sphere of cells, or trophoblast, enters the maternal endometrium and contributes to the placenta.

5). Which forms first during gastrulation of a frog embryo?
      a). mouth
      b). anus
      c). dorsal lip
      d). gut

The correct answer is b...
A. Answer a is incorrect because the mouth forms after the anus, which arises from the blastopore.

The correct answer is b--anus
B. Early in gastrulation of frog embryos, a layer of surface cells invaginate to form a small crescent-shaped slit where the blastopore will soon be located. The anus forms from the blastopore.

The correct answer is b...
C. Answer c is incorrect because the dorsal lip is not considered an opening.

The correct answer is b...
D. Answer d is incorrect because the gut itself is not considered an opening. Rather, the gut arises from the archenteron and the opening of the archenteron is the blastopore, which gives rise to the anus.

6). Gastrulation in mammals and birds is similar in that
     a). cells migrate over the dorsal lip to generate the archenteron in the anterior hemisphere of the embryo.
     b). cells migrate inward from the upper layer of the blastodisc to form the mesoderm.
     c). cells migrate outward from the upper layer of the blastodisc to form the mesoderm.
     d). cells migrate inward from the lower layer of the blastodisc to form the mesoderm.

The correct answer is b...
A. Answer a is incorrect because this description applies to gastrulation in most aquatic vertebrates, not mammals and birds.

The correct answer is b--cells migrate inward from the upper layer of the blastodisc to form the mesoderm
B. Shortly after the ectoderm and endoderm form, cells from the upper layer invaginate and involute to form the mesoderm.

The correct answer is b...
C. Answer c is incorrect because, cells migrate inward, not outward, from the upper layer of the blastodisc to form the mesoderm.

The correct answer is b...
D. Answer d is incorrect because cells migrate inward from the upper layer, not the lower layer, of the blastodisc to form the mesoderm.

7). Neural crest cells break off from the _____ and later move to the sides of the developing embryo.
     a). placodes
     b). ectoderm
     c). notochord
     d). neural tube

The correct answer is d...
A. Answer a is incorrect because placodes arise from clusters of ectodermal cells that are associated with, but distinct from, the neural crest cells.

The correct answer is d...
B. Answer b is incorrect because, although the neural tube is an ectodermal structure, neural tube is a more precise answer.

The correct answer is d...
C. Answer c is incorrect because neural crest cells do not break off from the notochord, but rather from the nearby neural tube.

The correct answer is d--neural tube
D. Just before the neural tube closes, its edges pinch off, forming a small strip of cells called the neural crest.

8). The cells of the Spemann organizer are responsible for
      a). notochord development.
      b). cell transplantation.
      c). dorsal lip formation.
      d). development of the eye through an induction mechanism.

The correct answer is a--notochord development.
A. By using genetically different donor and host blastulas in cell transplantation experiments, Spemann and Mangold were able to demonstrate that the notochord was induced to develop by the cells of the dorsal lip. This group of cells was termed the Spemann organizer.

The correct answer is a...
B. Answer b is incorrect because while cell transplantation experiments were used to identify the Spemann organizer, it is not responsible for cell transplantation.

The correct answer is a...
C. Answer c is incorrect because the cells of the Spemann organizer are located in the dorsal lip, but they are not required for its formation.

The correct answer is a...
D. Answer d is incorrect because while the eye is formed by induction, the cells of the Spemann organizer are not involved in this process.

9). All of the following structures are derived from the mesoderm *except*
      a). muscles.
      b). the liver.
      c). gonads.
      d). blood vessels.

The correct answer is b...
A. Answer a is incorrect because muscles are derived from the mesoderm. Remember, the question is which structure is not mesdodermally derived.

The correct answer is b--the liver.
B. The liver is derived from the endoderm.

The correct answer is b...
C. Answer c is incorrect because the gonads, or sex organs, are derived from the mesoderm. Remember, the question is which structure is not mesdodermally derived.

The correct answer is b...
D. Answer d is incorrect because blood vessels are derived from the mesoderm. Remember, the question is which structure is not mesdodermally derived.

10). Most fetal growth occurs in
    a). the first trimester.
    b). the second trimester.
    c). the third trimester.
    d). the postnatal period.

The correct answer is c...
A. Answer a is incorrect because, while much development, including organogenesis and morphogenesis, takes place in the first trimester, most fetal growth occurs in the third trimester.

The correct answer is c...
B. Answer b is incorrect because while some growth occurs in the second trimester, it is not as much as in the third trimester.

The correct answer is c--the third trimester.
C. The third trimester is predominantly a period of growth rather than development.

The correct answer is c...
D. Answer d is incorrect because while much growth does occur postnatally, the question is referring to fetal growth, which occurs before birth.

Test Your Visual Understanding

1). In this picture of a newly fertilized frog embryo, where would you predict that the sperm entered the egg? Draw a sperm at the approximate location of sperm entry.
Answer: The gray crescent forms on the side of the egg opposite from the point of penetration by the sperm. You should have drawn in a sperm in a location similar to that shown in figure 51.4.

Apply Your Knowledge

1). You are preparing for a debate on the use of embryonic stem cells in research. What are the pros and cons of this practice?
Answer: There is no one correct answer to this question.

2). Comparative embryology of vertebrates has led to the phrase *ontogeny recapitulates phylogeny*. This biogenic law, although not strictly true, supports evolution. Why?
Answer: The phrase *ontogeny recapitulates phylogeny* implies that embryonic development exhibits a progression of changes indicative of evolutionary origin. However, it is important to realize that embryonic stages are not equivalent to adult ancestral forms. Rather, early developmental stages of an embryo often reflect the embryonic stages of its evolutionary ancestors. This biogenic law supports evolution because the evolution of organisms is essentially "descent with modification" and dependent on changes in the developmental program. In this way, evolution is very closely related to development. Early patterns of development in chordate groups share very similar features, suggesting that these patterns have been built up in incremental steps over the evolutionary history of those groups.

3). What would happen if a mammalian embryo failed to produce sufficient amounts of human chorionic gonadotropin (hCG) in early pregnancy?
Answer: The pregnancy would terminate because hCG is required for production of progesterone and estrogen by the corpus luteum in the first trimester. Progesterone is particularly important for the maintenance of a pregnancy. Without hCG, the corpus luteum would degenerate, and menstruation would occur as in a normal menstrual cycle.

Inquiry Questions

FIGURE 52.4

The genetics of learning. Selection experiments in the laboratory established a genetic basis for differences in the ability to learn to run through a maze.
What would happen if, after the seventh generation, rats were randomly assigned mates regardless of ability to learn the maze?

Answer: Selection for learning ability would cease, and thus change from one generation to the next in maze learning ability; would only result from random genetic drift.

FIGURE 52.6

Genetically caused defect in maternal care. (*a*) In mice, normal mothers take very good care of their offspring, retrieving them if they move away and crouching over them.
(*b*) Mothers with the mutant *fosB* allele perform neither of these behaviors, leaving their pups exposed. (*c*) Amount of time female mice were observed crouching in a nursing posture over offspring. (*d*) Proportion of pups retrieved when they were experimentally moved.
Why does the lack of *fosB* alleles lead to maternal inattentiveness?

Answer: Normal *fosB* alleles produce a protein that in turn affects enzymes that affect the brain. Ultimately, these enzymes trigger maternal behavior. In the absence of the enzymes, normal maternal behavior does not occur.

FIGURE 52.26

Optimal diet. The shore crab selects a diet of energetically profitable prey. The curve describes the net energy gain (equal to energy gained minus energy expended) derived from feeding on different sizes of mussels. The bar graph shows the numbers of mussels of each size in the diet. Shore crabs tend to feed on those mussels that provide the most energy.
What factors might be responsible for the slight difference in peak prey length relative to the length optimal for maximum energy gain?

Answer: Many factors affect the behavior of an animal other than its attempts to maximize energy intake. For example, avoiding predation is also important. Thus, it may be that larger prey take longer to subdue and ingest, thus making the crabs more vulnerable to predators. Hence, the crabs may trade off decreased energy gain for decreased vulnerability for predators. Many other similar explanations are possible.

FIGURE 52.29

The advantage of male mate choice. Male mormon crickets choose heavier females as mates, and larger females have more eggs. Thus, male mate selection increases fitness.
Is there a benefit to females for mating with large males?

Answer: Yes, the larger the male, the larger the prenuptial gift, which provides energy that the female converts into egg production.

FIGURE 52.30

Products of sexual selection. Attracting mates with long feathers is common in bird species such as (*a*) the African paradise whydah and (*b*) the peacock, which show pronounced sexual dimorphism. (*c*) Female peahens prefer to mate with males with greater numbers of eyespots in their tail feathers.
Why do females prefer males with more spots?

Answer: A question that is the subject of much current research. Ideas include the possibility that males with longer tails are in better condition (because males in poor condition couldn't survive the disadvantage imposed by the tail). The advantage to a female mating with a male in better condition might be either that the male is less likely to be parasitized, and thus less likely to pass that parasite on to the female, or the male may have better genes, which in turn would be passed on to the offspring. Another possibility is the visual system for some reason is better able to detect males with long tails, and thus long-tailed males are preferred by females simply because the longer tails are more easily detected and responded to.

FIGURE 52.36
Flocking behavior decreases predation. As the size of a pigeon flock increases, hawks are less successful at capturing pigeons. Also, when more pigeons are present in the flock, they can detect hawks at greater distances, thus allowing more time for the pigeons to escape. **Would living in a flock would affect the time available for foraging in pigeons?**

Answer: Yes. If more birds are present, then each one can spend less time watching for predators, and thus have more time for foraging.

Self Test

1). A male stickleback's display of aggression at a red object is an example of
       a). innate behavior.
       b). operant conditioning.
       c). associative learning.
       d). habituation.

The correct answer is a--innate behavior.
A. An innate behavior is that which is "inborn," also called instinctive behavior. These are behaviors that are based on preset paths in the nervous system. With innate behaviors, a sign stimulus, in this case a red object, triggers a response in the nervous system that elicits the behavior such as aggressive activity.

The correct answer is a...
B. Answer b is incorrect because operant conditioning is the result of associating a behavior with a reward or punishment. The stickleback receives no reward or punishment for its aggressive behavior and therefore, it doesn't associate anything with its behavior.

The correct answer is a...
C. Answer c is incorrect because associate learning is the development of behaviors in response to a reward or punishment—the association of a behavior with a result. The stickleback receives no reward or punishment for its aggressive behavior and therefore, it doesn't associate anything with its behavior.

The correct answer is a...
D. Answer d is incorrect because habituation is the decrease in frequency of a behavior in response to a repeated stimulus. The stickleback's aggressive response to a red object in this example is not of decreasing frequency.

Hint: Early research in the field of animal behavior focused on behavioral patterns that appeared to be instinctive or innate. Because behavior is often stereotyped (appearing in the same way in different individuals of the same species), they argued that it must be based on preset paths in the nervous system. In their view, these paths are structured from genetic blueprints and cause animals to show essentially the same behavior from the first time it is produced throughout their lives. Examples of innate behaviors include egg retrieval by geese and territorial defense by male stickleback fish.

2). What type of behavior is associated with a "critical period" in which a stimulus must be detected to trigger the response?
 a). cognitive behavior
 b). taxis
 c). imprinting
 d). associative learning

The correct answer is c...
A. Answer a is incorrect because cognitive behavior is the ability to process information and respond in a manner that suggests thinking. Cognitive behavior occurs throughout life and is not isolated to a critical period of exposure.

The correct answer is c...
B. Answer b is incorrect because taxis is the behavior in which an animal moves toward or away from a stimulus. This is a behavior that occurs throughout life and is not isolated to a critical period of exposure.

The correct answer is c--imprinting
C. Imprinting is formation of social interactions and attachments that will direct future behaviors. Parent/offspring imprinting, called filial imprinting, occurs during a critical period in the offspring's development and is important for the formation of the bond of offspring with say a mother who will "teach" them other important species-specific behaviors.

The correct answer is c...
D. Answer d is incorrect because associative learning is the process by which a stimulus is linked to a behavior. This behavior occurs throughout life and is not isolated to a critical period of exposure.

Hint: As an animal matures, it may form social attachments to other individuals or form preferences that will influence behavior later in life. This process, called imprinting, is sometimes considered a type of learning. Imprinting occurs during a sensitive phase, or critical period, when the success of imprinting is highest.

3). The study of song development in sparrows showed that
 a). the acquisition of a species-specific song is innate.
 b). there are two components to this behavior—a genetic template and learning.
 c). song acquisition is an example of associative learning.
 d). All of these are correct.

The correct answer is b...
A. Answer a is incorrect because song development in sparrows showed that while their is an genetic component in song development, the young needed to hear the correct song in order for them to sing the correct song. Song development is not innate in sparrows but may be in some other species of birds, such as the cuckoos.

The correct answer is b--there are two components to this behavior—a genetic template and learning.
B. Song development in sparrows demonstrates the interaction between instinct and learning. Sparrows have a genetic template or instinctive program that guides them to learn their species-specific song but they also have to hear their song in order to learn it correctly. The genetic template alone is not sufficient for the sparrow to learn its song.

The correct answer is b...
C. Answer c is incorrect because song acquisition is a partially learned behavior but not through associative learning. Associative learning involves the association of a stimulus and a response

or the association between two stimuli. Song acquisition in sparrows does not involve this type of learning. Song acquisition is learned more through practice.

The correct answer is b...
D. Answer d is incorrect because there is only one correct answer, answer b. Although there is a genetic component of song development in sparrows, there is also a learning component and so it is not completely innate. And while there is a learning component, it is more by practice than by associative learning.

Hint: The work of Peter Marler and his colleagues on the acquisition of courtship song by white-crowned sparrows provides an excellent example of the interaction between instinct and learning in the development of behavior. His experiments suggested that these birds have a genetic template, or instinctive program, that guides them to learn the appropriate song. During a critical period in development, the template will accept the correct song as a model. Thus, song acquisition depends on learning, but only the song of the correct species.

4). The level of specificity in courtship signaling is often
        a). individual-specific.
        b). anonymous.
        c). species-specific.
        d). any of these.

The correct answer is c...
A. Answer a is incorrect because the goal of courtship signaling is to identify other members of the same species, not specific individuals. Individual-specific signaling is used in identifying individuals in neighboring territories, so a male doesn't waste energy defending its territory from its neighbors.

The correct answer is c...
B. Answer b is incorrect because the goal of courtship signaling is to identify other members of the same species and so the signal must be more specific than an anonymous level of specificity. Anonymous signaling is usually used in alarm calls to warn all individuals, regardless of species, of a predator.

The correct answer is c--species-specific.
C. The goal of courtship signaling is to identify individuals of the same species. An animal doesn't want to waste time and energy pursuing another individual of a different species. The species-specific signaling allows an individual to attract a potential conspecific mate and then other signaling occurs to exhibit/determine fitness.

The correct answer is c...
D. Answer d is incorrect because answer c is the signaling used most often in mating. Occasionally, there could be individual-specific signaling in courtship but anonymous signaling would not be used in courtship. The goal of courtship is to find a mate of your same species and anonymous signaling does not help achieve that goal.

Hint: During courtship, animals produce signals to communicate with potential mates and with other members of their own sex. A stimulus-response chain sometimes occurs, in which the behavior of one individual in turn releases the behavior by another. The level of specificity relates to the function of the signal. Many courtship signals are species-specific to help animals avoid making errors in mating that would produce nonviable hybrids or otherwise waste reproductive effort.

5). Which of the following is not a function of pheromones?
   a). sex attractants
   b). trigger alarm behaviors
   c). trail markers
   d). All of these are functions of pheromones.

The correct answer is d...
A. Answer a is incorrect because although pheromones are used to attract mates, this isn't the only correct answer.

The correct answer is d...
B. Answer b is incorrect because although pheromones are used in social insects as alarms to trigger attack behaviors, this isn't the only correct answer.

The correct answer is d....
C. Answer c is incorrect because although pheromones are used as trail markers to mark the path to a food source, this isn't the only correct answer.

The correct answer is d--All of these are functions of pheromones.
D. Pheromones are chemicals released by animals to communicate with other animals of their same species. These chemicals can communicate a desire to mate, a warning of danger, the location of a viable food source, or other messages to conspecific individuals.

Hint: Chemical signals also mediate interactions between males and females. Pheromones, chemical messengers used for communication between individuals of the same species, serve as sex attractants and other functions in societal groups of animals such as alarm calls, and trail markers.

6). Behavioral ecology is the study of
   a). how natural selection shapes behaviors.
   b). how environmental conditions affect animal behaviors.
   c). how feeding opportunities affect animal behaviors.
   d). how interactions with other individuals of the same species affects behaviors.

The correct answer is a--how natural selection shapes behaviors.
A. Behaviors, which in some cases involve physical characteristics, can maximize or minimize survival and reproduction and so these behaviors can be formed and influenced by natural selection. The area of study that addresses these types of issues is called behavioral ecology.

The correct answer is a...
B. Answer b is incorrect because although environmental conditions can affect animal behaviors, these are not the issues examined by behavioral ecologists. Other factors besides just the environment can affect behavior and behavioral ecology examines how all of these ecological factors affect behavior through natural selection.

The correct answer is a...
C. Answer c is incorrect because although feeding opportunities affect behavior, this is but one aspect of behavior that is examined by behavioral ecologists.

The correct answer is a...
D. Answer d is incorrect because although interactions with other individuals of the same species affect behaviors, this is but one aspect of behavior that is examined by behavioral ecologists.

Hint: Tinbergen is credited with being one of the founders of the field of behavioral ecology, the study of how natural selection shapes behavior. This branch of ecology examines the adaptive significance of behavior, or how behavior may increase survival and reproduction.

7). Which of the following would be most likely to occur according to the optimal foraging theory?
    a). Shore crabs eat the largest mussels even though they're harder to crack open.
    b). Columbian ground squirrels eat more because larger squirrels produce more offspring.
    c). Smaller yellow-eyed juncos eat larger prey, although they are harder to manage.
    d). An antelope will venture out on the open plain to feed even though lions are around.

The correct answer is b...
A. Answer a is incorrect because according to the optimal foraging theory, animals tend to feed on prey that maximize their net energy intake per unit of foraging time/energy. If larger mussels are harder to crack open, it is less likely that a crab would expend the extra energy to crack them open rather then selecting smaller mussels.

The correct answer is b--Columbian ground squirrels eat more because larger squirrels produce more offspring.
B. According the optimal foraging theory, natural selection will favor behavior that maximizes energy acquisition if increased energy leads to increases in reproductive success. The Columbian squirrel will exert more energy in foraging if it increases reproductive success.

The correct answer is b...
C. Answer c is incorrect because according to the optimal foraging theory animals tend to feed on prey that maximize their net energy intake per unit of foraging time/energy. Therefore, smaller yellow-eyed juncos would not eat larger prey because if they are harder to manage then the net energy intake would be reduced.

The correct answer is b...
D. Answer d is incorrect because according to the optimal foraging theory, behavior that maximizes energy intake is not the one that minimizes predation risk. If increased foraging increases predation risks then that foraging behavior will be reduced.

Hint: Foraging behaviors occur when the net energy gained by feeding is maximized such that the energy content of the prey minus the energy costs of pursuing and handling it. The optimal foraging theory suggests that natural selection favors individuals who tend to feed on prey that maximizes their net energy intake per unit of foraging time/energy. Natural selection also favors behaviors that maximize energy acquisition if increased energy reserves leads to increases in reproductive success.

8). Which of the following statements about territories is true?
    a). Territories and home ranges describe the same area of land.
    b). The defense of a territory is always beneficial to the animal.
    c). A territory contains resources exclusively for the animal that defends it.
    d). Territories overlap in time or space with other territories.

The correct answer is c...
A. Answer a is incorrect because territories and home ranges are not the same thing. Home ranges are larger areas of land that animals may move around in and may overlap with another's home range but a territory is a smaller area of land within the home range that is defended by an animal and is used exclusively by that animal and its mates.

The correct answer is c...
B. Answer b is incorrect because in certain situations the defense of a territory is not beneficial. When food, mates, and other resources are plentiful it is a waste of energy to defend a territory and may lead to the unnecessary exhaustion of the animal defending the territory.

The correct answer is c--A territory contains resources exclusively for the animal that defends it.
C. An animal defends a territory within its home range as a way to obtain and secure resources it needs to maximize its survival, such as food, space, safety, mates, etc. If the territory is defended successfully, these resources are not available to any other animal.

The correct answer is c...
D. Answer d is incorrect because territories do not overlap with other territories, but home ranges do. Territories are areas within home ranges that are defended and serve an individual exclusively. Home ranges however, may contain several territories and home ranges may overlap with others' home ranges.

Hint: Animals often move over a large area, or home range, during their daily course of activity. In many animal species, the home ranges of several individuals may overlap in time or space, but each individual defends a portion of its home range and uses it exclusively. This behavior, in which individual members of a species maintain exclusive use of an area that contains some limiting resource, such as foraging ground, food, or potential mates, is called territoriality.

9). In the haplodiploidy system of sex determination, males are
      a). haploid.
      b). diploid.
      c). sterile.
      d). not present because bees exist as single-sex populations.

The correct answer is a--haploid.
A. In the haplodiploidy system of sex determination, the males are haploid and the females are diploid but sterile (except for the queen). The males fertilize the queen and because the male is haploid, all offspring will inherit all of the father's alleles.

The correct answer is a...
B. Answer b is incorrect because the males are haploid, not diploid. The non-queen females are diploid but sterile.

The correct answer is a...
C. Answer c is incorrect because the males have to be fertile; it is their "job" to fertilize the queen. They wouldn't be much use to the hive if they were sterile.

The correct answer is a...
D. Answer d is incorrect because male bees do exist but as in all eusocial systems; they have their "job" within the society and their job is to fertilize the queen.

Hint: The origin of eusociality in hymenopterans (that is, bees, wasps, and ants) can be viewed in terms of kin selection. In these insects, males are haploid and females are diploid. This unusual system of sex determination, called haplodiploidy, leads to an unusual situation. If a single male fertilizes the queen, then all female offspring will inherit exactly the same alleles from their father.

10). According to kin selection, saving the life of your _____ would do the least for increasing your inclusive fitness.
      a). mother
      b). brother
      c). sister-in-law
      d). niece

The correct answer is c...
A. Answer a is incorrect because in saving the life of your mother you save 1/2 of your alleles, which can then be passed on to another offspring. This will increase your inclusive fitness.

The correct answer is c...
B. Answer b is incorrect because in saving the life of your brother you save 1/2 of your alleles, which can then be passed on to another generation of offspring. This will increase your inclusive fitness.

The correct answer is c--sister-in-law
C. Because your sister-in-law isn't a "blood" relation, you share no alleles with her. Saving your sister-in-law will do nothing to increase your inclusive fitness.

The correct answer is c...
D. Answer d is incorrect because in saving the life of your niece you save 1/8 to 1/4 of your alleles, which can then be passed onto another generation of offspring. This will increase your inclusive fitness.

Hint: Selection that favors altruism directed toward relatives is called kin selection. Although the behaviors being favored are cooperative, the genes are actually "behaving selfishly," because they encourage the organism to support copies of themselves in other individuals. On average, full siblings will share half of their alleles with each other and will also share half of their alleles with each parent. By contrast, cousins will, on average, only share one-eighth of their alleles.

Test Your Visual Understanding

1). Can you predict what the graph in the seventh generation would look like if instead of mating the maze-bright rats with each other and the maze-dull rats with each other, you always mated maze-bright rats with maze-dull rats?
Answer: After always mating the two extremes, maze-bright and maze-dull rats, with each other, the subsequent generations will tend to become more homogeneous and cluster around the middle of the graph. The bell-shaped curve in the graph will contain a higher peak in the center and the range of abilities on the x-axis will cluster closer to the center peak.

Applying Your Knowledge

1). Imagine an animal society in which the individuals share an average of one-third of their alleles with one another. If the benefits to an individual of performing an altruistic act are twice the costs, does the kin selection model predict that these individuals are likely to be altruistic? Explain your reasoning.
Answer: The animals in this society would be altruistic according to the kin selection model because when the benefit times the coefficient of relatedness are greater than the cost then the model predicts altruism:

$$rb>c$$

so in this case:

$$r=0.333$$
$$b=(2c)$$

so that:
$0.333(2c) = 0.666c$ and $0.666c$ is greater than c

2). If a young animal exhibits a behavior immediately after being born or hatched, is it reasonable to conclude that the behavior is instinctive rather than learned? If not, what sorts of experiments might be performed to distinguish between these two possibilities?
Answer: It is reasonable to conclude that the behavior is instinctual but because there could be some influence from the mother or siblings, an experiment should be performed that would separate the offspring from its parents and siblings prior to hatching or just after birth, in the case of a live birth. If the individual still exhibits the behavior after being isolated from parents and siblings, then it can be concluded with more confidence that the behavior is instinctual.

3). Swallows often hunt in groups, while hawks and other predatory birds usually are solitary hunters. What do you think is the basis for this difference?

Answer: The swallows, being smaller birds, receive protection from predators when hunting with a flock, while hawks and other predatory birds have very few predators themselves to worry about. Swallows may also benefit from the flock by being able to obtain easier access to food by "news" spreading through the flock and by the sharing of large food sources. Birds of prey hunt what they need and don't usually require the assistance of another bird to capture their prey.

Inquiry Questions

FIGURE 53.3
Morphological adaptation. Fur thickness in North American mammals has a major impact on the degree of insulation the fur provides.
Polar bears are able to live in zoos in warm climates. How thick would you expect the hair of a polar bear to be in a zoo in Miami, Florida?

Answer: It depends on what factors regulate hair growth. If hair growth responds to temperature, then we would expect hair length to be much lower in the Arctic because it is much warmer in Miami. If hair length is triggered by shorter day lengths, a sign of impending winter, then we would expect hair length to increase as winter approaches; however, even in the heart of winter, day length is much longer in Florida than in the Arctic, so hair length might also be shorter in Miami for that reason.

FIGURE 53.4
Behavioral adaptation. The Puerto Rican lizard *Anolis cristatellus* maintains a relatively constant temperature by seeking out and basking in patches of sunlight; in shaded forests, this behavior is not possible, and body temperature conforms to the surroundings.
When given the opportunity, lizards regulate their body temperature to maintain a temperature optimal for physiological functioning. Would lizards in open habitats exhibit different escape behaviors than lizards in shaded forest?

Answer: Very possibly. How fast a lizard runs is a function of its body temperature. Researchers have shown that lizards in shaded habitats have lower temperatures and thus lower maximal running speeds. In such circumstances, lizards often adopt alternative escape tactics that rely less on rapidly running away from potential predators.

FIGURE 53.11
The relationship between body size and generation time. In general, larger animals have longer generation times, although there are exceptions.
If resources became more abundant, would you expect smaller or larger species to increase in population size more quickly?

Answer: Because of their shorter generation times, smaller species tend to reproduce more quickly, and thus would be able to respond more quickly to increased resources in the environment.

FIGURE 53.13
Survivorship curve for a cohort of the meadow grass *Poa annua*. After several months of age, mortality increases at a constant rate through time.
Suppose you wanted to keep meadow grass in your room as a houseplant. Suppose, too, that you wanted to buy a plant that was likely to live as long as possible. What age plant would you buy?

Answer: As young a plant as possible, because survival rates decline with age.

FIGURE 53.14
Reproduction has a price. Increased fecundity in birds correlates with higher mortality in several population of birds, ranging from the albatross (lowest) to the sparrow (highest). Birds that raise more offspring per year have a higher probability of dying during that year.
Do you think that species in this graph are ordered by body size?

Answer: Yes, larger species tend to have lower birth and death rates. Thus, body size will tend to decrease along the x-axis.

FIGURE 53.15

Reproductive events per lifetime. Adding eggs to nests of collared flycatchers (which increases the reproductive efforts of the female rearing the young) decreases clutch size the following year; removing eggs from the nest increases the next year's clutch size. This experiment demonstrates the trade-off between current reproductive effort and future reproductive success. **Why does this relationship exist?**

Answer: Probably because a relationship exists between the number of offspring raised and the amount of energy expended. Thus, birds that raise fewer offspring probably retain larger energy stores, which makes them better able to raise more offspring the following year.

FIGURE 53.16

The relationship between clutch size and offspring size. In great tits, the size of the nestlings is inversely related to the number of eggs laid. The more mouths they have to feed, the less the parents can provide to any one nestling. **Would natural selection favor producing many small young or a few large ones?**

Answer: It depends on the situation. If only large individuals are likely to reproduce (as is the case in some territorial species, in which only large males can hold a territory), then a few large offspring would be favored; alternatively, if body size does not affect survival or reproduction, then producing as many offspring as possible would maximize the representation of an individual's genes in subsequent generations. In many cases, intermediate values are favored by natural selection.

FIGURE 53.19

Relationship between population growth rate and population size. Populations far from the carrying capacity (K) will have large growth rates—positive if the population is below K, and negative if it is above K. As the population approaches K, growth rates approach zero. **Why does the growth rate converge on zero?**

Answer: Because when the population is below carrying capacity, the population increases in size. As it approaches the carrying capacity, growth rate slows down either from increased death rates, decreased birthrates, or both, becoming zero as the population hits the carrying capacity. Similarly, populations well above the carrying capacity will experience large decreases in growth rate, resulting either from low birthrates or high death rates, that also approach zero as the population hits the carrying capacity.

FIGURE 53.20

Many populations exhibit logistic growth. (*a*) A fur seal (*Callorhinus ursinus*) population on St. Paul Island, Alaska. (*b*) Laboratory populations of two populations of the cladoceran *Bosmina longirsotris*. Note that the populations first exceeded the carrying capacity, before decreasing to a size that was then maintained. **Why is there a hump in the population growth curve in (*b*), followed by a decline in the population?**

Answer: There are a number of possible explanations. One is that the population overshot the carrying capacity and then declined back to it. Another is that the carrying capacity decreased, perhaps due to environmental change.

FIGURE 53.21

Density-dependent population regulation. Density-dependent factors can affect birthrates, death rates, or both. **Why might birthrates be density-dependent?**

Answer: There are many possible reasons. Perhaps resources become limited, so that females are not able to produce as many offspring. Another possibility is that space is limited so that, at higher populations, individuals spend more time in interactions with other individuals and squander energy that otherwise could be invested in producing and raising more young.

FIGURE 53.22
Density dependence in the song sparrow (*Melospiza melodia*) on Mandarte Island. Reproductive success decreases and mortality rates increase as population size increases. **What would happen if researchers supplemented the food available to the birds?**

Answer: The answer depends on whether food is the factor regulating population size. If it is, then the number of young produced at a given population size would increase and the juvenile mortality rate would decrease. However, if other factors, such as the availability of water or predators, regulated population size, then food supplementation might have no effect.

FIGURE 53.24
Fluctuations in the number of pupae of four moth species in Germany. The population fluctuations suggest that density-independent factors are regulating population size. The concordance in trends through time of the species suggests that the same factors are regulating population size in all species.
What might those factors be?

Answer: Most likely some aspect of the environment, such as winter severity, drought occurrence, or predator population size.

FIGURE 53.25
Linked population cycles of the snowshoe hare and the northern lynx. These data are based on records of fur returns from trappers in the Hudson Bay region of Canada. The lynx population carefully tracks that of the snowshoe hare, but lags behind it slightly.
Suppose experimenters artificially kept the hare population at a high and constant level; what do you think would happen to the lynx population? Conversely, if experimenters artificially kept the lynx population at a high and constant level, what would happen to the hare population?

Answer: If hare population levels were kept high, then we would expect lynx populations to stay high as well because lynx populations respond to food availability. If lynx populations were maintained at a high level, we would expect hare populations to remain low because increased reproduction of hares would lead to increased food for the lynxes.

FIGURE 53.26
History of human population size. Temporary increases in death rate, even severe ones such as that occurring during the Black Death of the 1300s, have little lasting impact. Explosive growth began with the industrial revolution in the 1800s, which produced a significant long-term lowering of the death rate. The current world population is 6.3 billion, and at the present rate, it will double in 53 years.
Based on what we have learned about population growth, what would you predict will happen to human population size?

Answer: If human populations are regulated by density-dependent factors, then as the population approaches the carrying capacity, either birthrates will decrease or death rates will increase, or both. If populations are regulated by density-independent factors, then if environmental conditions change, then either both rates will decline, death rates will increase, or both.

FIGURE 53.27
Why the population of Mexico is growing. The death rate (*red line*) in Mexico fell steadily throughout the last century, while the birthrate (*blue line*) remained fairly steady until 1970. The difference between birth and death rates has fueled a high growth rate. Efforts begun in 1970 to reduce the birthrate have been quite successful, but the growth rate remains high.

Is population growth rate increasing?

Answer: No, population growth rate, the difference between birthrate and death rate, is decreasing. Nonetheless, it is still positive, which means that population size is increasing.

FIGURE 53.28

Population pyramids from 2000. Population pyramids are graphed according to a population's age distribution. Kenya's pyramid has a broad base because of the great number of individuals below childbearing age. When the young people begin to bear children, the population will experience rapid growth. The Swedish pyramid exhibits a slight bulge among middle-aged Swedes, the result of the "baby boom" that occurred in the middle of the twentieth century. **What will the population distributions look like in 20 years?**

Answer: The answer depends on whether age-specific birth and death rates stay unchanged. If they do, then the Swedish distribution would remain about the same. By contrast, because birthrates are far outstripping death rates, the Kenyan distribution will become increasingly unbalanced as the bulge of young individuals enter their reproductive years and start producing even more offspring.

FIGURE 53.29

Distribution of population growth. Most of the worldwide increase in population since 1950 has occurred in developing countries. The age structures of developing countries indicate that this trend will increase in the near future. World population in 2050 likely will be between 7.3 and 10.7 billion, according to a recent United Nations study. Depending on fertility rates, the population at that time will either be increasing rapidly or slightly, or possibly, in the best case, declining slightly.
Is this an example of density-dependent population regulation? If so, what factors are regulating population size?

Answer: Yes. Birthrates around the world are declining. Nonetheless, in some places, death rates are increasing as population increases; thus, both birth and death rates appear to be density-dependent.

FIGURE 53.30

Ecological footprints of individuals in different countries. An ecological footprint calculates how much land is required to support a person through his or her life, including the acreage used for production of food, forest products, and housing, in addition to the forest required to absorb the carbon dioxide produced by the combustion of fossil fuels.
Which is a more important cause of resource depletion, overpopulation or overconsumption?

Answer: Both are important causes and the relative importance of the two depends on which resource we are discussing. One thing is clear: The world cannot support its current population size if everyone lived at the level of resource consumption of people in the United States.

Self Test

1). The term *homeostasis* refers to
      a). the maintenance of a consistent internal environment.
      b). the ability to conform internal temperature to environmental temperature.
      c). an organism's biotic potential.
      d). the carrying capacity of a population.

The correct answer is a--the maintenance of a consistent internal environment.
A. Answer a is correct. Homeostasis refers to the maintenance of a consistent internal environment.

The correct answer is a...
B. Answer b is incorrect. Organisms that are able to conform their internal temperature to environmental temperatures do not maintain temperature homeostasis.

The correct answer is a...
C. Answer c is incorrect. Biotic potential refers to the rate at which a population will increase if no limits are placed on its rate of growth.

The correct answer is a...
D. Answer d is incorrect. The carrying capacity of a population is the maximum number of individuals that the environment can support.

Hint: Homeostasis is a term that refers to a steady-state internal environment. Organisms that maintain homeostasis have a variety of adaptations that allow them to resist internal changes that could result from changes in the external environment.

2). Which of the following is *not* considered a population?
      a). the ginkgo trees (*Ginkgo biloba*) in New York City
      b). the birds in your hometown
      c). the human inhabitants of Pennsylvania
      d). the grizzly bears (*Ursus arctos*) of Alaska

The correct answer is b...
A. Answer a is incorrect because all ginkgos are the same species and those that live in New York City can be considered a population.

The correct answer is b--the birds in your hometown
B. Answer b is correct because all of the birds found in an area would constitute more than one species. A population is comprised of individuals of the same species.

The correct answer is b...
C. Answer c is incorrect because humans are all the same species and the residents of Pennsylvania can be considered a population.

The correct answer is b...
D. Answer d is incorrect because grizzly bears are the same species and those that live in Alaska can be considered a population.

Hint: A population is defined as a group of individuals of the same species living in the same geographic area.

3). A clumped population may be due to
      a). weak interactions between the members of a population.
      b). intense competition for uniformly distributed resources.
      c). uneven distribution of resources in the environment.
      d). intense territoriality.

The correct answer is c...
A. Answer a is incorrect because weak interactions between individuals results in a random distribution of individuals.

The correct answer is c...
B. Answer b is incorrect because intense competition of uniformly distributed resources results in a uniform distribution of individuals.

The correct answer is c--uneven distribution of resources in the environment.
C. Answer c is correct because a clumped distribution is due to an uneven distribution of resources in the environment.

The correct answer is c...
D. Answer d is incorrect because intense territoriality results in a uniformly distributed population.

Hint: Organisms distribute themselves in response to the distribution of resources in the environment. Clumped resources will result in a clumped distribution of individuals in a population.

4). The tidewater goby (*Eucyclogobius newberryi*) is an endangered species of fish that occurs as metapopulations in isolated coastal wetlands of California. Large wetlands serve as sources of individuals for populations in small wetlands, which function as sinks due to inferior habitat quality. What effect would most likely be seen on the population of gobies if a barrier to migration between wetlands developed?
    a). The populations in the small and large wetlands would evolve independently of each other.
    b). The populations in the large wetlands would most likely go extinct.
    c). The populations in the small wetlands would most likely go extinct.
    d). The populations in the small and large wetlands would most likely go extinct.

The correct answer is c...
A. Answer a is incorrect because most likely the populations in the small wetlands will go extinct due to a lack of immigration of individuals from the source population.

The correct answer is c...
B. Answer b is incorrect because the large wetlands serve as a refuge for a source population. The source population is less likely to be negatively impacted by an absence of migration between populations.

The correct answer is c--The populations in the small wetlands would most likely go extinct.
C. Answer c is correct because the small wetlands serve as sinks. The small wetlands are a poorer habitat than the large wetlands and have negative population growth.

The correct answer is c...
D. Answer d is incorrect because the large wetlands serve as a refuge for a source population and are less likely to go extinct.

Hint: Species that occur in distinct metapopulations often occur in source-sink metapopulations. The source population occurs in more suitable habitat and has a positive growth rate. Individuals often emigrate from these populations. The sink population occurs in less suitable habitat and has a negative population growth rate. Individuals often immigrate to these areas from the source population.

5). Which of the following factors does *not* determine the growth rate of a population?
    a). the population's sex ratio.
    b). the species' generation time.
    c). the age structure of the population.
    d). the optimal temperature at which an organism can reproduce

The correct answer is d...
A. Answer a is incorrect because the sex ratio of a population does affect its growth rate.

The correct answer is d...
B. Answer b is incorrect because the species generation time does affect its growth rate.

The correct answer is d...
C. Answer c is incorrect because the age structure of the population does affect its growth rate.

The correct answer is d--the optimal temperature at which an organism can reproduce
D. Answer d is correct because an organism's preferred environmental conditions do not influence its growth rate. Environmental extremes may decrease an organism's ability to reproduce but there is no single temperature range at which all species reproduce at the greatest rate.

Hint: The growth rate of a population is determined by the population's sex ratio, generation time, age structure, birth rate and death rate. Environmental conditions (such as pollution) can lower a population's growth rate; however, each species has a separate range of environmental conditions under which population growth will be optimal.

6). A population with a larger proportion of older individuals than younger individuals will likely
       a). grow larger and then decline rapidly.
       b). continue to grow larger indefinitely.
       c). grow smaller and may stabilize at a smaller population size.
       d). not experience a change in population size.

The correct answer is c...
A. Answer a is incorrect because a population with a larger proportion of older individuals than younger individuals will most likely experience a negative population growth (death rate will be higher than birth rate), which will decrease population size.

The correct answer is c...
B. Answer b is incorrect because a population with a larger proportion of older individuals than younger individuals will most likely experience a negative population growth (death rate will be higher than birth rate), which will decrease population size.

The correct answer is c--grow smaller and may stabilize at a smaller population size.
C. Answer c is correct because a population with a larger proportion of older individuals than younger individuals will most likely experience a negative population growth (death rate will be higher than birth rate), which will decrease population size.

The correct answer is c...
D. Answer d is incorrect because a population with a larger proportion of older individuals than younger individuals will most likely experience a negative population growth (death rate will be higher than birth rate), which will decrease population size.

Hint: Older individuals are post-reproductive. A population with a larger proportion of older individuals than younger individuals will experience negative population growth. As long as the young cohorts continue to reproduce the population will eventually stabilize at a smaller population size.

7). Humans are an example of an organism with a type I survivorship curve. This means
       a). mortality rates are highest for younger individuals.
       b). mortality rates are highest for older individuals.
       c). mortality rates are constant over the life span of individuals.
       d). the population growth rate is high.

The correct answer is b...
A. Answer a is incorrect because organisms with a type I survivorship curve show the highest mortality in the older age classes.

The correct answer is b--mortality rates are highest for older individuals.
B. Answer b is correct because organisms with a type I survivorship curve show the highest mortality in the older age classes.

The correct answer is b…
C. Answer c is incorrect because organisms with a type I survivorship curve show the highest mortality in the older age classes.

The correct answer is b…
D. Answer d is incorrect because survivorship curves provide information about survival rates across age groups and not about growth rates of populations.

Hint: Type I survivorship curves are typical of organisms with higher mortality in older age classes.

8). According to the Population Reference Bureau (2002), the worldwide intrinsic rate of human population growth (r) is currently 1.3%. In the United States, $r = 0.6\%$. How will the U.S. population change relative to the world population?
       a). The world population will grow, while the population of the United States will decline.
       b). The world population will grow, while the population of the United States will remain the same.
       c). Both the world and the U.S. populations will grow, but the world population will grow more rapidly.
       d). The world population will decline, while the U.S. population will increase.

The correct answer is c…
A. Answer a is incorrect because both populations exhibit a positive value of r. This means both populations will increase.

The correct answer is c…
B. Answer b is incorrect because both populations exhibit a positive value of r. This means both populations will increase.

The correct answer is c--Both the world and the U.S. populations will grow, but the world population will grow more rapidly.
C. Answer c is correct because both populations exhibit a positive value of r. This means both populations will increase. Because the value of r for the world is larger, the world will exhibit faster population growth.

The correct answer is c…
D. Answer d is incorrect because both populations exhibit a positive value of r. This means both populations will increase.

Hint: The intrinsic rate of population growth (r) = birth rate (b) – death rate(d). Any time $r > 0$ a population will increase. The larger the value of r, the faster the rate of population growth.

9). The logistic population growth model, $dN/dt = rN[(K - N)/K]$, describes a population's growth when an upper limit to growth is assumed. This upper limit to growth is known as the population's _____, and as N gets larger, dN/dt _____.
       a). biotic potential/increases
       b). biotic potential/decreases
       c). carrying capacity/increases
       d). carrying capacity/decreases

The correct answer is d…
A. Answer a is incorrect because the upper limit to a population's growth is known as its carrying capacity and as population size (N) increases the change in population size (dN/dt) decreases.

The correct answer is d…
B. Answer b is incorrect because the upper limit to a population's growth is known as its carrying capacity.

The correct answer is d…
C. Answer c is incorrect because as population size (N) increases the change in population size (dN/dt) decreases.

The correct answer is d--carrying capacity/decreases
D. Answer d is correct because the upper limit to a population's growth is known as its carrying capacity and as population size (N) increases the change in population size (dN/dt) decreases.

Hint: The theoretical upper limit to a population's size is known as that population's carrying capacity (K). In the logistic growth model, the closer the population size gets to the carrying capacity the slower the population size increases. Once the carrying capacity is reached population growth ceases.

10). Which of the following is *not* an example of a density-dependent effect on population growth?
      a). an extremely cold winter
      b). competition for food resources
      c). stress-related illness associated with overcrowding
      d). competition for nesting sites

The correct answer is a--an extremely cold winter
A. The correct answer is a because an extremely cold winter is a density-independent effect. An environmental factor such as temperature will affect individuals regardless of population size.

The correct answer is a...
B. Answer b is incorrect because competition for food resources is a density-dependent effect. The more individuals there are in the population, the greater the competition for food resources.

The correct answer is a...
C. Answer c is incorrect because stress-related illness associated with overcrowding is a density-dependent effect. The more individuals there are in the population, the greater the potential for stress.

The correct answer is a...
D. Answer d is incorrect because competition for nesting sites is a density-dependent effect. The more individuals there are in the population, the greater the competition for nesting sites.

Hint: Density-dependent effects are factors that change in response to population size. Density-independent effects are factors that do not change in response to population size.

Test Your Visual Understanding

1). The song sparrow *Melospiza melodia* exhibits density-dependent population growth on Mandarte Island. List three reasons that the number of young per female may be sensitive to population size.
Answer: Competition for food results in decreased nutritional status for females, competition for food results in decreased nutritional status for offspring, reduced food availability requires parents to be away from the nest for longer periods of time which leaves the young vulnerable to

predation, competition for nesting sites, and stress-related responses to increased population size.

Apply Your Knowledge

1). Throughout most of North America, large carnivores have either been extirpated (driven to local extinction) or their populations are at extremely low levels. Explain how the loss of carnivore populations may have changed the vegetation of North America.
Answer: Decreases in carnivore populations often lead to an increase in herbivore populations. As herbivore populations increase they consume more vegetation. This can lead to large-scale changes in vegetation abundance and distribution. This phenomenon can be observed on the small scale by looking at a pasture full of cows. All of the vegetation that is palatable to the cows will be grazed. Those plants that the cows do not eat (such as thistle) will be ungrazed.

2). Do humans show more *r*-selected life-history traits or *K*-selected traits? How does this correlate with current global human population growth?
Answer: In general, humans show more *K*-selected life history traits. For example, humans have a late age at first reproduction; have a long lifespan, a low mortality rate, and extensive parental care. Currently, human population growth is showing an exponential rate of increase. This is due to technological advances, which have made human populations less density-dependent.

3). Give your opinion: What constitutes the greatest threat to the future of the planet, the rapidly growing population in developing parts of the world or high resource consumption in the developed world?
Answer: Opinion.

FIGURE 54.3

Abundance of tree species along a moisture gradient in the Santa Catalina Mountains of southeastern Arizona. The species' patterns of abundance are independent of each other. Thus, community composition changes continuously along the gradient.
Why do species exhibit different patterns of response to change in moisture?

Answer: There are many possible reasons. Each species may have its own adaptive characteristics. Moreover, species may respond differently to the presence of other species, including competitors, predators, and parasites.

FIGURE 54.4

Change in community composition across an ecotone. The plant communities on normal and serpentine soils are greatly different, and the transition from one community to another occurs over a short distance.
Why is there a sharp transition between the two community types?

Answer: The different soil types require very different adaptations, and thus different species are adapted to each soil type.

FIGURE 54.8

Character displacement in Darwin's finches. These two species of finches (genus *Geospiza*) have bills of similar size when allopatric, but different size when sympatric.
Why do populations have different bill sizes when they occur with other species?

Answer: When the two species live on different islands they most likely consume similar foods and so their beaks are similar in size. When they occur in the same area, their niches overlap and there would be great competition for the same resources. Under these circumstances, one species would usually outcompete the other driving it to extinction. But what often happens is that selection will favor a splitting up of the resources, called resource partitioning, and under these circumstances, each species may become more "specialized" for its portion of the niche, resulting in different morphologies, called character displacement.

FIGURE 54.9

Detecting interspecific competition. This experiment tests how removal of kangaroo rats affects the population size of other rodents. Immediately after kangaroo rats were removed, the number of other rodents increased relative to the enclosures that still contained kangaroo rats. Notice that population sizes (as estimated by number of captures) changed in synchrony in the two treatments, probably reflecting changes in the weather.
Why are there more individuals of other rodent species when kangaroo rats are excluded?

Answer: The kangaroo rats competed with all the other rodent species for resources, keeping the size of other rodent populations smaller. In the absence of competition when the kangaroo rats were removed, there were more resources available which allowed the other rodent populations to increase in size.

FIGURE 54.10

Predator-prey in the microscopic world. When the predatory *Didinium* is added to a *Paramecium* population, the numbers of *Didinium* initially rise, while the numbers of *Paramecium* steadily fall. When the *Paramecium* population is depleted, however, the *Didinium* individuals also die.
Can you think of any ways this experiment could be changed so that *Paramecium* might not go extinct?

Answer: This could be accomplished in a variety of ways. One option would be to provide refuges to give some *Paramecium* a way of escaping the predators. Another option would be to include predators of the *Didinium,* which would limit their populations (see Ecosystem chapter).

FIGURE 54.22
Change in ant population size after the removal of rodents. Ants initially increased in population size relative to ants in the two enclosures from which rodents weren't removed, but then these ant populations declined.
Why do ant populations increase and then decrease in the absence of rodents?

Answer: At first, the number of small seeds available to ants increases due to the absence of rodents. However, over time, plants that produce large seeds outcompete plants that produce small seeds, and thus fewer small seeds are produced and available to ants; hence, ant populations decline.

Self Test

1). The entire range of factors an organism is able to exploit in its environment is its
      a). community.
      b). realized niche.
      c). fundamental niche.
      d). habitat.

The correct answer is c…
A. Answer a is incorrect because a community is a group of organisms that live together in an area; it is not the factors in an environment that are used by a particular organism.

The correct answer is c…
B. Answer b is incorrect because a realized niche is the actual niche that the organism occupies which may be a subset of the entire niche. Although an organism may be capable of utilizing more resources in its environment, it is limited by interactions with other organisms, such that it lives in its realized niche.

The correct answer is c--fundamental niche.
C. A fundamental niche is all the available resources in an area that an organism is able to utilize based on its resource needs and physical limitations. However, because of interactions with other organisms, any given organism may not be able to utilize all available resources.

The correct answer is c…
D. Answer d is incorrect because an organism's habitat is the physical space in which it lives, not the resources in the area that it utilizes. For example, a bird's habitat may be a tree; its niche is the food and shelter available in the tree.

Hint: The entire niche that a species is capable of using, based on its physiological tolerance limits and resource needs, is called the fundamental niche. The actual niche the species occupies is called its realized niche. Because of interspecific interactions, the realized niche of a species may be considerably smaller than its fundamental niche.

2). The phenomenon known as character displacement is associated with
      a). sympatric species.
      b). allopatric species.
      c). competitive exclusion.
      d). primary succession.

The correct answer is a--sympatric species.
A. Sympatric species are similar species that occupy the same habitat but coexist by utilizing different resources in the habitat (occupy different niches). In communities where two species coexist, they tend to have greater differences in morphology or utilize different resources than the same species living apart from each other. These differences are called character displacement.

The correct answer is a...
B. Answer b is incorrect because allopatric species are similar species that are living in different geographical areas. As such, they are not competing for resources and so they do not exhibit differences in morphology or utilize different resources, which is referred to as character displacement. However, if these same species lived in the same geographical area, they would exhibit these differences.

The correct answer is a...
C. Answer c is incorrect because competitive exclusion is the situation where two species are competing for a limited resource and the species that utilizes the resource more efficiently will eliminate the other species in that community. Character displacement is when the two species coexist in the same geographical area by utilizing different resources, but they also may evolve different morphologies.

The correct answer is a...
D. Answer d is incorrect because primary succession is the process whereby organisms begin inhabiting a bare, lifeless substrate and does not usually involve character displacement where two species coexist in the same geographical area by utilizing different resources but they also may evolve different morphologies.

Hint: Where two species co-occur, they tend to exhibit greater differences in morphology and resource use than do allopatric populations of the same species. Called character displacement, the differences evident between sympatric species are thought to have been favored by natural selection as a mechanism to facilitate habitat partitioning and thus reduce competition.

3). As the number of individuals of the predatory species increases, the prey population
    a). increases.
    b). decreases.
    c). stabilizes.
    d). first increases, and then begins to decrease.

The correct answer is b...
A. Answer a is incorrect because as the number of predators increases, they consume more and more of the prey; therefore the size of the prey population decreases, not increases.

The correct answer is b--decreases.
B. The size of the predator population increases when food is available. As more and more predators are present in an area the number of individuals of the prey species decreases as they are consumed by the predators.

The correct answer is b...
C. Answer c is incorrect because an increasing number of predators means more hunting and more consuming of individuals of the prey population. The only way that the prey species population will stabilize is if the predator population does not increase in size.

The correct answer is b...
D. Answer d is incorrect because this is a prediction of what occurs in the predator population, not in the prey population. While food is available, the predator population will initially increase but as the food supply diminishes, the predators will begin dying out and their population size will begin to decrease.

Hint: When the predatory *Didinium* is added to a *Paramecium* population, the numbers of *Didinium* initially rise, while the numbers of *Paramecium* steadily fall. When the *Paramecium* population is depleted, however, the *Didinium* individuals also die.

4). In order for mimicry to be effective in protecting a species from predation, it must
        a). occur in a palatable species that looks like a distasteful species.
        b). have cryptic coloration.
        c). occur such that mimics look and act like models.
        d). occur in only poisonous or dangerous species.

The correct answer is c…
A. Answer a is incorrect because although Batesian mimicry involves the evolution of a palatable species to look like a distasteful species, thereby avoiding predation, this isn't the only type of mimicry. Müllerian mimicry involves the evolution of different but poisonous or dangerous species to look like each other. None of them are palatable.

The correct answer is c…
B. Answer b is incorrect because although cryptic coloration is a defensive mechanism, it usually is not involved in mimicry. Cryptic coloration, which involves coloring of the animal so that it blends with its surroundings, is usually not the case with Batesian or Müllerian mimicry. With mimicry, the models and mimics usually have warning coloration.

The correct answer is c--occur such that mimics look and act like models.
C. In Batesian mimicry, a harmless mimic looks and acts like its dangerous model species and with Müllerian mimicry, all of the species are dangerous and they all look and act like each other.

The correct answer is c…
D. Answer d is incorrect because although mimicry does occur in only poisonous or dangerous species, such is the case in Müllerian mimicry, Batesian mimicry involves harmless species. In Batesian mimicry, a harmless, palatable species will look and act like a distasteful or dangerous species. Predators will avoid the palatable species thinking it is the dangerous species.

Hint: In both Batesian and Müllerian mimicry, mimic and model must not only look alike but also act alike if predators are to be deceived. For example, the members of several families of insects that closely resemble wasps behave surprisingly like the wasps they mimic, flying often and actively from place to place.

5). Brightly colored poison-dart frogs are an example of
        a). Batesian mimicry.
        b). Müllerian mimicry.
        c). cryptic coloration.
        d). aposematic coloration.

The correct answer is d…
A. Answer a is incorrect because Batesian mimicry is an evolutionary phenomenon where a relatively harmless species has come to resemble distasteful species that exhibit warning coloration. Although Batesian mimicry could occur where another frog species evolves to resemble the poison-dart frog, the poison-dart frog's coloration is not an example of Batesian mimicry.

The correct answer is d…
B. Answer b is incorrect because Müllerian mimicry is an evolutionary phenomenon where several unrelated but protected animal species come to resemble one another. If animals that resemble one another are poisonous or dangerous, they gain an advantage because a predator will learn to quickly avoid all animals that look like that. Although Müllerian mimicry could occur

where other poisonous frogs acquire the coloration of the poison-dart frog but the poison-dart frog's coloration is not an example of Müllerian mimicry.

The correct answer is d...
C. Answer c is incorrect because cryptic coloration is an evolutionary phenomenon where an animal that has no chemical defenses have coloration that allow them to blend in with their surroundings, which is their defense mechanism. Such camouflaging hides the individual from predators. The poison-dart frog does not have cryptic coloration but rather has brightly colored skin that is a warning to all predators that it is poisonous.

The correct answer is d--aposematic coloration.
D. Aposematic coloration or warning coloration is an evolutionary phenomenon where a poisonous or dangerous animal has acquired brightly colored skin that "advertises" itself to predators. This coloration is a defensive mechanism. The poison-dart frog produces toxic chemicals that is secretes on its skin. These chemicals are deadly to predators. Its brightly colored skin is readily identifiable by predators and they stay away.

Hint: Animals also manufacture and use a startling array of substances to perform a variety of defensive functions. The poison-dart frogs of the family Dendrobatidae produce toxic alkaloids in the mucus that covers their brightly colored skin; these alkaloids are deadly to animals that try to eat the frogs. Many animals advertise their poisonous nature using an ecological strategy known as warning coloration, or aposematic coloration.

6). Which of the following is an example of commensalism?
   a). a tapeworm living in the gut of its host
   b). a clownfish living among the tentacles of a sea anemone
   c). a lichen
   d). bees feeding on nectar from a flower

The correct answer is b...
A. Answer a is incorrect because this is an example of parasitism. In this relationship, the tapeworm benefits from living inside the host because the host provides food and protection for the tapeworm. In turn, the tapeworm harms the host by denying it full nutritional benefit for the food it eats.

The correct answer is b--a clownfish living among the tentacle of a sea anemone
B. This type of relationship is commensalism because the sea anemone provides the fish with food, the detritus left on its tentacles following a meal. However, the sea anemone itself receives no real benefit from the relationship, but also, it is not harmed.

The correct answer is b...
C. Answer c is incorrect because a lichen is an example of mutualism. In this relationship, fungi associate with green algae or cyanobacteria in such a way that both individuals benefit. The fungi provide protection to the algae or cyanobacteria but in turn, the fungi receives nutrients from the photosynthetic algae or cyanobacteria.

The correct answer is b...
D. Answer d is incorrect because bees feeding on nectar from a flower is an example of mutualism. In this relationship, the bees obtain nutrients from the flowers but they in turn help the flowers cross-pollinate by transporting pollen from one flower to the next.

Hint: Commensalism is a symbiotic relationship that benefits one species and neither hurts nor helps the other. One of the best-known examples of symbiosis involves the relationship between certain small tropical fishes and sea anemones. These fish evolved the ability to live among the stinging tentacle of the sea anemone, feeding off of the detritus left on its tentacles. The sea anemone is not harmed by this relationship nor does there seem to be a real benefit for it either.

7). A parasite that feeds on its host from inside is a(n)
   a). endoparasite.
   b). ectoparasite.
   c). parasitoid.
   d). predator.

The correct answer is a--endoparasite.
A. An endoparasite is a parasite that lives inside the body of its host, either feeding on the host or robbing the host of its own food.

The correct answer is a…
B. Answer b is incorrect because an ectoparasite is a parasite the feeds on the exterior surface of an organism. Many examples of ectoparasites are known in both plants and animals.

The correct answer is a…
C. Answer c is incorrect because a parasitoid is an insect that lays its eggs on the host and the larvae feed on the host, often killing it. Parasitism is common among wasps.

The correct answer is a…
D. Answer d is incorrect because a predator, although like a parasite in that it feeds on a host, is usually larger than their host, which is called prey. It attacks it prey and usually eats it beginning on the outside.

Hint: Parasites that feed on the exterior surface of an organism are external parasites, or ectoparasites. Vertebrates are parasitized internally by endoparasites, members of many different phyla of animals and protists. Internal parasitism is generally marked by much more extreme specialization than external parasitism.

8). A species that interacts with many other organisms in its community in critical ways can be called a
   a). predator.
   b). primary succession species.
   c). secondary succession species.
   d). keystone species.

The correct answer is d…
A. Answer a is incorrect because although a predator may interact with many other organisms in a community these interactions may not necessarily be critical in the community.

The correct answer is d…
B. Answer b is incorrect because a primary succession species is a species that inhabits a barren environment with no soil and usually doesn't interact with many other organisms.

The correct answer is d…
C. Answer c is incorrect because a secondary succession species is a species that inhabits an environment that has been cleared of plant life but the soil still remains. These types of organisms usually don't interact with many other organisms.

The correct answer is d--keystone species.
D. A keystone species is a species that has particularly strong effects on the composition of a community. Predators often serve as keystone species because their presence restrains competition among other species, maintaining high species richness. A keystone species might also affect the environment by creating new habitats or niches for other species. When the keystone species is removed from a community, the community itself is disrupted.

Hint: Species that have particularly strong effects on the composition of communities are termed keystone species. Predators, such as the starfish, can often serve as a keystone species by preventing one species from outcompeting others, thus maintaining high levels of species richness in a community.

9). Succession that occurs on abandoned agricultural fields is best described as
        a). coevolution.
        b). primary succession.
        c). secondary succession.
        d). prairie succession.

The correct answer is c...
A. Answer a is incorrect because coevolution is the modifications or adaptations that evolve in two or more species that interact with each other in the same community. This is not the same as succession, which is changing of a community from simple to more complex over time.

The correct answer is c...
B. Answer b is incorrect because primary succession is the emergence of new life on a bare or lifeless substrate, such as rocks, where organisms gradually move into the area and change its nature. An abandoned agricultural field is not a bare, lifeless substrate.

The correct answer is c--secondary succession.
C. Succession is the changing of a community from simple to more complex over time. There are two types of succession, primary and secondary. Primary succession occurs on bare substrate such as rock, where soil isn't even present. Secondary succession is an area where the existing community has been disturbed, such as by a fire or logging, but where soil still remains. Secondary succession is what occurs in an abandoned field, where grasses and small shrubs begin to appear.

The correct answer is c...
D. Answer d is incorrect because there are only two types of succession, primary and secondary. Although succession occurs on a prairie, where a community increases in complexity over time, there is no category of succession specifically for prairies.

Hint: Communities have a tendency to change from simple to complex in a process called succession. If a wooded area is cleared and left alone, plants will slowly reclaim the area. Eventually, the area will be transformed into woods again. This kind of succession, which occurs in areas where an existing community has been disturbed, but soil remains, is called secondary succession. In contrast, primary succession occurs on bare, lifeless substrate, such as rocks.

10). Lichen growing on the surface of rocks provides an example of
        a). facilitation.
        b). tolerance.
        c). inhibition.
        d). secondary succession.

The correct answer is b...
A. Answer a is incorrect because facilitation is a process in succession whereby the original species that move into a newly opened habitat alter the environment in such a way as to allow new species to move in. Lichens are not part of this step in the process of succession.

The correct answer is b--tolerance.
B. Succession happens because species alter the habitat in ways that permit other species to enter it. Tolerance is the first step in this process, where hardy, more weedlike species that are tolerant of harsh, lifeless conditions become established in barren areas. Lichens are able to

grow on rocks or other abiotic substrates and so are usually a species that appears during the tolerance phase of succession.

The correct answer is b...
C. Answer c is incorrect because inhibition is a process in succession whereby changes in the habitat caused by one species actually favors another species, which inhibits the growth of the original species. Lichens are not part of this step in the process of succession.

The correct answer is b...
D. Answer d is incorrect because secondary succession involves succession, the changing of a community from simple to more complex, in areas where an existing community has been disturbed but soil still remains. Lichens are involved in primary succession, not secondary succession.

Hint: Succession happens because species alter the habitat and resources in ways that favor other species. Three dynamic concepts are of critical importance in the process: tolerance, facilitation, and inhibition. Tolerance involves the early successional stages where weedy *r*-selected species that are tolerant of the harsh, abiotic conditions are able to grow in barren areas. Abiotic barren areas include rocks. Lichens are the first vegetation able to grow under such conditions.

Test Your Visual Understanding

1). The graph above shows three general stages of succession indicated by the labels *a*, *b*, and *c* that occurred after the receding of a glacier at Glacier Bay, Alaska. Using the concepts of tolerance, facilitation, and inhibition, explain what is happening at each stage of succession.
Answer: Stage *a* corresponds to tolerance, where weedy *r*-selected species (the mosses) that are tolerant of the harsh conditions. After the glacier receded, the substrate was barren, covered with rocks. Mosses, and similarly lichens, are some of only a few species that are able to inhabit abiotic, barren substrates. They introduce nitrogen and other minerals into the soil that forms and permits other species of plants to grow.
     Stage *b* corresponds to facilitation, where the mosses elevated the levels of nitrogen to the point where other plant species could survive. The alder plants moved in and further altered the environment, lowering the pH of the soil. The continuous changing of the environment allowed still more species to live in the community.
     Stage *c* corresponds to inhibition, where the alders change the soil in such a way as to favor larger trees of spruce and hemlock. Eventually, the trees outcompeted the alders for soil and other forms of vegetation gradually replaced the alders.

Apply Your Knowledge

1). Through genetic engineering, bacterial toxin genes from a soil bacterium, *Bacillus thuringiensis* (Bt), have been inserted into corn plants, making them resistant to certain insects. The corn plants produce the toxin that kills insects but doesn't harm the plant or people. However, because the corn pollen, which also contains the toxins, could spread to neighboring milkweed plants, there was a concern that monarch butterflies, which are killed by the toxin, could be at risk. The lethal dose of toxin consists of 2500 pollen grains/in^2 of milkweed leaf. Milkweed plants within a field of corn contain on average 500 pollen grains/in^2 of milkweed leaf. Assume that the level of pollen decreases by 60% with every 10 feet. How much pollen will reach milkweed plants that are 10 feet from the cornfield? 20 feet from the cornfield?
Answer: Milkweed plants in the cornfield contain 500 pollen grains/in^2 of milkweed leaf. If the rate of dispersion drops by 60% for every 10 feet then only 40% make it onto a plant 10 feet away. Therefore, a milkweed plant that is 10 feet away from the cornfield will receive 500 x 0.4 or 200 pollen grains/in^2 of milkweed leaf. A milkweed plant that is 20 feet away will receive 500 x 0.4 x 0.4 or 80 pollen grains/in^2 of milkweed leaf.

Inquiry Questions

FIGURE 55.11

The food chain in Cayuga Lake. Autotrophic plankton (algae and cyanobacteria) fix the energy of the sun, heterotrophic plankton feed on them, and both are consumed by smelt. The smelt are eaten by trout, with about a fivefold loss in fixed energy. For humans, the amount of smelt biomass is at least five times greater than that available in trout, although humans prefer to eat trout.

Why does it take so many calories of algae to support so few of humans?

Answer: At each link in the food chain, only a small fraction of the energy at one level is converted into mass of organisms at the next level. Much energy is dissipated as heat or excreted.

FIGURE 55.12

Ecological pyramids. Ecological pyramids measure different characteristics of each trophic level. (*a*) Pyramid of numbers. (*b*) Pyramids of biomass, both normal (*top*) and inverted (*bottom*). (*c*) Pyramid of energy.

How can the existence of inverted pyramids of biomass be explained?

Answer: In the inverted pyramid, the primary producers reproduce quickly and are eaten quickly, so that at any given time, a small population of primary producers exist relative to the heterotroph population.

FIGURE 55.13

Trophic cascades. Streams with trout have fewer herbivorous invertebrates and more algae than streams without trout.

Why do streams with trout have more algae?

Answer: Because the trout eat the invertebrates which graze the algae. With fewer grazers, there is more algae.

FIGURE 55.14

Four-level trophic cascades. Streams with large, carnivorous fish have fewer lower- level predators, such as damselflies, more herbivorous insects (exemplified by the number of chironomids, a type of aquatic insect), and lower levels of algae.

What might be the effect if snakes that prey on fish were added to the enclosures?

Answer: The snakes might reduce the number of fish, which would allow an increase in damselflies, which would reduce the number of chironomids and increase the algae. In other words, lower levels of the food chain would be identical for the "snake and fish" and "no fish and no snake" treatments. Both would differ from the enclosures with only fish.

FIGURE 55.15

Bottom-up effects. At low levels of productivity, herbivore populations cannot be maintained. Above some threshold, increases in productivity lead to increases in herbivore biomass; vegetation biomass no longer increases with productivity because it is converted into herbivore biomass. Similarly, above another threshold, herbivore biomass gets converted to carnivore biomass. At this point, vegetation biomass is no longer constrained by herbivores, and so again increases with increasing productivity.

Why are there portions of the curves where vegetation biomass does not increase as productivity increases?

Answer: Because the increase in vegetational mass is all eaten by herbivores and is translated into greater herbivore biomass.

FIGURE 55.16
Bottom-up effects on a stream ecosystem. Increases in the amount of light hitting the stream lead to increases in the amount of vegetation. However, herbivore biomass does not increase with increased productivity because it is converted into predator biomass.
Why is the amount of light an important determinant of predator biomass?

Answer: More light means more photosynthesis. More plant material means more herbivores, which translates into more predator biomass.

FIGURE 55.17
Effect of species richness on ecosystem stability and productivity. (*a*) One of the Cedar Creek experimental plots. (*b*) Community stability can be assessed by looking at the effect of species richness on community invasibility. Each dot represents data from one experimental plot in the Cedar Creek experimental fields. Plots with more species are harder to invade by non-native species, which occur in surrounding agricultural fields.
How could you devise an experiment on invasibility that didn't rely on species from surrounding areas?

Answer: Introduce them yourself. For example, each spring, you could place a premeasured number of seeds of a particular invasive species in each plot. Such an experiment would have the advantage of more precisely controlling the opportunity for invasion, but also would be less natural, which is one of the advantages of the Cedar Creek study site: the plots are real ecosystems, interacting with their surrounding environment in natural ways.

FIGURE 55.18
Factors that affect species richness. (*a*) *Productivity*: In fynbos plant communities of mountainous areas of South Africa, species richness of plants peaks at intermediate levels of productivity (biomass). (*b*) *Spatial heterogeneity*: The species richness of desert lizards is positively correlated with the structural complexity of the plant cover in desert sites in the American Southwest. (*c*) *Climate*: The species richness of mammals is inversely correlated with monthly mean temperature range along the west coast of North America.
(*a*) Why is species richness greatest at intermediate levels of productivity? (*b*) Why do more structurally complex areas have more species? (*c*) Why do areas with less variation in temperature have more species?

Answer: (*a*) Perhaps because an intermediate number of predators is enough to keep numbers of superior competitors down. (*b*) Perhaps because there are more habitats available and thus more different ways of surviving in the environment. (*c*) Hard to say. Possibly more stable environments permit greater specialization, thus permitting coexistence of more species.

FIGURE 55.20
The equilibrium model of island biogeography. (*a*) Island species richness reaches an equilibrium (*black dot*) when the colonization rate of new species equals the extinction rate of species on the island. (*b*) The equilibrium shifts depending on the rate of colonization, the size of an island, and its distance to sources of colonists. Species richness is positively correlated with Island size and inversely correlated with distance from the mainland. Smaller islands have higher extinction rates, shifting the equilibrium point to the left. Similarly, more distant islands have lower colonization rates, again shifting the equilibrium point leftward. (*c*) The effect of distance from a larger island, which can be the source of colonizing species, is readily apparent. More distant islands have fewer species compared to nearer islands of the same size.
Do islands with the same number of species necessarily have the same extinction rate?

Answer: No. Examine figure 55.20b. The equilibrium number of species can be the same for two islands, but the rates of extinction and colonization can be different due to island size and distance to the mainland.

1). Over land, most of the water in the atmosphere results from _____, whereas over the oceans, most of the water in the atmosphere results from _____.
      a). evaporation/transpiration
      b). evaporation/evaporation
      c). transpiration/evaporation
      d). transpiration/transpiration

The correct answer is c...
A. Answer a is incorrect because the main loss of water from terrestrial systems is through transpiration whereas the main loss from the oceans is through evaporation.

The correct answer is c...
B. Answer b is incorrect because the main loss of water from terrestrial systems is through transpiration whereas the main loss from the oceans is through evaporation.

The correct answer is c--transpiration/evaporation
C. Answer c is correct because the main loss of water from terrestrial systems is through transpiration whereas the main loss from the oceans is through evaporation.

The correct answer is c...
D. Answer d is incorrect because the main loss of water from terrestrial systems is through transpiration whereas the main loss from the oceans is through evaporation.

Hint: Approximately 90% of the water in the atmosphere over land is from transpiration from the surface of plants. Over the oceans, the majority of water in the atmosphere comes from evaporation of seawater.

2). Which of the statements about groundwater is *not* accurate?
      a). In the U.S., groundwater provides 50% of the population with drinking water.
      b). Groundwaters are being depleted faster than they can be recharged.
      c). Groundwaters are becoming increasingly polluted.
      d). Removal of pollutants from groundwaters is easily achieved.

The correct answer is d...
A. Answer a is incorrect because groundwater supplies drinking water to 50% of the U.S. population.

The correct answer is d...
B. Answer b is incorrect because groundwaters are being depleted faster than they can be recharged.

The correct answer is d...
C. Answer c is incorrect because groundwater contamination is a growing problem.

The correct answer is d--Removal of pollutants from groundwaters is easily achieved.
D. Answer d is correct because it is nearly impossible to clean pollutants from groundwater aquifers.

Hint: Groundwater aquifers are large and inaccessible. Additionally, the rate of turnover in aquifers is slow. These factors make it difficult to clean pollutants from groundwaters.

3). The largest store of carbon molecules on earth is in
    a). the atmosphere.
    b). fossil fuels.
    c). marine sediments.
    d). living organisms.

The correct answer is c…
A. Answer a is incorrect because marine sediments are the largest store of carbon.

The correct answer is c…
B. Answer b is incorrect because marine sediments are the largest store of carbon.

The correct answer is c--marine sediments.
C. Answer c is correct because marine sediments are the largest store of carbon.

The correct answer is c…
D. Answer d is incorrect because marine sediments are the largest store of carbon.

Hint: When marine organisms die, their bodies sink into the sediments at the bottom of the ocean. The carbon from their bodies is released to these sediments and marine sediments are the largest store of carbon on earth.

4). Some bacteria have the ability to "fix" nitrogen. This means
    a). they convert ammonia into nitrites and nitrates.
    b). they convert atmospheric nitrogen gas into biologically useful forms of nitrogen.
    c). they break down nitrogen-rich compounds and release ammonium ions.
    d). they convert nitrate into nitrogen gas.

The correct answer is b…
A. Answer a is incorrect because the conversion of ammonia into nitrites and nitrates is not nitrogen fixation.

The correct answer is b--they convert atmospheric nitrogen gas into biologically useful forms of nitrogen.
B. Answer b is correct because nitrogen fixation is the process of converting atmospheric nitrogen gas into a biologically useful form.

The correct answer is b…
C. Answer c is incorrect because the breaking down of nitrogen-rich compounds with the subsequent release of ammonium ions is a process known as ammonification.

The correct answer is b…
D. Answer d is incorrect because the process of converting nitrate into nitrogen gas is known as denitrification.

Hint: Nitrogen fixation is the process whereby certain types of bacteria are able to cleave atmospheric nitrogen to produce biologically useful forms of nitrogen such as nitrites and nitrates.

5). The phosphorous cycle differs from the water, carbon, and nitrogen cycles in that
    a). the reservoir for phosphorous exists in mineral form in rocks rather than in the atmosphere.
    b). phosphorous is far more abundant than water, carbon, or nitrogen.
    c). phosphorous is less important to biological systems than water, carbon, or nitrogen.
    d). phosphorous, once used by an organism, does not cycle back to the environment.

The correct answer is a--the reservoir for phosphorous exists in mineral form in rocks rather than in the atmosphere.
A. Answer a is correct because phosphorous reservoirs are in the mineral form, or rock.

The correct answer is a...
B. Answer b is incorrect because phosphorous is relatively scarce in the environment.

The correct answer is a...
C. Answer c is incorrect because phosphorous is important to biological organisms and is often a limiting nutrient to plants.

The correct answer is a...
D. Answer d is incorrect because the phosphorous cycle is a complete cycle—phosphorous that is found in organisms cycles back to the environment.

Hint: The reservoir of phosphorous exists in mineral form.

6). In the Hubbard Brook experiments, which of the following situations did *not* occur?
        a). The undisturbed forests were effective at retaining nutrients.
        b). The deforested areas gained nitrogen.
        c). The deforested areas lost more water to runoff than the undisturbed forests.
        d). The deforested areas lost more minerals to runoff than the undisturbed forests.

The correct answer is b...
A. Answer a is incorrect because the undisturbed forests were effective at retaining nutrients.

The correct answer is b--The deforested areas gained nitrogen.
B. Answer b is correct because the deforested areas lost nitrogen rather than gained it.

The correct answer is b...
C. Answer c is incorrect because the deforested areas lost more water to runoff than the undisturbed forests.

The correct answer is b...
D. Answer d is incorrect because the deforested areas lost more minerals to runoff than the undisturbed forests.

Hint: The undisturbed sites accumulated nitrogen at a rate of 2 kilograms per hectare per year. The disturbed sites lost nitrogen at a rate of 120 kilograms per hectare per year.

7). What percentage of the energy that hits a plant's leaves is converted into chemical (food) energy?
        a). 1%
        b). 5%
        c). 10%
        d). 20%

The correct answer is a--1%
A. Answer a is correct. Approximately 1% of the energy that hits a plants leaves is converted into chemical energy.

The correct answer is a...
B. Answer b is incorrect. 5% is the amount of energy that a carnivore is able to convert from food energy to energy in its own body.

The correct answer is a...
C. Answer c is incorrect. 10% is the amount of energy that an invertebrate is able to convert from food energy to energy in its own body.

The correct answer is a...
D. Answer d is incorrect. 20% is the amount of energy that an herbivore is able to convert from food energy to energy in its own body.

Hint: Within ecosystems, energy transformations are not 100% efficient. Only 1% of the sun's energy that hits the surface of a plant is converted into chemical energy in the plant.

8). According to the trophic cascade hypothesis, the removal of carnivores from an ecosystem may result in
        a). a decline in the number of herbivores and a decline in the amount of vegetation.
        b). a decline in the number of herbivores and an increase in the amount of vegetation.
        c). an increase in the number of herbivores and an increase in the amount of vegetation.
        d). an increase in the number of herbivores and a decrease in the amount of vegetation.

The correct answer is d...
A. Answer a is incorrect. Removing predators will result in an increase in herbivores, which will result in a decrease in vegetation.

The correct answer is d...
B. Answer b is incorrect. Removing predators will result in an increase in herbivores, which will result in a decrease in vegetation.

The correct answer is d...
C. Answer c is incorrect. Removing predators will result in an increase in herbivores, which will result in a decrease in vegetation.

The correct answer is d--an increase in the number of herbivores and a decrease in the amount of vegetation.
D. Answer d is correct. Removing predators will result in an increase in herbivores, which will result in a decrease in vegetation.

Hint: The trophic cascade hypothesis is a top-down system of ecosystem control. Organisms at one trophic level have effects on organisms at lower trophic levels. If top carnivores are removed from a system the number of herbivores is likely to increase. This will exert increased herbivory pressure on the vegetation of the system and most likely result in a decrease in vegetation.

9). Experimental evidence from the Cedar Creek Natural History Area supports the hypothesis that
        a). species richness is related to community stability.
        b). human activities are upsetting the trophic cascade.
        c). bottom-up effects can regulate the number of top carnivores in a system.
        d). some aquatic ecosystems have inverted biomass pyramids.

The correct answer is a--species richness is related to community stability.
A. Answer a is correct. Researchers at Cedar Creek Natural History Area have performed field experiments that suggest species richness and community stability are related.

The correct answer is a...
B. Answer b is incorrect. Researchers at Cedar Creek Natural History Area have performed field experiments that suggest species richness and community stability are related.

The correct answer is a...
C. Answer c is incorrect. Researchers at Cedar Creek Natural History Area have performed field experiments that suggest species richness and community stability are related.

The correct answer is a...
D. Answer d is incorrect. Researchers at Cedar Creek Natural History Area have performed field experiments that suggest species richness and community stability are related.

Hint: Experiments performed at the Cedar Creek Natural History Area involved counting the number of different plant species in 207 different plots of land over an 11-year period. The plots with the greatest number of species showed less year-to-year variation in biomass production, which indicates that these plots are more stable.

10). The equilibrium model of island biogeography suggests all of the following *except*
      a). larger islands have more species than smaller islands.
      b). the species richness of an island is determined by colonization and extinction.
      c). smaller islands have lower rates of extinction.
      d). islands closer to the mainland will have higher colonization rates.

The correct answer is c...
A. Answer a in incorrect because, in general, larger islands have greater species richness than smaller islands.

The correct answer is c...
B. Answer b is incorrect because the equilibrium model states that species richness is a balance between colonization and extinction.

The correct answer is c--smaller islands have lower rates of extinction.
C. Answer c is correct because smaller islands tend to have higher rates of extinction than larger islands.

The correct answer is c...
D. Answer d is incorrect because islands closer to the mainland have higher colonization rates than more distant islands.

Hint: Smaller islands will have smaller populations of individuals living on them because there will be fewer resources to support these populations. Small populations have a higher chance of going extinct than larger populations.

Test Your Visual Knowledge

1). Using this table relate productivity to species richness.
Answer: Highly productive ecosystems can support more species than less productive ecosystems. The tropical rainforests have the greatest net primary productivity (NPP) and also have the greatest diversity. In comparison, the deserts have low NPP and low species diversity.

Apply Your Knowledge

1). Nitrogen is a limiting nutrient to plant growth in most ecosystems. To increase plant production, fertilizers that contain nitrogen (and phosphorous) are used. What effects might this influx of nitrogen have on ecosystems?
Answer: Increased nitrogen has allowed for increased plant growth in areas where plant growth was normally limited. This has had a major impact on many ecosystems. This is most obvious in lakes where runoff of fertilizers containing nitrogen and phosphorous have stimulated plant growth and caused lakes to become choked with aquatic vegetation.

2). Many communities in the U.S. struggle with issues of deer overpopulation. Explain how human activities have created this situation.

Answer: Humans have removed most of the deer's normal predators. This has helped deer populations to grow. Additionally, humans have fragmented forests and subsequently created habitats that deer are able to exploit more readily than large contiguous forests. This has also contributed to an increase in deer populations.

FIGURE 56.5

Temperature varies with latitude. The blue line represents the annual mean temperature at latitudes from the North Pole to Antarctica.
Why is it hotter at low latitudes?

Answer: The tropics are warmer than temperate regions because the sun's rays arrive almost perpendicular to regions near the equator. Near the poles, the angle of incidence of the sun's rays spreads them out over a much greater area, providing less energy per unit of area.

FIGURE 56.8

The effects of precipitation and temperature on primary productivity. The net primary productivity of ecosystems at 52 locations around the globe depends significantly upon (*a*) mean annual precipitation and (*b*) mean annual temperature.
Why does productivity increase with increasing precipitation and temperature?

Answer: This is one of the great questions in ecology. Many factors are involved, and scientists are not entirely in agreement. Increasing precipitation is responsible for increased plant growth. Increased temperature is related to many factors, but perhaps the most important is the increased availability of energy from the sun, which plants can convert into plant tissue through photosynthesis.

FIGURE 56.25

The greenhouse effect. The concentration of carbon dioxide in the atmosphere has steadily increased since the 1950s (*blue line*). The red line shows the general increase in average global temperature for the same period of time.
Why has temperature change been erratic, even though carbon dioxide levels have risen steadily?

Answer: Because other factors beside CO_2 concentrations affect global temperatures. For example, in 1991 the eruption of Mount Pinatubo in the Philippines produced much ash that circulated in the atmosphere, blocking the sun and leading to a short-term decrease in temperature.

Self Test

1). A rain shadow results in
      a). extremely wet conditions due to loss of moisture from winds rising over a mountain range.
      b). dry air moving toward the poles that cools and sinks in regions 15° to 30° north/south latitude.
      c). global polar regions that rarely receive moisture from the warmer, tropical regions, and are therefore dryer.
      d). desert conditions on the down-wind side of a mountain due to increased moisture-holding capacity of the winds coming from the seas.

The correct answer is d...
A. Answer a is incorrect because a rain shadow results in a desert on the down-wind side of the mountain. Extremely wet conditions occur on the up-wind side of the mountain when rising air releases precipitation.

The correct answer is d...
B. Answer b is incorrect because dry air moving toward the poles that sinks at 15-30 degrees latitude describes how the major deserts are formed.

The correct answer is d...
C. Answer c is incorrect because global polar regions that rarely receive moisture are frigid deserts.

The correct answer is d--desert conditions on the down-wind side of a mountain due to increased moisture-holding capacity of the winds coming from the seas.
D. Answer d is correct. A rain shadow results in desert conditions on the down-wind side of a mountain.

Hint: Rain shadows are produced when moisture-laden winds from the ocean encounter a mountain range. The winds are pushed upward and as they cool, they release moisture. As the air descends on the other side of the mountain it is able to hold moisture and there is little precipitation in the "shadow" of the mountain.

2). What two factors are most important in biome distribution?
 a). temperature and latitude
 b). rainfall and temperature
 c). latitude and rainfall
 d). temperature and soil type

The correct answer is b...
A. Answer a is incorrect. Rainfall and temperature are the two most important factors in biome distribution.

The correct answer is b--rainfall and temperature
B. Answer b is correct. Rainfall and temperature are the two most important factors in biome distribution.

The correct answer is b...
C. Answer c is incorrect. Rainfall and temperature are the two most important factors in biome distribution.

The correct answer is b...
D. Answer d is incorrect. Rainfall and temperature are the two most important factors in biome distribution.

Hint: There are eight major biome categories (some ecologists recognize more) that are defined by average annual rainfall (or available moisture) and average annual temperatures.

3). Savannas are best described as areas with
 a). extremely dry conditions and sparse vegetation.
 b). cold, dry conditions with herbs and few trees.
 c). warm summers, cool winters, and abundant rainfall which promotes tree growth.
 d). seasonal rainfall, few trees, and abundant grasses.

The correct answer is d...
A. Answer a is incorrect because these conditions describe a desert.

The correct answer is d...
B. Answer b is incorrect because these conditions describe the tundra.

The correct answer is d...
C. Answer c is incorrect because these conditions describe temperate deciduous forests.

The correct answer is d--seasonal rainfall, few trees, and abundant grasses.
D. Answer d is correct because these conditions describe a savanna.

4). The cacti that are found in the deserts of North and South America look very much like the euphorbs that are found in the deserts of Africa. However, these plants are not closely related. The similarities in these plants are due to

     a). convergent evolution as a result of similar environmental pressures.
     b). artificial selection for these similar traits.
     c). differences in rainfall between the two deserts.
     d). differences in pollinator species in the two deserts.

The correct answer is a--convergent evolution as a result of similar environmental pressures.
A. Answer is correct. Cacti and euphorbs have similar morphological characteristics because they both live in dry environments and have evolved similar adaptations for water conservation.

The correct answer is a…
B. Answer b in incorrect. The characteristics of cacti and euphorbs are the result of natural selection, not artificial selection.

The correct answer is a…
C. Answer c is incorrect. American and African deserts are both characterized by extremely low precipitation.

The correct answer is a…
D. Answer d is incorrect. There are different plant pollinators in American and African deserts however, these different pollinators are not responsible for the similarities between cacti and euphorbs.

Hint: Plants that occur in similar environments tend to evolve similar adaptive responses to these environments. Both cacti and euphorbs have fleshy stems for storing water and spinelike structures to reduce surface area for water loss. However, cacti and euphorbs are not closely related.

5). Which of the following is not a result of an El Niño event?
     a). The trade winds relax in the central and western Pacific.
     b). The sea surface is about a meter higher at the Philippines than at Ecuador.
     c). A rise in sea surface temperature and a decline in primary productivity adversely affect fisheries in Ecuador and Peru.
     d). Flooding and strong winter storms occur in California.

The correct answer is b…
A. Answer a in incorrect. An El Niño results when the trade winds across the Pacific diminish and stop driving the movement of warm water from western South America to Australia and the Philippines.

The correct answer is b--The sea surface is about a meter higher at the Philippines than at Ecuador.
B. Answer b is correct. During a non-El Niño year, the sea surface is about a meter higher at the Philippines than at Ecuador.

The correct answer is b…
C. Answer c is incorrect. An El Niño results in a rise in sea surface temperature, which adversely affects the commercial fisheries of Ecuador and Peru.

The correct answer is b…
D. Answer d is incorrect. A strong El Niño year results in global climate disruption, which includes violent winter storms and flooding in California.

Hint: El Niño events occur when the trade winds that normally blow from western South America to Australia and the Philippines are diminished. The result is that cool, nutrient-rich waters can no longer rise to the surface and primary productivity decreases. This adversely affects the commercial fisheries of Peru, Chile, and Ecuador as well as disrupts global climate patterns.

6). The neritic zone is best described as the
     a). area of water above the ocean floor where a diversity of plankton species are concentrated.
     b). ocean floor that is made up of mud and other fine particles that have settled from the water.
     c). area less than 300 meters below the surface of the oceans along the coasts of continents and islands.
     d). part of the ocean floor that drops to depths where light does not penetrate.

The correct answer is c…
A. Answer a is incorrect. The area of water above the ocean floor is known as the pelagic zone.

The correct answer is c…
B. Answer b in incorrect. The ocean floor is known as the benthic zone.

The correct answer is c--area less than 300 meters below the surface of the oceans along the coasts of continents and islands.
C. Answer c is correct. The area along the coasts of continents and islands is the neritic zone.

The correct answer is c…
D. Answer d is incorrect. The part of the ocean floor where light does not penetrate is known as the abyssal zone.

Hint: The neritic zone is the area less than 300 meters below the surface of the oceans along the coasts of continents and islands. The neritic zone is the location of the most important commercial fisheries.

7). The limnetic zone of a lake is best described as the
     a). shallow area along the shore.
     b). area below the limits where light can penetrate.
     c). zone where photosynthesis cannot occur.
     d). well-illuminated surface waters away from the shore.

The correct answer is d…
A. Answer a is incorrect. The shallow area along the shore of a lake or pond is known as the littoral zone.

The correct answer is d…
B. Answer b is incorrect. The area below the limits where light can penetrate into a lake or pond is known as the profundal zone.

The correct answer is d…
C. Answer c is incorrect. The zone where photosynthesis cannot occur in a lake or pond is known as the aphotic zone.

The correct answer is d--well-illuminated surface waters away from the shore.
D. Answer d is correct. The well-illuminated surface waters away from the shore of a lake or pond is known as the limnetic zone.

Hint: The limnetic zone is the well-illuminated surface waters away from the shore of a lake or pond. These waters receive enough light to support high levels of primary productivity and are populated by photosynthetic plankton and the species that feed on the plankton.

8). In temperate regions, lakes are thermally stratified, with warm waters at the top and cooler waters at the bottom during the summer. The region of abrupt change between these layers is known as the

        a). thermocline.
        b). hypolimnion.
        c). epilimnion.
        d). fall overturn.

The correct answer is a--thermocline.
A. Answer a is correct. The region of abrupt change between the layer of warm water and the layer of cold water in a lake is known as the thermocline.

The correct answer is a…
B. Answer b is incorrect. The hypolimnion is the layer of cold water at the bottom of a lake.

The correct answer is a…
C. Answer c is incorrect. The epilimnion is the layer of warm water at the surface of a lake.

The correct answer is a…
D. Answer d is incorrect. The fall overturn is mixing of the epilimnion and the hypolimnion that occurs every fall when the epilimnion cools to the same temperature as the hypolimnion.

Hint: The thermocline is the region where the warm water of the epilimnion meets the cold water of the hypolimnion.

9). Oligotrophic lakes can be turned into eutrophic lakes as a result of human activities such as
        a). overfishing of sensitive species, which disrupts fish communities.
        b). introducing nutrients into the water, which stimulates plant and algal growth.
        c). disrupting terrestrial vegetation near the shore, which causes soil to run into the lake.
        d). spraying pesticides into the water to control aquatic insect populations.

The correct answer is b…
A. Answer a is incorrect. Overfishing is a problem that affects some lakes but it does not turn oligotrophic lakes into eutrophic lakes.

The correct answer is b--introducing nutrients into the water, which stimulates plant and algal growth.
B. Answer b is correct. Oligotrophic lakes can be made eutrophic if excess nutrients are introduced into the lake.

The correct answer is b…
C. Answer c is incorrect. Many lakes are negatively impacted by the removal of vegetation near the shore, which causes problems with soil runoff. However, this does not turn an oligotrophic lake eutrophic.

The correct answer is b…
D. Answer d is incorrect. Pesticides in the water can negatively affect water quality but it does not cause an oligotrophic lake to become eutrophic.

Hint: Oligotrophic lakes are characterized by scarce nutrients and limited plant growth. Eutrophic lakes are nutrient-rich and support high levels of plant growth. Oligotrophic lakes can be made eutrophic when excess nutrients (such as from fertilizer runoff from agricultural fields and yards) enter the lake system.

10). The loss of the ozone layer has serious implications for the quality of the environment because
     a). ozone (O_3) protects organisms from ultraviolet radiation that can cause cancer.
     b). a depleted ozone layer causes rainwater to have a lower pH that kills plant life.
     c). loss of the ozone layer causes the sun's rays to get trapped in the atmosphere and increase global temperatures.
     d). a depleted ozone layer can interact with toxic chemicals to increase their effect on organismal health.

The correct answer is a--ozone (O_3) protects organisms from ultraviolet radiation that can cause cancer.
A. Answer a is correct. The ozone layer helps to shield the earth from ultraviolet radiation. UV radiation can mutate DNA and cause cancer and other diseases.

The correct answer is a…
B. Answer b is incorrect. Acid precipitation is due to the release of nitric and sulfuric acids into the atmosphere.

The correct answer is a…
C. Answer c is incorrect. The release of greenhouse gases (such as carbon dioxide) into the atmosphere creates a situation known as the greenhouse effect. Solar radiation that would normally be reflected back into space becomes trapped in the atmosphere and causes the atmosphere to heat up. This situation has resulted in global warming.

The correct answer is a…
D. Answer d is incorrect. The depleted ozone layer does not interact with toxic chemicals to increase their effect.

Hint: The ozone layer protects biological organisms from harmful UV radiation. Life was not able to become established on land until the early atmosphere was effective at blocking UV radiation. Excessive exposure to UV radiation causes cancer and other diseases.

Test Your Visual Knowledge

1). Predict what changes to global climate would occur if the earth's axis were not tilted.
Answer: The earth's axis is tilted by 23.5 degrees relative to its plane of orbit around the sun. This results in seasonal variation at the poles as the earth travels around the sun. If the earth were perpendicular relative to its plane of orbit around the sun there would be no seasonal variation at temperate latitudes.

Apply Your Knowledge

1). Some vegetarians argue that it is more ethical to eat "lower on the food chain" (eat more grains and vegetables) than to consume meat. Explain this argument in terms of energy conversions in ecosystems.
Answer: Energy transformations through trophic levels are not 100% efficient and energy is lost with each transfer. Eating meat instead of grains adds a link to the food chain, which decreases energy efficiency.

2). The Clean Water Act protects wetlands. Under the act, there is to be no net loss of wetlands and any wetland losses should be offset through restoration projects or creation of new wetlands. Why are wetlands given this status?

Answer: Wetlands are highly productive systems that are the homes to many different species of plants and animals. In addition, wetlands provide "ecosystem services" such as flood abatement and filtering pollutants from water.

3). The concentration of CO_2 in the atmosphere has steadily increased since the 1950s. A general increase in average global temperature has already occurred. How is global climate change predicted to affect the area where you live?
Answer: Answer will vary.

Inquiry Questions

FIGURE 57.3
Trends in species loss. These graphs present data on recorded animal extinctions since 1600. The majority of extinctions have occurred on islands, with birds and mammals particularly affected (although this may reflect to some degree our more limited knowledge of other groups).
Why are extinction rates highest for birds and mammals?

Answer: Perhaps attributes of birds and mammals, such as higher energetic requirements due to being endothermic, make them more susceptible to extinction. Alternatively, these data may reflect insufficient information. Other groups are less well studied than are birds and mammals. We simply are unaware of many extinctions in these groups.

FIGURE 57.5
Human populations in hotspots. The rich biodiversity in many hotspots is under pressure from (a) dense and (b) rapidly growing human populations.
Why do population density and growth rates differ among hotspots?

Answer: Many factors affect human population trends, including resource availability, governmental support for settlement in new areas or for protecting natural areas, and the extent to which governments attempt to manage population growth.

FIGURE 57.7
The economic value of maintaining habitats. (a) Mangroves in Thailand and (b) rainforests in Cameroon provide more economic benefits left standing than if they are destroyed and the land used for other purposes.
If shrimp farms established on cleared mangrove habitats make money, how can clearing mangroves not be an economic plus?

Answer: The mangroves provide many economic services. For example, without them, fisheries become less productive and storm damage increases. However, because the people who benefit from these services do not own the mangroves, governmental action is needed to ensure that the value of what are economists call "common goods" is protected.

FIGURE 57.12
Extinction and the species-area relationship. The data present percent extinction rates as a function of habitat area for birds on a series of Finnish islands. Smaller islands experience far greater local extinction rates.
Why does extinction rate increase with decreasing island size?

Answer: On smaller islands, populations tend to be smaller. As we discuss later in this chapter, small populations are vulnerable to many problems, which individually or in concert can heighten the risk of extinction.

FIGURE 57.16
World catch of whales in the twentieth century. Each species is hunted in turn until its numbers fall so low that hunting it becomes commercially unprofitable.
Why might whale populations fail to recover once hunting is stopped?

Answer: As discussed in this chapter, populations that are small face many problems that can reinforce one another and eventually cause extinction.

FIGURE 57.22
Loss of genetic variability in small populations. The percentage of polymorphic genes in isolated populations of the tree *Halocarpus bidwilli* in the mountains of New Zealand is a sensitive function of population size.

Why do small populations lose genetic variation?

Answer: As we discussed in chapter 21, allele frequencies change randomly in a process called genetic drift. The smaller the population size, the greater these random fluctuations will be. Thus, small populations are particularly prone to one allele being lost from a population due to these random changes.

Self Test

1). Historically, island species have tended to become extinct faster than species living on a mainland. Which of the following reasons cannot be used to explain this phenomenon?
      a). Island species have often evolved in the absence of predators and have no natural avoidance strategies.
      b). Humans have introduced diseases and competitors to islands, which negatively impacts island populations.
      c). Island populations are usually smaller than mainland populations.
      d). Island populations are usually less fit than mainland populations.

The correct answer is d…
A. Answer a is incorrect. Island species have often evolved in the absence of predators and cannot defend against human hunters or other introduced predators such as rats and cats.

The correct answer is d…
B. Answer b is incorrect. As humans move around to new areas they carry germs and other species with them. These new diseases can rapidly deplete a susceptible population. Introduced species can often outcompete native species and drive their populations to extinction.

The correct answer is d…
C. Answer c is incorrect. Island populations are usually smaller than mainland populations and small populations have a higher extinction rate.

The correct answer is d--Island populations are usually less fit than mainland populations.
D. Answer d is correct. Island populations are well adapted to their native environments. However, when their environment is dramatically changed they may not be able to avoid extinction.

Hint: In the past, most extinction took place on islands. Island species are often unable to defend against predators, have no immunity to introduced diseases, cannot outcompete introduced species, and have smaller population sizes. All of these factors contribute to a higher probability of extinction.

2). An endemic species is
      a). one found in many different geographic areas.
      b). one found naturally in just one geographic area.
      c). one found only on islands.
      d). one that has been introduced to a new geographic area.

The correct answer is b…
A. Answer a is incorrect because a species that is found in many different geographic areas is not an endemic species.

The correct answer is b--one found naturally in just one geographic area.
B. Answer b is correct. Species that are found in just one geographic area are endemic species.

The correct answer is b...
C. Answer c is incorrect. Many island species are endemic but there are also mainland endemic species.

The correct answer is b...
D. Answer d is incorrect. A species that has been introduced to a new geographic area is an introduced or exotic species.

Hint: An endemic species is one that is found in just one geographic area. Endemic species, because of their limited ranges, are more prone to extinction.

3). Conservation hotspots are best described as
a). areas with large numbers of endemic species that are disappearing rapidly.
b). areas where people are particularly active supporters of biological diversity.
c). islands that are experiencing high rates of extinction.
d). areas where native species are being replaced with introduced species.

The correct answer is a--areas with large numbers of endemic species that are disappearing rapidly.
A. Answer a is correct. Hotspots are recognized as areas with large numbers of endemic species that are rapidly being lost.

The correct answer is a...
B. Answer b is incorrect. Hotspots are recognized as areas with large numbers of endemic species that are rapidly being lost.

The correct answer is a...
C. Answer c is incorrect. Some hotspots are islands; however, many mainland areas are also conservation hotspots.

The correct answer is a...
D. Answer d is incorrect. Introduced species can contribute to extinction of endemics but it is not the only factor that results in production of a hotspot.

Hint: Hotspots are areas with a large number of endemic species that are disappearing rapidly. Conservation biologists often focus their efforts on these conservation hotspots.

4). Which of the following does *not* distinguish the current mass extinction event from past events?
a). This is the only extinction event to be triggered by a single species.
b). This is the only extinction event from which biodiversity may not recover.
c). This is the only extinction event in which the majority of losses are occurring in mainland areas.
d). This is the only extinction event in which the majority of losses are occurring on islands.

The correct answer is d...
A. Answer a is incorrect because the current extinction event is the only event to be triggered by a single species.

The correct answer is d...
B. Answer b is incorrect because the current extinction event is the only event from which biodiversity may not recover.

The correct answer is d...
C. Answer c is incorrect because in the current extinction event, most recent losses are from mainland areas.

The correct answer is d--This is the only extinction event in which the majority of losses are occurring on islands.
D. Answer d is correct because in historic extinction events, most losses are from island areas.

Hint: Our current mass extinction event is unique from historic extinction events. It has been triggered by a single species, biodiversity may not recover, and currently, the majority of losses are from mainland areas.

5). The ability of an intact ecosystem, such as a wetland, to buffer against flooding and filter pollutants from water is a(n) _____ value of biodiversity.
  a). direct economic
  b). indirect economic
  c). ethical
  d). aesthetic

The correct answer is b...
A. Answer a is incorrect because direct economic benefits of biodiversity include a species' value as food, medicine, clothing, fuel, etc.

The correct answer is b--indirect economic
B. Answer b is correct. Indirect economic benefits of biodiversity include an intact ecosystem's ability to buffer against environmental damage.

The correct answer is b...
C. Answer c is incorrect. Ethical arguments for the preservation of biodiversity center on the belief that every species is of value in its own right.

The correct answer is b...
D. Answer d is incorrect. Aesthetic values of biodiversity include the enjoyment humans receive from experiencing plants and animals.

Hint: Intact ecosystems can provide indirect economic values such as maintaining flood waters, cleaning water and air, and preserving soils. These indirect economic values are often of greater benefit than the direct benefits of exploiting individual species within an ecosystem.

6). Which of the following is currently considered the leading cause of extinction?
  a). overexploitation of species
  b). competition from introduced species
  c). habitat loss
  d). pollution

The correct answer is c...
A. Answer a is incorrect. Historically, overexploitation has been a leading factor in the extinction of some species. However, presently habitat loss is the main factor leading to extinctions.

The correct answer is c...
B. Answer b is incorrect. Competition from introduced species is an important factor in extinction, however, presently habitat loss is the main factor leading to extinctions.

The correct answer is c--habitat loss
C. Answer c is correct. Presently, habitat loss is the main factor leading to extinctions.

The correct answer is c...
D. Answer d is incorrect. Pollution can be an important factor in extinction of species, particularly if it results in habitats becoming so degraded that they are essentially lost to organisms. However, presently habitat loss is the main factor leading to extinctions.

Hint: Presently, habitat loss is the main factor leading to extinctions.

7). What percentage of Madagascar's original forests have been lost due to human activity?
      a). 10%
      b). 30%
      c). 60%
      d). 90%

The correct answer is d...
A. Answer a is incorrect. 90% of Madagascar's original forests have been lost.

The correct answer is d...
B. Answer b is incorrect. 90% of Madagascar's original forests have been lost.

The correct answer is d...
C. Answer c is incorrect. 90% of Madagascar's original forests have been lost.

The correct answer is d--90%
D. Answer d is incorrect. 90% of Madagascar's original forests have been lost.

Hint: 90% of Madagascar's original forests have been lost.

8). Numbers of migratory songbirds are declining in North America. Which of the following factors is important in this decline?
      a). pollution
      b). human disruption of breeding behavior
      c). habitat fragmentation in the United States
      d). global climate change

The correct answer is c...
A. Answer a is incorrect. Pollution has been shown to have negative effects on plant and animal populations, however, songbird declines are linked to habitat fragmentation in the United States (and habitat loss in their wintering grounds).

The correct answer is c...
B. Answer b is incorrect. Human disruption of breeding behavior has caused negative consequences for some species (such as cave-dwelling bats), however, songbird declines are linked to habitat fragmentation in the United States (and habitat loss in their wintering grounds).

The correct answer is c--habitat fragmentation in the United States
C. Answer c is correct. Songbird declines are linked to habitat fragmentation in the United States (and habitat loss in their wintering grounds).

The correct answer is c...
D. Answer d is incorrect. Songbird declines are linked to habitat fragmentation in the United States (and habitat loss in their wintering grounds).

Hint: Both habitat fragmentation in the United States and loss of habitat in tropical wintering grounds have contributed to the decline of North American songbirds.

9). Most large whale species have been driven to the brink of extinction. Which of the following is the most accepted explanation for this situation?
     a). overexploitation
     b). habitat loss
     c). pollution
     d). competition from introduced species

The correct answer is a…
A. Answer a is correct. Most large whale species have been hunted to near extinction.

The correct answer is a--overexploitation
B. Answer b is incorrect. Most large whale species have been hunted to near extinction.

The correct answer is a…
C. Answer c is incorrect. Most large whale species have been hunted to near extinction.

The correct answer is a…
D. Answer d is incorrect. Most large whale species have been hunted to near extinction.

Hint: Overharvesting of whales had driven their populations to near extinction.

10). A keystone species is one that
     a). has a higher likelihood of extinction than a nonkeystone species.
     b). exerts a strong influence on an ecosystem.
     c). causes other species to become extinct.
     d). has a weak influence on an ecosystem.

The correct answer is b…
A. Answer a is incorrect. Keystone species do not have a higher likelihood of extinction than nonkeystone species.

The correct answer is b--exerts a strong influence on an ecosystem.
A. Answer b is correct. A keystone species has a strong influence on an ecosystem and the other species that comprise that ecosystem.

The correct answer is b…
C. Answer c is incorrect. A keystone species does not cause other species to go extinct. However, if a keystone species goes extinct it may lead to the extinction of other dependent species.

The correct answer is b…
D. Answer d is incorrect. A keystone species has a strong influence on an ecosystem, not a weak influence.

Hint: Keystone species are species that exert a strong influence on an ecosystem. Flying foxes are a keystone species because without them many plants are not being pollinated and their seeds are not being dispersed. This has had a major impact on forest ecosystems in places such as Guam.

Test Your Visual Knowledge

1). List the possible factors that explain the trend in the graph.
Answer: ban on DDT spraying, captive breeding programs, public support for conservation, providing adequate nesting areas

Apply Your Knowledge

1). Do you know of any endangered or threatened species that live near you? What factors have led to their decline? What efforts are being made to preserve any endangered species in your area?
Answer: Answer will vary.

2). Exotic species can have detrimental impacts on native species. Are all exotics bad? Can you name any instances in which exotics have not had detrimental effects?
Answer: Exotic species that do not outcompete native species for access to resources usually do not have a detrimental effect on ecosystems. The ring-necked pheasant is an exotic species that was intentionally introduced to the United States. It has not been a problem species and there are many efforts to keep its populations in the United States healthy.

3). Recent advances in genetic technologies have allowed scientists to develop microbes that can metabolize toxins in the environment, such as pesticides and oil slicks. What are the dangers of releasing these genetically modified organisms into the wild?
Answer: Species introductions can often have negative consequences for native species. Releasing genetically modified microbes may cause a change in microbe communities that could, in turn, have negative consequences on organisms that interact with those microbes.

ISBN 0-07-310923-1

90000

9 780073 109237